Maintenance Arc Welding

Maintenance Arc Welding

Erratum

Price

$.50 in U. S. A.
$.75 Elsewhere
Postage Prepaid

This book may be ordered through any
recognized book dealer or direct from

THE JAMES F. LINCOLN ARC WELDING FOUNDATION
CLEVELAND . . . . OHIO

Published by

THE JAMES F. LINCOLN ARC WELDING FOUNDATION

First Printing, November, 1943

Printed in U. S. A.

Permission to reproduce any material contained herein, either in whole or in part, is granted provided proper credit is given to The James F. Lincoln Arc Welding Foundation.

Copyright 1943

Preface

"MAINTENANCE Arc Welding" is the first volume to be published by the Lincoln Foundation on the important application of the arc welding process in maintenance of metal equipment and structures. Maintenance work, in which the welding arc had its original application, has always been and will remain a most important field of usefulness. Ever responsible for tremendous savings in the industrial field, maintenance arc welding has been indispensable in maintaining the tremendous war production machine. In countless instances, it has kept machinery and plants in operation where otherwise production would have stopped. With critical shortages of both materials and equipment, the arc welding process has made it possible for industry to effect repairs without which scrapping would be the only alternative. This has applied not only in the reclamation of broken and worn parts of machinery and structures but also in the fabrication of replacements with tremendous economy.

"Maintenance Arc Welding," the second book to develop from the 1940-42 Progress Program, contains 25 award papers which were selected as outstanding in the program's maintenance classification. The other book, "Studies in Arc Welding," comprises 98 award papers on design, manufacture and construction.

In selecting the papers for the present volume, the entire group of 55 papers which received awards in the maintenance classification were considered in the light of originality, value of information and thoroughness in treatment of subject matter. Since all papers possessed unquestioned merit, the omission of any one paper is in no sense of the word a reflection or criticism.

Those papers which were considered too lengthy for complete reproduction were briefed without loss of any pertinent text matter nor illustrations. The attention of the reader is called to the number of different industries represented by the papers and also to the great diversity in the subject matter itself. A brief description at the beginning of each chapter serves as a guide to the content of the particular paper. "Maintenance Arc Welding" is believed a most valuable contribution to furthering scientific and industrial progress by furnishing new case-study data under the authorship of men whose careers, for the most part, are devoted to the important field of maintenance.

The Lincoln Foundation herewith expresses its appreciation to all those who participated in the Progress Program. Without the interest and effort of those who submitted papers on maintenance, the information contained herein would not have been made available for the general benefit of industry.

—A. F. DAVIS AND ED. C. POWERS, EDITORS

Table of Contents

	Page
Chapter I — Modern Bakery, by William E. Dalton	1
Chapter II — Welded Blast Furnace Shell, by Thomas J. Peiffer	7
Chapter III — Cement Plant, by Harry A. Cozad	26
Chapter IV — Ceramic Plant, by Carlman Martin Rinck	47
Chapter V — Chemical Plant, by J. E. Gurvin	55
Chapter VI — Coke Oven Doors, by H. A. Immisch	60
Chapter VII — Copper Plant, by Gordon B. Forbes	67
Chapter VIII — Cracking Still Charging Pump, by George M. Heath	82
Chapter IX — Drill Pipe of Integral-Joint Construction, by H. N. Keener and C. F. Underwood	85
Chapter X — Farm Machinery, by Leslie Swick	91
Chapter XI — Fibre and Plastics Plant, by Arthur B. Eastman	96
Chapter XII — Foundry Sand Rammers, by Michael F. Streidl	110
Chapter XIII — Furniture Manufacturing Plant, by William H. Dietrichs	114
Chapter XIV — Gravel Plant, by Henry Barrett	124
Chapter XV — Machine Tools, by H. W. Rushmer	134
Chapter XVI — Oil Still Tubes, by L. V. Hile	143
Chapter XVII — Power Generating Station, by R. C. Fitzgerald	149
Chapter XVIII — Railway Bridge, by A. M. Knowles	157
Chapter XIX — Corrosion Control in Refinery Pressure Vessels, by W. W. McClow	165
Chapter XX — Saw Mill, by Robert Schliewe	183
Chapter XXI — Steel Mill, by J. B. Whitlock	196
Chapter XXII — Stud Bolts Removed Quickly When Broken, by Alex F. Morton and William F. Kramer	205
Chapter XXIII — Trestle for Stocking Iron Ore, by Earl M. Ver Bunker	210
Chapter XXIV — Truck Wheel Carrier, by Clinton Stutter	215
Chapter XXV — Hydraulic Turbine Maintenance on Municipal Power System, by Eric F. Bladholm	219

Maintenance Arc Welding

Chapter 1—Modern Bakery

By WILLIAM E. DALTON,

Chief Engineer, Continental Baking Co., Toledo, Ohio.

William E. Dalton

Subject Matter: With the use of arc welding equipment, the following maintenance jobs were completed: 1, Repairing and welding aluminum cake pans; 2, Repairing window handles throughout the plant; 3, Repairing pan washing machine track; 4, Extracting broken-off studs; 5, Redesigning the monorail system.

In addition, a newly designed and fabricated conveyor system was installed by the maintenance crew. The cost of conveyor was $1,281.99 as against $2,202.59 from an outside source. A gross saving of $920.60.

A modern bakery consists of automatic mixers, scales, dough tracks and chutes, depositor machines, ovens, monorail-track systems, pan-washing machines, cooling conveyors, icing machines and conveyors, wrapping machines and conveyors, steel-production racks, tables, steel cupboards, mixing bowls and icing bowls, gas cookers, steam-jacket kettles, refrigerators, sugar pulverizer, flour-conveying system, blending machines, boilers, shipping room storing racks and storage compartments.

Considering the repair and maintenance on all this equipment, I felt it would be an asset to have an electric welding machine in the plant. At this time my superiors did not understand the value a machine of this type could have in the upkeep of the plant. After this difficulty I took it upon myself to personally purchase a 200-ampere welder.

Some of the problems that we have faced since the purchase of this machine were the repairing and welding of aluminum cake pans, window handles throughout the plant, pan-washing machine track for conveyor chain, extracting broken-off studs, re-designing our monorail system and many more too numerous to mention.

These were just small maintenance jobs compared to the new re-designed and fabricated conveyor system.

We shall now go into full detail of all maintenance jobs as listed above.

We had in our plant approximately 700 aluminum cupcake pans which are 39 inches long, 10 inches wide and 2 inches deep, 1 and 7/8 inches at top, 1 and 1/8 inches at bottom. Each pan consists of six sections and each

1

section consists of six cups. Six sections riveted to a steel band forming the complete pan. The partition between each of these cast aluminum cups was placed in such a way that the usage broke the partition out and made about ⅔ of the side wall of the cup break out with it, rendering the cup useless. Before the purchase of my machine, these sections of pans that were broken, were scrapped. These pans were brought to the plant maintenance repair shop. We built a tank to fit about ten pans and we boiled these pans in a solution of tri-sodium phosphate to remove any surplus grease that might have been on the pans. We then proceeded to build a copper back-up that fit the pan internally, two cups at a time. We placed the cups over this die and welded from the back of the cups. No machine work was required as the inside of the cups were completely smooth. These pans after being welded were much stronger because the build up at this particular point was sufficient to increase the strength of the partition as this seemed to be the weak point in the casting. Since this material could not be purchased, we repaired such pans and also created a savings for the company plus the fact that they still had the pans in service, amounting to approximately $0.45 per section. We completely finished about 1000 sections before we were unable to purchase aluminum rod for this purpose.

During the winter months it seemed that the condensation in our plant gathered around the window frames, freezing the window frame and sash together. At such a time our employees would wish to open a window, these frames being froze together would break the cast iron handles that were riveted to the frame. These handles had to be replaced. In order to do this, it would have required a lot of labor to remove the frame, window glass and re-rivet new handles in place, then replace the frame and re-glaze the glass. The way we overcame the excessive labor cost of the job was to form the handles from ⅜ inch cold rolled steel, slightly raise the window, place asbestos paper between the glass and the handle and proceed to weld the handle in place with E-6010 rod. The complete job of approximately 40 windows with two handles each was completed in a course of six hours.

The pan washer in our plant is 35 feet long, 6 feet high and 5 feet wide. It has a cyclone wire-mesh conveyor traveling over an angle iron track, passing through a hot water spray and over a gas flame for drying. This machine being in operation for a number of years, the angle iron track on each side of the wire-mesh conveyor had rusted partially away, leaving the wire-mesh conveyor drop down out of line at the partially-worn spots. This angle iron was formerly formed and then welded to the side walls of the pan-washing machine. The top flange or track of this angle was the part that was rusted away, leaving the part that was welded to the side walls in good condition. So by taking 2 inch x ¼ inch flat cold rolled steel and forming into place as we welded to the other angle, created an enormous savings over the method of having to cut this angle iron completely out, reforming, machining and replacing. The way we did this job on our pan-washing machine, we kept our normal production on schedule which could not have been accomplished by any other method.

We had to change a switch spur on our overhead monorail track system due to the installation of a new machine. Instead of drilling, bolting and fastening this spur in place by our former method which would have taken too long to have it in service at the proper time, we welded it in place in order to meet our schedule.

A very small but very important job I did that would have necessitated a complete shut down of the plant and having to completely tear down a cookie depositor thus causing 40 employees to lose a day's work was accomplished by burning a 3/16 inch rod into a 3/8 inch broken-off stud, backing the stud out and replacing a new 3/8 inch cap screw. This job was completed in ten minutes.

The new re-designed and fabricated conveyor system completed with our own maintenance crew will now be explained in detail also the figures of an outside welding company and by machine fabrication.

The former conveyor was inadequate due to increased production and more modern handling facilities which also damaged our cake in transit due to a cast-aluminum spiral chute that was used to transfer the product from the ceiling of the first floor to the 29 3/4 inch level of the horizontal belt. The problem that we faced with large changeover was to do this enormous amount of work and still not interrupt our normal production. We also faced the problem of securing the necessary steel to do this work by the machine-fabricating process. We started to think seriously of welding. In doing so we found we could use every bit of material that was in the old conveyor plus a small amount of new material.

We planned this work to be fabricated in three sections, keeping our plant on normal production at all times. Each of these sections was taken out, re-designed and completely welded on the day that the plant was not in operation. This day falls on the last of the week which is Friday. From the time the plant was down on Thursday evening and it started again Friday evening each section had to be in place and in working order. We found on the completion of this job that we could operate with approximately $20.00 less labor per day. This conveyor also gives our plant enlarged operating facilities and handles our product more efficiently. Since this job had to be completed and not shut our plant down as we would have lost a large volume of business, I feel it was a great savings to the firm by electric welding this conveyor with our own maintenance help.

We started first with section BB, Fig. 1, fabricating a three-pulley device beforehand. This three-pulley device was designed for the purpose of deflecting the travel of the belt from a horizontal plane to an angle plane, approximately 30 degrees, to do away with the cast-aluminum spiral chute and deliver the product from the ceiling belt of the first floor to our shipping room belt with a 1/4 turn. The construction of this three-pulley device consisted of two 2 inch x 2 inch x 1/4 inch angle irons 31 inches long as the height of the horizontal conveyor is 31 inches, also two 2 inch by 2 inch x 1/4 inch 34 inches long as the angling part of our conveyor is 34 inches high. The level of the top of the two idlers were 29 3/4 inches. These idlers were constructed from 3 inch steel pipe with steel plugs welded in the ends with a shaft protruding about 3 1/4 inches on each end to make up our idler pulleys. This shaft was 1 1/4 inches in diameter. Since we used standard pillow blocks for bearings for these idlers we could not get the ends of the pillow block bearings close enough to give us a 1 inch opening between the two idlers, so we cut 3/4 inch off one side of each pillow block, butting the two ends together and welding, giving us a double pillow block in one piece. Bolting this to the 2 inch x 2 inch x 1/4 inch angle iron on the horizontal plane of this device, this angle was welded to the outside frame of the three-pulley device. Immediately under the center of the opening between the two 3 inch idlers we placed another 3 inch idler, taking the belt over the one idler, under the bottom idler and over the top continuing on our horizontal plane. In doing this it was possible to use only one

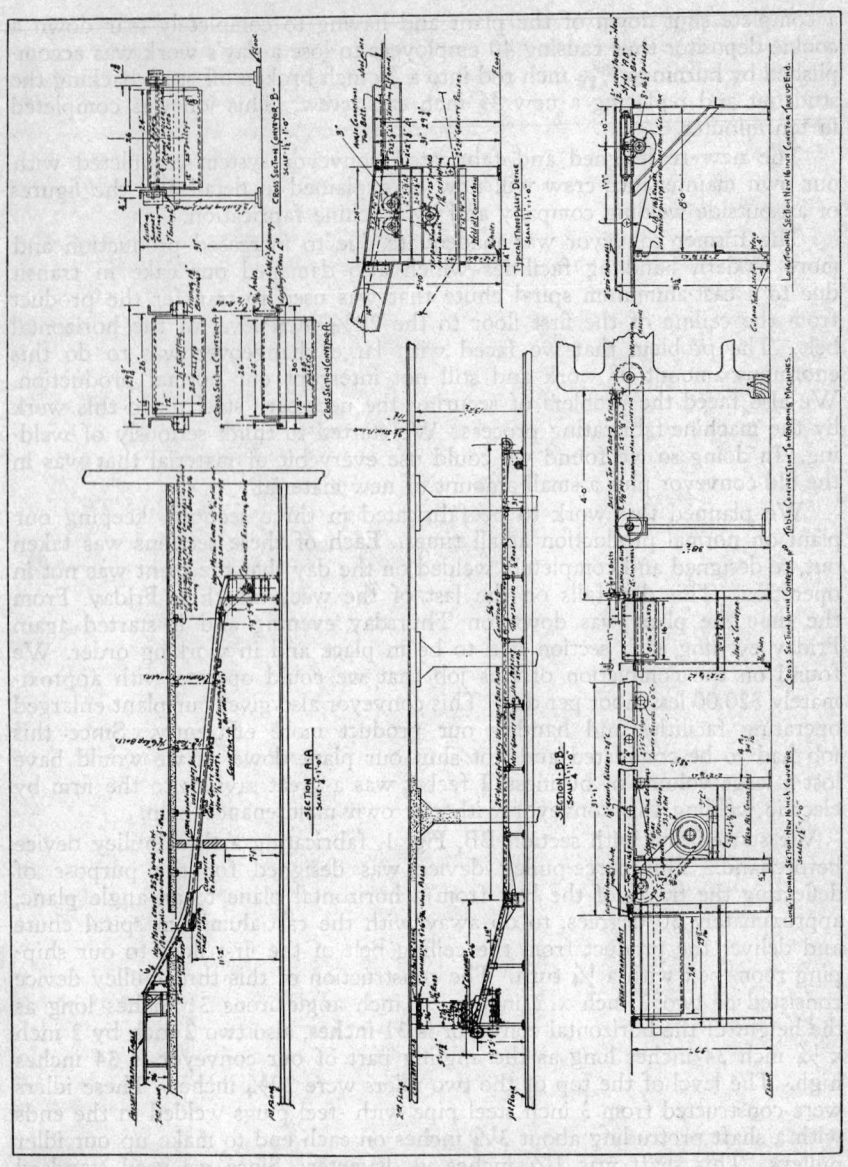

Fig. 1. Floor plans of production line.

drive. Another reason for having this three-pulley device was that we needed 56 feet 8 inches of level belt 29¾ inches from the floor in order to efficiently pack our product from the belt. We also wanted this belt to be continuous. For the return side of the belt on the three-pulley device, we attached two 2 inch x 24 inch gravity rollers taking our belt under these for clearing the three idlers in the top part of the device. Since this device was constructed before hand, we dismounted the entire 73 feet 2 inches of the flat conveyor leaving all the standards and floor flanges intact to the side channel iron frame of the old conveyor. Taking out the old spacing rods, gravity rollers, welding in new spacing rods 26 inches long and measuring back from center of drive-in pulley 55 feet 8 inches, we burnt our conveyor in two, welding this section of the conveyor frame to the 31 inch side of our three-pulley device. This giving us an overall length of 57 feet 8 inches. We completely lined and anchored this section, this leaving us 15 feet 6 inches of the conveyor to be raised at the idling end of the belt 5 feet 9 inches from the floor to the center of the idling pulley. We cut our pipe legs to the right length and raised this conveyor, setting it in place and burnt it to fit our three-pulley device, then welding it to the floor.

To connect this conveyor with section AA, Fig. 1, which was still a 16 inch belt we had to install a temporary chute until the following week end when the shop was not operating. The first thing we had to do when

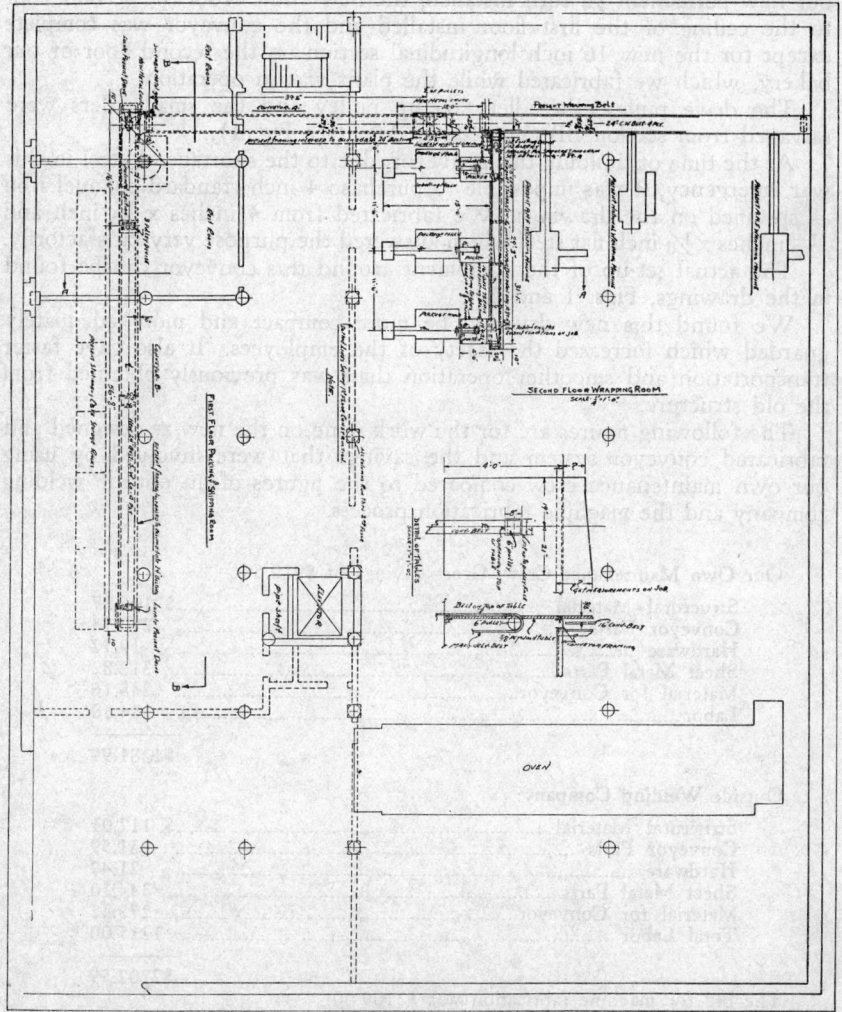

Fig. 2. Floor plan of shipping room.

we started on conveyor "A" was to disassemble the old 16 inch conveyor, enlarge our opening in the wall. The drive that powered this section of the conveyor was hanging on the ceiling so this had to come down and a hanger was designed at the end and underneath of section BB, Fig. 1, and installed here. This was done in order to shorten our drive centers, make it easier to service the drive, to streamline and create a more efficient drive. Our hanger plates on the ceiling had to be made longer because this conveyor was wider. We cut small pieces of 3 inch channel irons 30¼ inches apart, thus having the ceiling-hanger rods just on the outside of the conveyor channel iron. We welded 8 inches on to one end of the channel iron previously supporting the former conveyor, welding these channel irons in place on the new conveyor, putting our stay rods through with nuts and pulling up into place.

Fabricating a guard for the power unit from a 16 gauge black iron, we had our new permanent ¼ turn installed, the new chute from the second floor to the ceiling of the first floor installed and the conveyor was complete except for the new 16 inch longitudinal section on the second floor of our bakery, which we fabricated while the plant was in operation.

The drive pulley, the idler take-up pulley and the small idlers were salvaged from section BB and section AA, (see Fig. 1).

At the time of building this conveyor, due to the shortage of steel in this war emergency, it was impossible to purchase 4 inch standard channel iron as specified on the drawings. We fabricated from 4 inches x ⅛ inch and 1½ inches x ⅛ inch flat steel which answered the purpose very satisfactorily.

The actual set-up of the equipment around this conveyor can be found in the drawings, Figs. 1 and 2.

We found this new drive to be more compact and more adequately guarded which increased the safety of the employees. It also gave faster transportation and smoother operation than was previously obtained from the old structure.

The following figures are for the work done on the new re-designed and fabricated conveyor system and the savings that were involved by using our own maintenance crew compared to the figures of an outside welding company and the machine fabrication process.

Our Own Maintenance Crew: Gross Savings of $920.60

Structural Material	$ 106.37
Conveyor Parts	210.54
Hardware	19.52
Sheet Metal Parts	312.82
Material for Conveyor	248.16
Labor	384.58
	$1281.99

Outside Welding Company:

Structural Material	$ 117.01
Conveyor Parts	231.59
Hardware	21.47
Sheet Metal Parts	344.10
Material for Conveyor	273.42
Total Labor	1215.00
	$2202.59

The bid for machine fabrication was $3109.00

Chapter II—Welded Blast Furnace Shell

By THOMAS J. PEIFFER,

Steel Works Engineer, Jones & Laughlin Steel Corp., Pittsburgh, Pa.

Subject Matter: Describes construction of arc welded ⅜-inch steel shell for large blast furnace for making iron. Author considers stresses for both riveted and welded joints and gives stress calculations and efficiency. Welding required only seven weeks while riveting would have required four to five months. Actual saving on construction only was $4,214 with a greater efficiency of joint strength by arc welding with less noise.

Thomas J. Peiffer

INTRODUCTION—The design of blast furnace shells in the past has been mostly confined to the riveted construction. There are a few exceptions on record of welded construction. However, riveting is the general practice. This may be partly traditional, or due to the reluctance of authorities to assume the responsibility of deviating from past accepted and tested standards.

The factor of cost was not so much of an objection as the idea involved that the strength of a welded joint depended upon the ability of the welder. This human element was one of the greatest hindrances to the progress of welding. Time has proven that these obstacles could be almost entirely eliminated and that a reliable weld could be made by a properly trained and experienced welder.

The application of welding in the field of maintenance has become almost indispensable and still it is often quite difficult to make an accurate estimate of the financial returns. This is especially true in the steel industry, around blast furnaces, pickling tanks and by-product coke plants where there is excessive corrosion to the steel work due to the sulphurous atmosphere. A badly corroded structural column or structural member may be repaired in a comparatively short time and without any disturbance to existing steel work by means of a reinforcing strap and a few hours of welding. Replacement of one of these members would quite often be almost impossible and the cost prohibitive.

It is the purpose of this article to determine with a reasonable amount of accuracy, the savings effected by the application of arc welding in the field of maintenance.

The Blast Furnace—The blast furnace, see Fig. 1, is a tall circular structure 90 to 100 feet high consisting of a steel shell shaped in the form of a frustrum of a cone. The bottom of this shell is securely riveted to a circular steel reinforcing ring known as the mantle. This structure constitutes the main body and is supported by 10 or 12 columns arranged in the form of

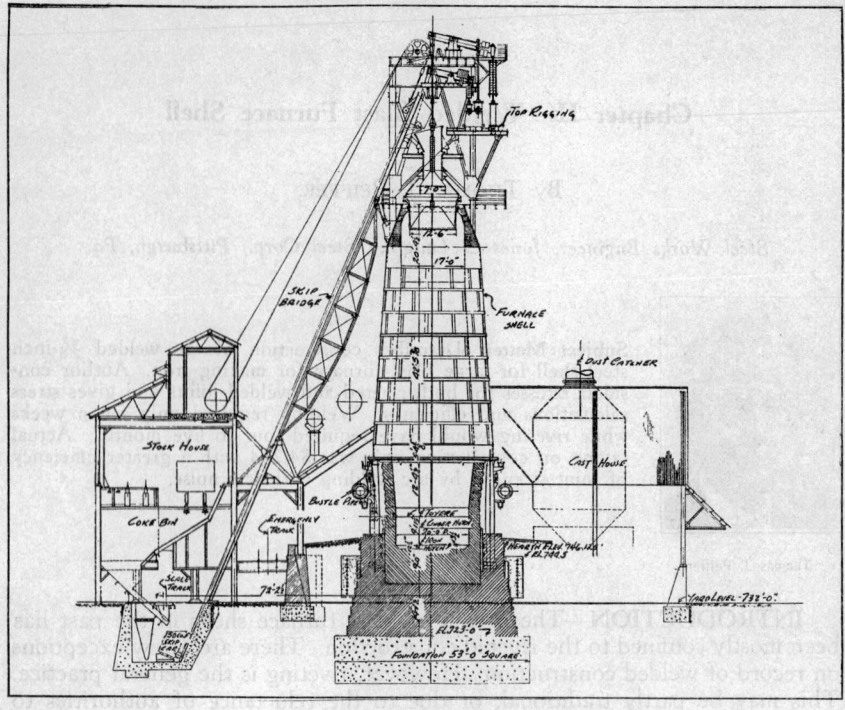

Fig. 1. Cross section of blast furnace.

a circle. The inside of the shell is lined with fire brick to a thickness of approximately four feet and is supported by the mantle.

The space inside the lining is divided into three main parts. The bottom section is cylindrical in form and is called the hearth. The second section extending about 12 feet higher is called the bosh. The section above the bosh extending upward about 68 feet is called the stack. The whole is now capped by the furnace top, which completes the gross features of the furnace proper.

Blast Furnace Rehabilitation—The rebuilding of blast furnaces quite often involves an extensive program; this article however will be confined to a special relining which required the replacement of the furnace shell and mantle, the original of which is shown by Fig. 2. The upper ring and furnace top had been replaced at some earlier date and were still in an excellent state of preservation. The problem, therefore, was to renew the shell without disturbing the furnace top, skip bridge and downcomers. By referring to Fig. 1 it will be noted that the furnace shell is supported by the mantle bearing on twelve columns, and that the top, skip bridge and downcomers are supported by the furnace shell.

Considerable time was spent in the engineering department making studies and layouts to determine the most feasible and economical methods of procedure. The method finally adopted was to construct a new welded shell enveloping the old riveted shell, see Fig. 4, section C-C and weld it to the top ring of the old structure which remained intact. The construction of the new work was necessarily a welding proposition due to the fact that

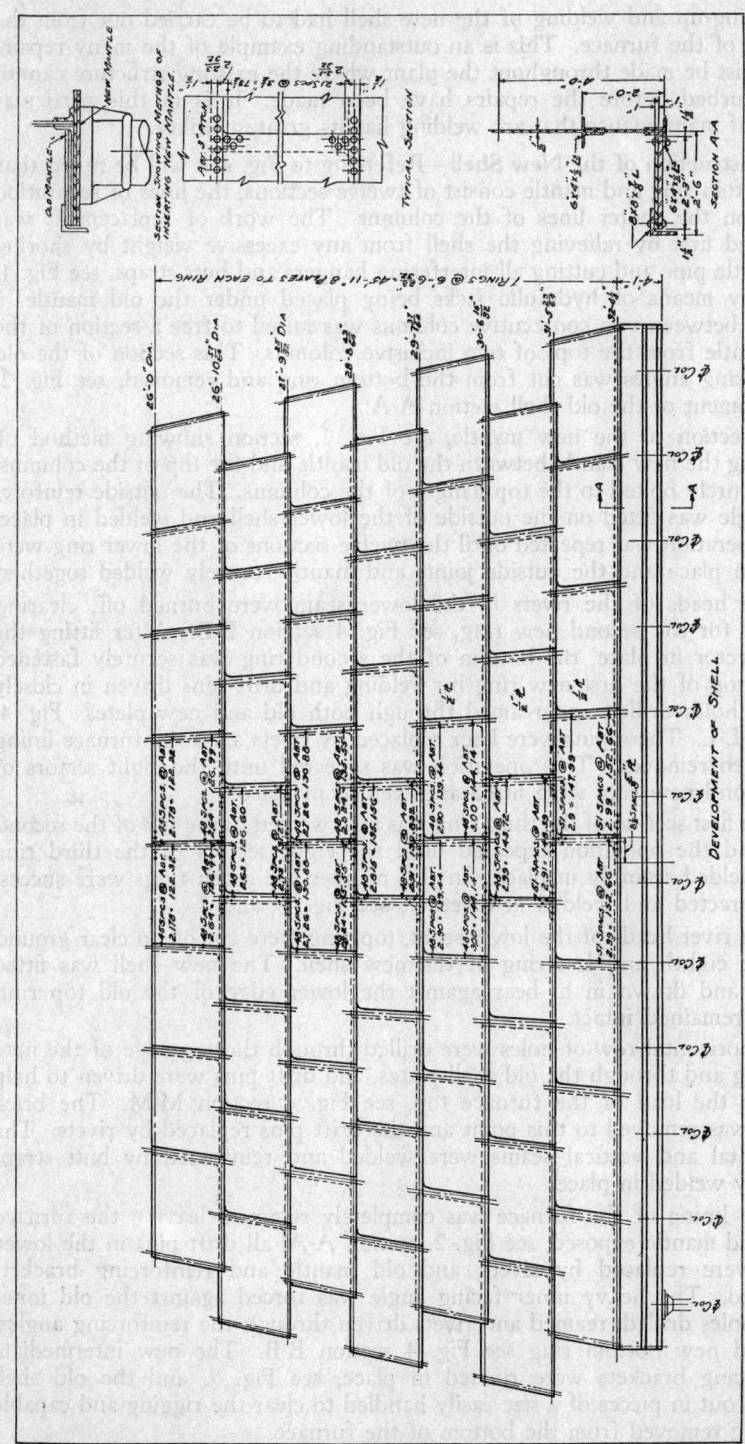

Fig. 2. Old riveted shell blast furnace.

the fitting-up and welding of the new shell had to be carried out from the outside of the furnace. This is an outstanding example of the many repairs that must be made throughout the plant where the existing structure cannot be disturbed before the repairs have been made. It is in this particular phase of maintenance that arc welding has its greatest utility.

Construction of the New Shell—Referring to Fig. 4 it will be noted that the bottom ring and mantle consist of twelve sections, the lines of separation being on the center lines of the columns. The work of replacement was preceded first by relieving the shell from any excessive weight by shoring the bustle pipe and cutting all interfering hangers and butt straps, see Fig. 1. Now by means of hydraulic jacks being placed under the old mantle, a section between two consecutive columns was raised to free a section of the old mantle from the tops of two inclusive columns. This section of the old reinforcing angles was cut from the bottom ring and removed, see Fig. 2, development of the old shell section A-A.

A section of the new mantle, see Fig. 2, section showing method of inserting the new mantle between the old mantle and the top of the columns, was securely bolted to the top flanges of the columns. The outside reinforcing angle was fitted on the outside of the lower shell and welded in place. This operation was repeated until the twelve sections of the lower ring were fitted in place and the outside joints and mantle securely welded together.

The heads of the rivets in the lower seam were burned off, clearing ground for the second new ring, see Fig. 4 section B-B. After fitting the plate sector in place, the bottom of the second ring was securely fastened to the top of the first new ring by welding and drift pins driven in closely spaced holes drilled and reamed through both old and new plates. Fig. 4, section L-L. These pins were later replaced by rivets after the furnace lining had been removed. This operation was repeated until the eight sectors of the second new ring were fitted and welded in place.

The first section of the third ring was now welded to the top of the second ring and the operation repeated until the eight sectors of the third ring were welded securely in place. In this manner the seven rings were successively erected and welded in together, see Figs. 7 and 8.

The rivet heads of the lower seam, top ring were cut off to clear ground for the eighth and last ring of the new shell. The new shell was fitted closely and drawn in to bear against the lower edge of the old top ring which remained intact.

A horizontal row of holes were drilled through the top edge of the new top ring and through the old shell plates, and drift pins were driven to help to take the load of the furnace top, see Fig. 4 section M-M. The brick lining was removed to this point and the drift pins replaced by rivets. The horizontal and vertical seams were welded and reinforced by butt straps securely welded in place.

The lining of the furnace was completely removed leaving the furnace shell and mantle exposed, see Fig. 2, section A-A, all drift pins in the lower shell were replaced by rivets, and old mantle and reinforcing brackets removed. The heavy inner facing angle was forced against the old inner shell, holes drilled, reamed and rivets driven through the reinforcing angles, old and new bottom ring see Fig. 4 section B-B. The new intermediate reinforcing brackets were riveted in place, see Fig. 9, and the old shell burned out in pieces of a size easily handled to clear the rigging and capable of being removed from the bottom of the furnace.

ARC WELDING

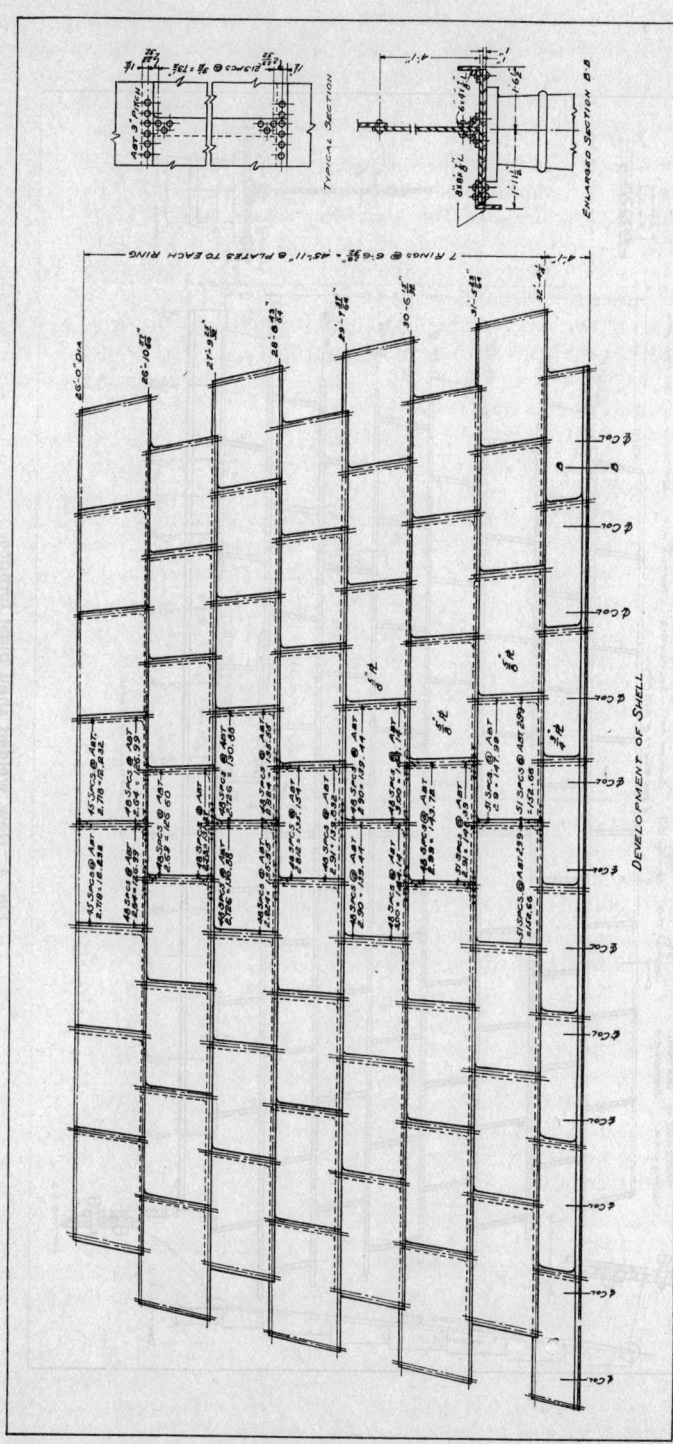

Fig. 3. New riveted shell blast furnace.

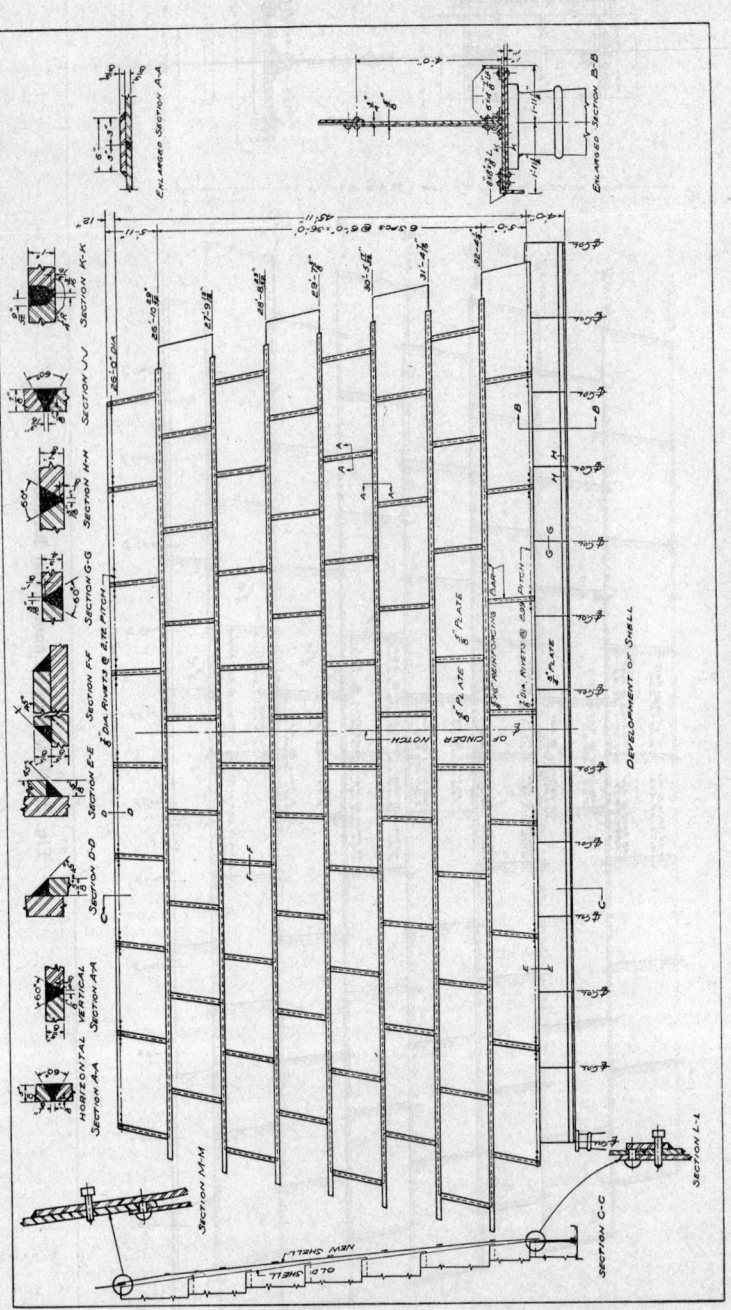

Fig. 4. New welded shell blast furnace.

ARC WELDING   13

Furnace Shell Stresses—The stresses in the furnace shell will be based on direct compression. Under simple compression the failure occurs for brittle material by oblique shearing and for plastic materials by enlargement and cracking. Referring to Fig. 1 it will be noted that, in addition to the static load of the furnace top, there is a superimposed load on the shell due to the weight of the skip bridge, downcomers and skip cars. The skip cars are coupled so that when the loaded car is at the top of the furnace, the empty car is in the skip pit. The maximum load imposed upon the shell is when the loaded car is at the top of the furnace.

Referring to Fig. 5 the superimposed loads on the furnace shell are: first, the forces due to the weight of the skip buckets; and second, the force due to the weight of the skip bridge.

The tension T_2 due to the weight of the empty skip bucket is determined by diagram No. 1 and is found to be 2250 pounds. The tension T_1 in the

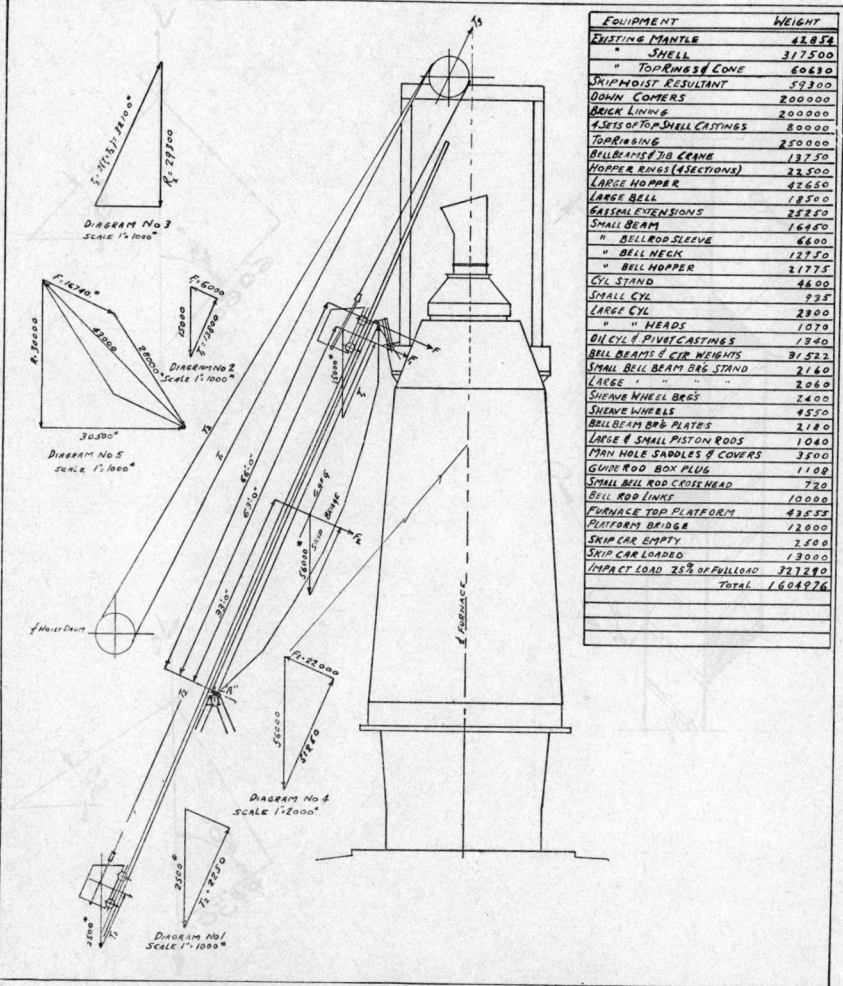

Fig. 5. Loading and stress diagrams of blast furnace.

cable supporting the loaded skip car is, according to diagram No. 2, 13800 pounds. These forces are directly transmitted to the furnace top through the bull wheel. Let T_3 be the resultant of these two loads.

$$\text{Then } T_3 = 2\ (T_1 + T_2) \text{ or } 32100 \text{ lbs.}$$

The load on the furnace shell due to the weight of the skip bridge is determined as follows: assume the weight of the bridge being concentrated at the center of gravity, then by means of diagram Fig. 4, the normal force F_2 will be 22000 pounds, and at a distance of 33 feet from the fulcrum point A. The component force F, due to the loaded skip bucket, and normal to the bridge will be 6000 pounds from diagram Fig. 2 and is at a distance of 63 feet from the center of rotation A.

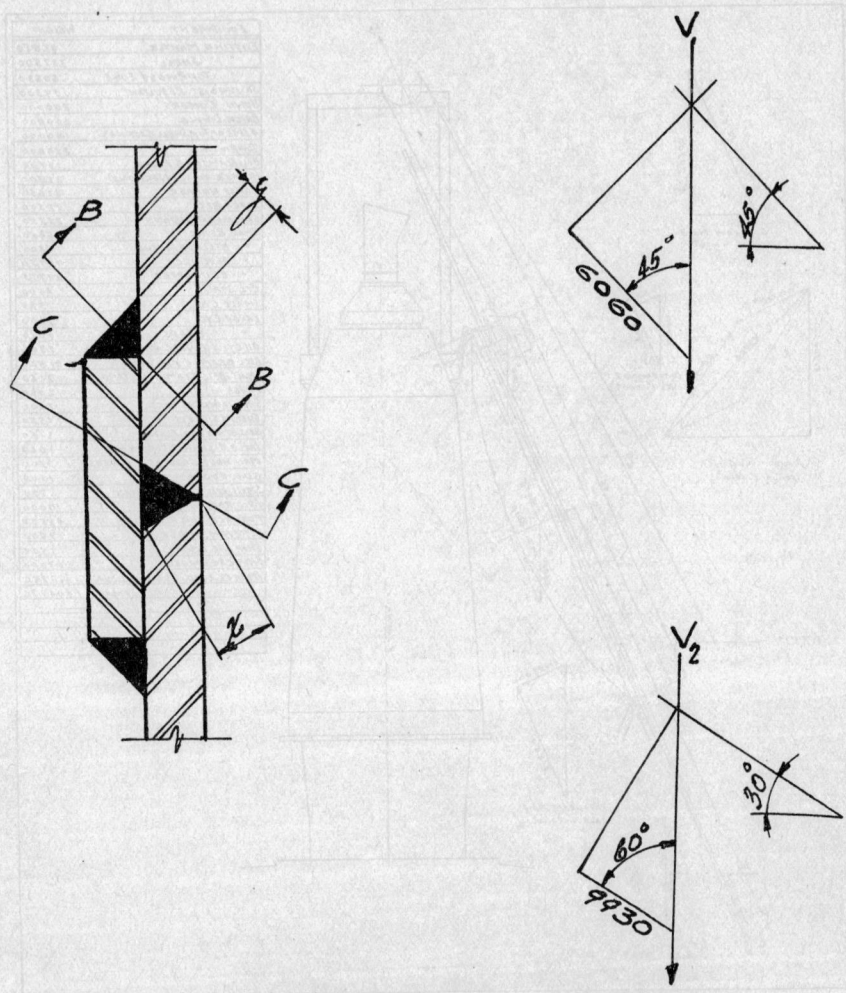

Fig. 6. Stress in welded joint.

ARC WELDING

The resultant force F normal to the bridge is found by taking moments about the center of rotation A and is expressed by the equation—

66 F = 63 × 6000 + 33 × 22000
F = 16740 lbs.

The force F acts through the connecting link between the skip bridge and furnace. The resulting vertical component, R is determined by diagram Fig. 5 and equals 30000 pounds.

The resultant vertical force R_2 due to the weight of the skip buckets is shown by diagram Fig. 3 and equals 29500 pounds. The total vertical load on the furnace due to the weight of the skip buckets and skip bridge is $R_1 + R_2$ or 59300 pounds.

The resultant vertical load must be added to the static load of the furnace shell Fig. 5 and is indicated under skip hoist resultant in the list of equipment.

In determining the stress in the furnace shell the maximum will appear in the smaller section which is in the top ring. To determine the stress at this section, the load of the shell and mantle will be excluded from the list of equipment as shown by Fig. 5.

Hypothetical New Riveted Shell, Fig. 3.

Minimum diameter of shell	26 feet
Section area for 5/8" shell 81.64 x 12 x .625	612 sq. in.
Net load on shell	1,400,000
Number of rivets in seam	360
Load per rivet	3900 lbs.
Stress in shell lbs. per sq. inch	2620

Joint Efficiency for 5/8" Plate

Let P equal tensile force transmitted from plate to plate	3900 lbs.
t equal thickness of plate	.625
p equal pitch of rivets	2.75"
d equal diameter of hole	.875"
S_t equal tensile unit stress—ultimate	55000 lbs. sq. in.
S_s equal unit stress in compression	45000 " " "
S_c equal unit stress in shear	55000 " " "

For Compression on Rivet

$$S_c = \frac{P}{td} = \frac{3900}{.625 \times .875} = 7140 \text{ lbs./sq. inch}$$

Shear in Rivet

$$S_s = \frac{P}{\frac{nd2}{4}} = \frac{3900}{.60} = 6500 \text{ lbs./sq. inch}$$

Let E = Efficiency of Joint in Compression

$$e = \frac{tds}{ptS_t} = \frac{ds_c}{pSt}$$

$$= \frac{.875 \times 55000}{2.75 \times 55000} = 31.8\%$$

Let e^1 = Efficiency of Joint in Shear

$$e^1 = \frac{\frac{nd^2 S_s}{4}}{ptS_t} = \frac{.60 \times 45000}{2.75 \times .625 \times 5500} = 28.6\%$$

Fig. 7. Erection of furnace shell.   Fig. 8. Another view of furnace shell erection.

The efficiency of the joint in shear is very low and could have been increased by a double row of rivets in the horizontal seams of the shell. Assuming a double row of rivets the efficiency will be increased as follows:

$$e^1 = \frac{2dS_c}{pS_t} = \frac{1.75}{2.75} = 63.6\%$$

This method of riveting is quite often adopted, however it is evident that this practice increases the cost of riveting considerably.

Cost of New Riveted Shell, Fig. 3—The cost of the new riveted shell will be based on similar relinings and replacements over a period of years with adjustments for 1940 labor rates. Referring to Fig. 3 which is the development of the riveted shell and the equivalent of the welded shell shown by Fig. 4.

Riveted Shell—Table 1.

Gross weight of steel allowing 8% for waste	168067 lbs.
Net weight	155617 "
Cost of plates 168067 lbs. @ 1.8¢ per lb.	$ 3110.00
Cost of rivets 9800 lbs. @ 2.89¢	283.00
Shop labor 155617 lbs. @ 3.8¢	5920.00
Assembly 155617 lbs. @ 1.68¢	2620.00
Riveting 11863 lbs. @ 20¢ each	2376.00
Burden and misc. 153347 lbs. @ .8¢ per lb.	1225.00
Total	$15534.00

Cost per lb. 10¢

The costs as shown in Table 1 are based on the complete dismantling of the furnace. This eliminates all interferences of the downcomers and skip bridge and greatly facilitates the erection of the new work.

ARC WELDING

Cost of Welded Shell Fig. 4—It will be noted that the installation of the welded shell was carried out under abnormal conditions involving **extra** labor in shoring and handicaps due to interferences which made erection exceedingly more difficult, see Figs. 7 and 8.

Welded Shell—Table 2.

Gross weight of steel allowing 8% for waste	175792 lbs.
Net weight	162778 "
Cost of plates 175792 lbs. @ 1.8¢ per lb	$ 3170.00
Shop labor 162778 lbs. @ 3.16¢	5140.00
Assembly 162778 lbs. @ 1.68¢	2740.00
Welding 162778 lbs. @ 1.24¢	2026.00
Rivets 1080 lbs. @ 20¢ each	216.00
Stub ends 600 lbs. @ 7.8¢ per lb	47.00
Burden and misc. 162778 lbs. @ .8¢ per lb	1300.00
Total	$14639.00

Cost per lb. 8.95¢

The erection of the welded shell was performed by a sub-contractor, direct figures were therefore not available. The cost of welding is based on field costs and data as recorded in the "Procedure Hand Book of Arc Welding."

The data in Table 3 are based on the following:

Operating factor—60%
Labor.........................$1.25 per hour
Power.........................1¢ per K.W.H.
Electrode cost per lb.—7.8¢

Table 3.

Section Mark Fig. 4	Electrode Dia. Inch	Current in Amps.	Minimum Volts	Arc Speed in Ft. of Joint per Hr.	Lbs. of Electrode per Ft. of Joint	Total Number of Feet	Total Weight of Electrode Lbs.	Cost per Foot of Weld $	Total Cost per Section $
A-A Hor.	3/16	150	25	2.4	.93	651	604	.621	398.00
A-A Vert.	3/16	150	25	3.6	.93	384	357	.451	173.00
D-D	1/4	190	25	4.0	1.26	935	1175	.429	400.00
E-E	3/16	150	25	2.0	1.26	753	950	.743	558.00
F-F	3/16	150	25	3.0	1.26	768	970	.535	410.00
G-G	3/16	150	25	2.0	1.50	48	72	.725	34.80
H-H	3/16	150	25	1.0	1.89	6	11	1.44	8.65
J-J	1/4	340	30	1.5	1.69	4	7.6	1.03	4.13
K-K	1/4	340	30	2.8	2.90	52	151	.765	39.60
							4297.6 lbs.		$2026.18

Stress in Welded Joint Fig. 6—The ultimate failure of the welded reinforced joint could occur in two ways. First, by shearing the welded metal along the lines B-B and C-C. Second, by crushing the welded seam. The analyses are based on the following values as given in the "Procedure Hand Book of Arc Welding."

Unit stress in tension $S_t = 15000$ lbs. per sq. inch
Unit stress in shear $S_s = 13600$ lbs. per sq. inch
Unit compression $S_c = 18000$ lbs. per sq. inch

Let $S_s = 13600$ lbs. per sq. in.

$$x = \frac{.625}{\cos 30°} = \frac{.625}{.857} = .728$$

Likewise

$y = .625 \text{ sine } 45°$
$= .625 \times .707$
$= .445$

For Shearing along B-B

$.445 \times 13600 = 6060$ lbs.

The sum total of shear along the lines B-B and C-C equals 15,990 lbs.

The resulting vertical components of the corresponding forces along the planes B-B and C-C, is expressed by the following equations:

$$V_1 = \frac{6060}{\cos 45°} = \frac{6060}{.707} \qquad V_2 = \frac{9930}{\cos 60°} = \frac{9930}{.5}$$

$V_1 = 8580$ lbs. $\qquad V_2 = 19860$ lbs.

Total vertical force $= V_1 + V_2 = 28440$ lbs.

S_s for shell per linear inch $= 55000 \times .625$
$= 34000$ lbs.

S_s for welded metal linear inch $= 28400$ lbs.

$$\text{Efficiency of joint} = \frac{28440}{34400}$$

82.8%

Relative Strength of Riveted and Welded Shell—The large diameter in comparison to the length of the shell brings the stresses almost in direct compression. This, however, is not altogether true. Experience has proven that a furnace shell when stressed to the ultimate performs like a plastic cylinder, namely by enlargement of the section area accompanied by the development of vertical cracks in the shell. Emergency repairs are made quite frequently by the installation of lateral reinforcing bands about the defective area.

It is obvious then that a welded reinforced joint is the proper construction since the plates are butted, the welded metal is in direct compression. In this manner it is quite possible to form a joint with a 100 percent efficiency.

The strength of the riveted shell is weakened by the rivet holes, and the strength of the structure so joined is determined by the strength of the joint. A riveted joint may yield in any one of three ways. First, by shearing; second, by the plate yielding in tension or compression; third, by the rivet tearing through the margin. If the stress becomes excessive the rivet is weakened to rsist shearing or the plate to resist compression and failure may occur. It is not possible to have a riveted joint with an efficiency of 100 percent. It will be noted that the unit stresses in the shell were very low. This seems to indicate that a lighter plate might prove more economical. There are, however, some important factors to be considered in the design of furnace shells. First, corrosion on the interior of the shell may become excessive in case of a badly eroded furnace lining, thereby greatly reducing the life of the shell. Second, there are undetermined stresses developed in the shell due to unequal expansion of the downcomers, shell, safety walk connections, skip bridge and comparative settling of the furnace foundation, and third, explosions in the furnace which may prove serious and endanger the lives of the operating crew. Considering all these advantages, the additional cost involved in the heavier shell is greatly justified.

The Relative Costs of Welded and Riveted Shell—According to cost analysis, see Tables 1 and 2, there was a difference of $895.00 in favor of the welded shell. It will be remembered that construction of the welded job was carried out under severe handicaps due to interferences of the existing structure, see Figs. 7 and 8. This is especially true of the old furnace mantle which was raised intermittently by means of hydraulic jacks and then cut out in sections to clear ground for the new steel work. It is evident that this method of procedure greatly increased the cost of the welded shell.

The cost of the new shell might have been reduced by the elimination of the vertical and horizontal butt straps. These were installed as an added precaution against a possible failure. There is no doubt that in the future this added expense will be avoided in consideration of the very low fibre stresses. The omission of this added material and labor would affect the cost as follows:

733 ft. of flat 3/4" fillet weld @ 42.0¢ per ft.	$ 314.00
733 ft. overhead 3/4" fillet weld @ 74.35¢ per ft.	543.00
128 ft. vertical 3/4" fillet weld @ 53.55¢ per ft.	59.00
1300 lbs. butt straps @ 7.4¢ per lb.	970.00
	$1886.00
Savings due to welding	895.00
Total	$2781.00

Fig. 9. Removal of old shell.

The cost of the riveted shell is based on single riveted horizontal seams with a joint efficiency of 28 percent. The double riveted seam would raise the joint efficiency to 63.6 percent with the corresponding increase in cost not including the shop labor for additional rivet holes.

Table 4.
Weight of 2335 rivets 7/8" dia. x 3 1/8" lg. @ 77 lbs. per 100.. 1770 lbs.
Cost of rivets 360 lbs. @ 2.89¢ per lb.................................$ 51.00
Cost of driving rivets 2335 @ 20¢ each.................................. 467.00

Total $518.00

The installation of riveted shell would require the complete dismantling of the furnace top, skip bridge and downcomers. It is assumed that the downcomers are in a good state of preservation and can be re-erected, which, in case of the structural steel, is not practical. The structural steel top and skip bridge will be considered as scrap and replaced by new steel work. This also applies to the brick lining in the downcomers. The mechanical parts of the furnace top can be salvaged and re-erected.

The total savings, therefore, will be based on the economy of the welded structure, labor and material saved due to non-disturbance of the existing equipment. The time element is also a very important factor which in case of the welded structure, required approximately seven weeks. This would not have been possible by the installation of the riveted shell which is a matter of approximately four to five months, depending upon the availability of the materials of construction. The loss of production during the period of reconstruction is of vital importance but will be excluded in this article.

Dismantling Downcomers—The downcomers are of riveted construction, see Figs. 7 and 8. The total length to be dismantled is 700 feet with an average diameter of six feet. The most economical method for dismantling is to cut the pipes into sections by flame cutting between the riveted joints. This method of procedure is preferable to cutting out rivets which would be prohibitive in cost, besides the injury that would result to rivet holes, making a satisfactory job of erection impossible.

Assuming the pipes are to be cut into 25-foot sections which is a convenient length for handling, there will be a total of 28 sections to be dismantled. The estimated amount of labor and material are shown in Table 5.

Table 5.
Number of sections—25 ft. lengths.................................. 28
Linear ft. of flame cutting 3/8" plate.................................. 485
Cutting speed per hour.. 69
Total time in hours.. 7
Oxygen consumption cu. ft. per hour................................. 24
Acetylene consumption cu. ft. per hour............................. 13
Total oxygen required in cu. ft... 336
Total acetylene required in cu. ft... 182

We find that the actual amount of time, labor and material do not conform with the foregoing estimate. This is due to amount of miscellaneous cutting which is very difficult to estimate in work of this type.

The actual amount of labor and material involved are:

Labor	Man Hours
Acetylene cutting	40
Carpenters	160
Common labor	116
Riggers	496
Boiler makers	48
Crane service	32
Total	892

Cost 892 man hours @ $1.02 per hour .... $ 917.00
Oxygen—3 tanks @ $2.31 .... 6.93
Acetylene—1 tank @ $5.30 .... 5.30

Total .... $ 929.23
Freight on brick bats 100 tons @ .50¢ per ton .... $ 50.00
Labor for loading 372 man hours @ .72½¢ 269.70
Burden and miscellaneous 25% 299.73

Total $1498.66
Total weight of downcomers .... 200,000 lbs.
Cost per lb. .... .75¢

Erecting Downcomers—In erecting the downcomers, assembly will be made on the basis of welded construction and by means of reinforcing butt straps. The application of these straps will greatly facilitate the erection and compensate for their added cost:

Material for butt straps 4 x 3/8 x 485 ft. lg. 2473 lb. @ 3¢ ...... $ 74.19
500 ft. of 3/8" flat fillet weld @ 54.2¢ per ft. 271.00
500 ft. of 3/8" overhead fillet weld @ 58.0¢ per ft. 290.00

Total $635.19

Labor	Man Hours
Boiler makers	1790
Riggers	650
Carpenters	624
Crane service	294
Machinists	126
Labor	428
Total	3912

Cost of 3912 man hours @ 1.02¢ per hour $3990.24
Painting—13500 sq. ft.
Paint coverage 600 sq. ft. per gal.
Labor 700 sq. ft. per 8 hour day.
Rate $5.80 per day.
Paint $1.85 per gal.
Time required—16.8 days.
Labor cost—16.8 days @ $5.80 per day $102.44
Material—22.5 gal. @ $1.85 per gal. 41.62

Total $144.06
Cost per sq. ft.—1.03¢
Total cost of erection—
Welding and material .... $ 635.19
Labor 3990.24
Painting—labor and material 144.06
Burden and miscellaneous 25% 1340.00

Total $6109.49

Cost per lb. = $\dfrac{6109.49}{200000}$ = 3.02¢

Relining Downcomers—
Material—30,000 brick @ $30.00 per M $900.00

Labor	Man Hours
Bricklayers	2718
Bricklayer helpers	2718
Carpenters	1196
Crane service	185
Labor	800
Total	7617 @ $.92

.... $7007.64
Burden and miscellaneous 25% 1751.91

Total cost $8759.55

Dismantling Top Structural Rigging—No attempt will be made to salvage the existing steel work. Referring to Fig. 1 it will be noted that it is an intricate construction. Past experience has proven that salvaging of this type of structure is impractical and that it is more economical to scrap the existing structure and erect a new structure.

Total weight of steel work.............................25000 lbs.

Labor	Man Hours
Boiler makers	325
Riggers	275
Carpenters	89
Crane service	320
Labor	420
Millwrights	82
Pipe fitters	80
Total	1591

Labor cost 1591 man hours @ 1.02¢=$1622.82.

Oxygen and acetylene required to dismantle steel work and cut into scrap for open hearth furnaces:

Oxygen—163 tanks @ $2.31	$ 376.53
Acetylene—28 tanks @ $5.30	148.40
Cutting scrap—labor and material	524.93
Dismantling labor	1622.82
Cutting up into scrap 125 tons @ $8.28	1035.00
Burden and miscellaneous 25%	795.00
Total	$3977.75

Cost per lb.—1.58¢

Dismantling Skip Bridge:

Total weight of steel work..................................56000 lbs.

Structural steel work dismantled and cut into scrap for open hearth furnace. Cost per lb. 1.58¢ for analysis:

Total cost—56000 @ 1.58¢.............................$884.80

Weight of Mechanical Top Rigging—see Fig. 1.

Equipment	Weight, Lbs.
Top shell castings	80,000
Bell beams and jib crane	13,750
Hopper rings	22,500
Large hopper	42,650
Small beam	16,450
Large bell	18,500
Small bell rod sleeve	6,600
Small bell neck	12,750
Small bell hoppers	21,775
Cylinder stand	4,600
Small cylinder	935
Large cylinder	2,300
Large cylinder head	1,070
Oil cylinder and pivot castings	1,390
Bell beams and counter weights	31,522
Small bell beam bearing stand	2,160
Large bell beam bearing stand	2,060
Sheave wheels	2,400
Bell beam bearing plates	2,180
Large and small piston rods	1,040
Manhole saddle and covers	4,500
Guide rod box plug	1,108
Small bell rod cross head	720
Bell rod links	10,000
Total weight	302,960

Dismantling Mechanical Top Rigging:

Total weight of equipment..................................302,260 lbs.

Labor	Man Hours
Riggers	1800
Boiler makers	332
Carpenters	142
Machinists	448
Labor	600
Crane service	400
Total	3722

Cost 3722 man hours @ $1.05 per hour...............$3908.10
Burden and miscellaneous 25%.................................. 975.00

Total..$4883.10

Cost per lb. $1.62¢

Erection of Mechanical Top Rigging

Total weight of equipment..................................302,260 lbs.

Labor	Man Hours
Riggers	2435
Boiler makers	665
Carpenters	234
Machinists	693
Crane service	849
Labor	976
Total	5852

Cost 5852 man hours @ $1.05 per hour...............$6144.60
Burden and miscellaneous 25%.................................. 1536.00

Total..$7680.60

Cost per lb. $2.54¢

Erection of New Top Structural Rigging

Structural steel 250,000 lbs. @ 3.78¢ per lb............$ 9450.00
Erection 250,000 lbs. @ 2.35¢ per lb....................... 5875.00
Painting (2 coats) 18,750 sq. ft. @ 1.03¢ x 2........... 387.25

Total..$15712.25

Cost per lb. .06⅓¢

Erection of New Skip Bridge

Structural steel 56,000 lbs. @ 3.78¢ per lb............$2116.80
Erection 56,000 lbs. @ 2.35¢ per lb....................... 1316.00
Painting (2 coats) 7,000 sq. ft. @ 1.03¢ x 2........... 144.20

Total..$3577.00

Table 6.
Summary of Savings

Welded shell	$ 895.00
Dismantling downcomers	1498.66
Erecting downcomers	6109.49
Relining downcomers	8759.55
Dismantling structural top	3977.75
Erecting structural top	15712.25
Dismantling skip bridge	884.80
Erecting skip bridge	3577.00
Dismantling mechanical top	4883.10
Erecting mechanical top	7680.60
Total	$46297.60

The saving as shown in Table 6 applies to a specific maintenance project and does not apply generally. In order to form a true comparison, field assembly of the riveted and welded shells must be on the same basis, that is, by complete dismantling of the furnace for both shells. In order to bring the efficiency of the riveted shell up to 63.6 percent it will be necessary to design the riveted shell with two horizontal rows of rivets per joint. This will add $518 to the cost of the riveted shell, see Table 5.

According to the stress analysis of the welded shell, see Fig. 6, it is evident that the horizontal and vertical butt straps could be eliminated and still retain a high degree of joint efficiency. This would reduce the cost of the welded shell by $2781.

Comparative costs—
Riveted shell $16052.00
Welded shell 11838.00

Savings..$ 4214.00

Assuming the average life of a furnace shell, by proper care, to be twenty years, the savings must be distributed over this period of time.

Savings per year per furnace $\frac{4214}{20}$ = $ 211.00

For 11 furnace............$211.00 × 11 = $2321.00

The comparative savings of steel—

Riveted Shell		Welded Shell	
Shell	138798 lbs.	Shell	130179 lbs.
Mantle	28678 lbs.	Mantle	28678 lbs.
Rivets	9800 lbs.	Weld metal	4300 lbs.
Total	177276 lbs.	Total	163157 lbs.

Savings per furnace................................14119 lbs.

Savings per year per furnace $\frac{14119}{20}$ = 710 lbs.

For 11 furnace......................710 × 11 = 7810 lbs.

There are approximately 231 active blast furnaces in the United States and 25 under construction, making a total of 256 furnaces. Assuming that all furnaces are of the riveted type, reconstruction of these furnaces to the welded type in the next 20 years would effect the following savings:

Economy in steel per furnace... 14119 lbs.
Total for 256 furnaces...3,614,464 lbs.
or.. 1800 tons
Savings per year.. 90 tons

The total economy in dollars based on the 1940 valuation is accordingly:

Savings per furnace per year...$ 211.00
Total for 256 furnaces... 54,016.00
Total savings per year... 2,700.00

These figures appear almost insignificant in comparison to the total production of steel in the United States. However, they are very conservative due to the fact that the furnace in discussion is of the average size, and that the general trend of modern furnaces is towards large capacities. There has also been a considerable increase in labor rates within the past year.

No claim is justified in the increased life of the furnace due to welding. Past experience has proven that deterioration in the furnace shell is general rather than localized.

Conclusion—It is evident from the analysis of the foregoing project, that some of the greatest advantages of arc welding are to be found in the field of maintenance. This is mostly due to the flexibility of its application to existing structures. Economy in maintenance bears a direct relation to efficient production.

The process of joining metals by means of arc welding has produced a joint of greater efficiency and reliability. The factor of doubt has been practically eliminated by the improvement of modern welding equipment, and the training of reliable and efficient welders working under favorable conditions.

Considerable sums of money are constantly being spent for the elimination of noise in industry. This is especially applicable to the construction of buildings in close proximity of office buildings and hospitals where the noise of the riveting hammer would be prohibitive. There can be no matter of doubt that arc welding has contributed to its fullest extent to our social and economic lives.

Chapter III—Cement Plant

By Harry A. Cozad,

Master Mechanic, Colorado Portland Cement Co., Portland, Colorado.

Harry A. Cozad

Subject Matter: Several examples are given of the use of arc welding in the maintenance of a cement plant. The fabrication of rotary feeders is described in which proper firmness of ingredients must be maintained. A gear train or transmission for a large rotary kiln is also described in detail. These are fabricated by arc welding. Repairs to a cast iron grinding mill head without extensive dismantling of mill was made possible by arc welding of steel ring in place.

This maintenance work is on the company's own equipment and is in the line of repairs, replacements, improvements and general upkeep. This equipment is used to make Portland cement and wall plaster. I am going to submit three subjects, as follows:

No. 1—Repairs to a 8 foot x 26 foot grinding mill head.

No. 2—The complete fabrication of nine rotary or star feeders.

No. 3—Gear train or transmission, for an $8\frac{1}{2}$ foot x 125 foot rotary cement kiln.

The following articles of equipment were designed by the author.

As the first subject, I will take up the repairs of a broken head of a 8 foot x 26 foot grinding mill where arc welding played an important part.

The head is 9 feet 6 inches in diameter, is 3 inches thick, has projecting hub on one side 56 inches in diameter which is bored to 46 inches, and is made of cast iron. The distance through hub is 10 inches. From this hub projection and tapering to rim are 8 "T" ribs cast integral. The ribs are $2\frac{1}{2}$ inches thick all ways and the top or cross of that section is 12 inches wide at or within 2 inches of hub. The ribs are a continuation, one with the other, and are 3 inches wide at rim or outside edge of head. At the rib intersections or at the continuation of one rib to the other, a "U" is formed of about a 10 inch radius. At center of this radius, or in bottom of "U", the rib stands up or out away from the hub proper 6 inches, behind the face of ribs at "U" and between "T" section of ribs and head; the hub proper is only $2\frac{1}{2}$ inches thick from bore out. As the journal is pressed into the bore of head, with a 5 inch flange on journal to bolt same to head; 24 $1\frac{1}{2}$-inch studs are employed for this purpose, it was necessary to cast 16 bosses against $2\frac{1}{2}$ inch wall of hub to receive the studs. The other 8 studs were in line with ribs. There were 5 fractures in head. All were in the same place and between 5 different ribs, starting in the bottom of "U" between ribs proper and continuing through to bore on outside and through bosses on the inside or behind the ribs, thus allowing head bore to open up and allowing press fit projection of journal to "work", breaking the studs as fast as they could be put in. The only repair that I could feature was something that would pull fractures together to restore the original bore of hub. The ribs at the shallow part or in bottom of "U" were 2½ inches thick, so a cross feed and compound from an old lathe was set up to turn a shoulder into ribs. This would weaken them further but it didn't matter as they were broken anyway. A shoulder 1 inch in width was turned ½ inch in diameter larger than the flange on the journal. The ribs being tapered to outside of head it was only necessary to face 10 inches of the ribs to secure the 1 inch shoulder at hub. Before the turning was started the mill was dumped of its 58-ton load of steel balls, and as these mills turn 17½ revolutions per minute, that was too fast to turn radius of that size. An 8 foot pulley was bolted on countershaft and an extra 75 horsepower motor was employed to turn mill. While machinist was turning shoulder on mill head the welder was busy rustling some 1 inch plate to make a circle to shrink onto shoulder. By using 4 separate pieces of 1 inch plate enough could be found to make a circle 55 inches inside and 77 inches outside. The circle was cut out with the torch and 2 halves were made. Permanent welds were made in the halves, and then the halves were tack welded together so the circle could be bored out to proper size. The circle was then set up on boring mill and bored to 56¾ inches while the shoulder on mill head was turned to 57 inches. After boring, the circle was laid out and drilled for four 1 inch bolts to go in each rib. The circle was then broken in two at point of tack welds and a ¾ inch square nut was welded on each side of fracture for ears to pass ⅝ inch bolts through to hold in place for welding after ring was in position to weld around journal. The ends of ring were scarfed to form about a 90 inch "V" for the weld. The ring was welded in place with very little, if any warp. As it was slightly larger than the flange of the journal, it was carried on this flange while being heated with two gas (natural) heaters. Meanwhile, the mill was rotated slowly and the heat was uniform. After 2½ hours of heating the flange was driven over the shoulder with two sections of 3 inch shafting on each side as battering rams, while mill was rotating. When ring was in place, the mill was stopped and the holes were drilled on through top or "T" section of ribs, and plate was drawn up against ribs which part we had machined. The mill has been running 12 weeks since repairing without the loosening of any of the studs and the cracks closed up entirely.

The total cost was—

E-6010 Electrodes	$ 1.20
Labor	60.40
Acetylene & Oxygen	2.50
	$64.10

The loss of time on grinding was 96 hours. The size of journal of this mill is 30 inches in diameter and 30 inches long. The mill weighs empty 80 tons, and the ball load is 58 tons, and the prime mover is a 600 horsepower, 60-cycle 2300 volt motor. Drive is through a magnetic clutch.

Had this ring been made in one piece and not welded in place, it would have been necessary to jack up the whole mill 16 inches, remove the feeder and main bearing or pillow block which would have cost $200 at least. We recently changed a head on a similar mill at a cost for labor $182. Being a discharge head it wasn't necessary to jack mill up, just take the weight at that end.

The 96 hours of lost time on mill was elapsed time and not actual labor

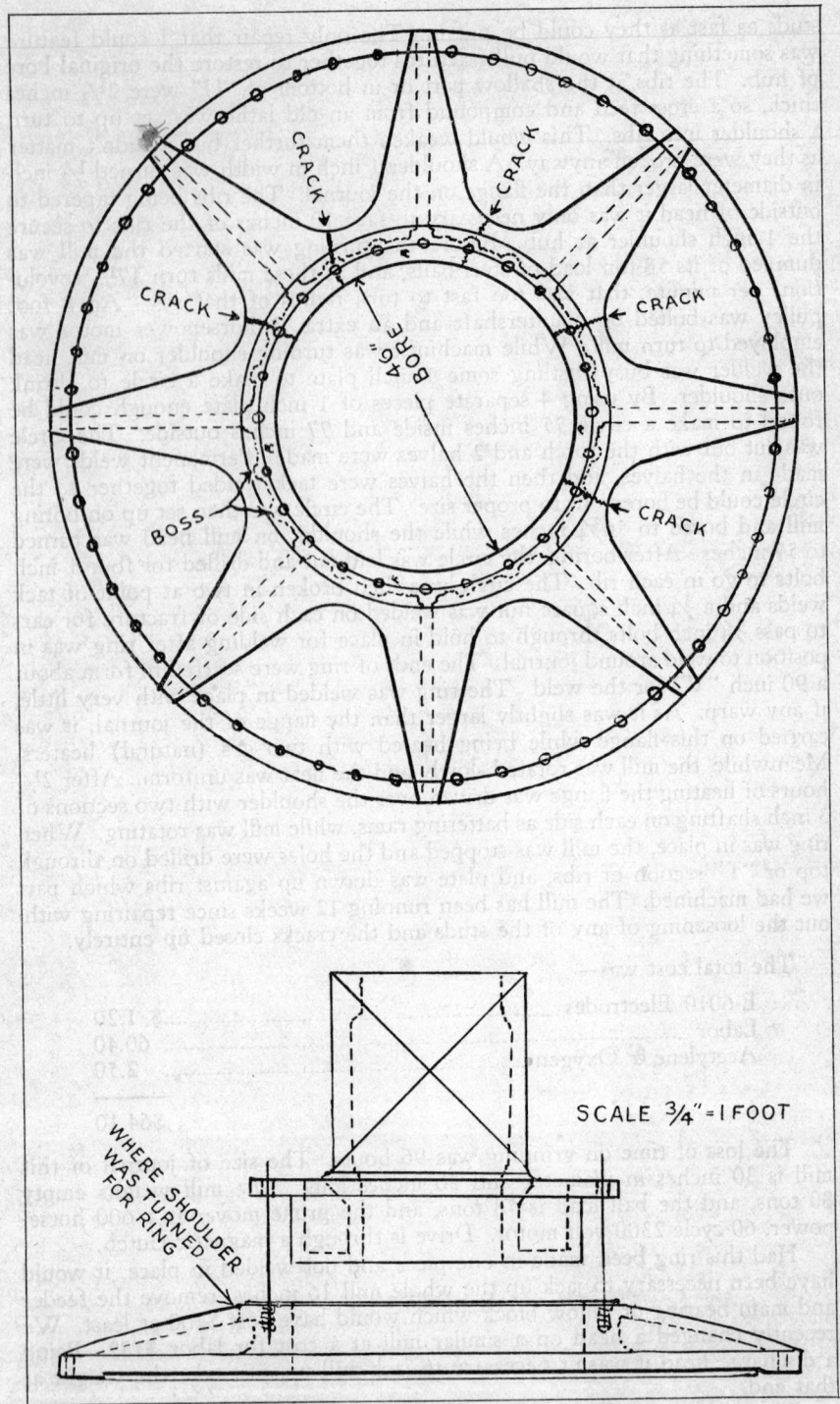

Fig. 1. Fractures in mill.

as only one crew of three men worked the day shift, plus some overtime. The cost of a new head for this mill is $1398.

As a second subject, I will take up the complete fabrication of nine star or rotary feeders. We needed these badly and for some cause or other we could not obtain them, so we proceeded to build them. The rotor of feeders is 10 inches in diameter and 12 inches in length and they have a maximum capacity of 75 barrels per hour. These were used on a circulating system in the raw mill of the cement plant and handle lime stone and shale that is ground to the fineness of 97 per cent passing a 100 mesh screen. The idea of a circulating system in the raw end of a cement plant is to flatten out the irregular raw mix by circulating about four times as much material through the circulating system as is being ground, by drawing from the rotary kiln bins and delivering back to them through a conveyor over bins. The raw mix is composed of high lime rock and low lime bearing shale which have to be properly proportioned by the chemical analysis. Sometimes for reasons beyond the chemist's control the mix will vary. Sometimes it will be too high in lime content and other times it might be on the low side. For instance, if mix goes up 1 per cent and mix that is already in bins is O.K. and we circulate four times as much of the mix that is already in bins and combine it with the new mix coming from mills, it will cut new mix four ways and reduce the rise to $1/4$ of 1 per cent. There are nine bins from which star feeders draw from, therefore there were nine feeders to be made. The feeders are mounted directly on the casing of a 16 inch screw conveyor and are driven by that same screw. The feeders were fabricated by electric arc, from $1/4$ inch sheet iron, $3/8$ inch x 2 inch flat iron, $1/4$ inch x 2 inch flat iron, 11 inch gas pipe, 2 inch gas pipe, $1\frac{1}{2}$ inch square key steel and some odds and ends. They were 12 inches in length and $10\frac{1}{4}$ inches inside with a 10 inch x 10 inch opening, short hopper on top, and a 10 inch x 11 inch short hopper on bottom, the 11 inch measurement running with pipe. The hopper on bottom to connect to angle iron on top of the 16 inch conveyor casing, will take one of the feeders only, balance of them being identically the same.

A $12\frac{1}{2}$ inch section of the 11 inch gas pipe was cut with torch as square as possible, a little in length being allowed to machine square later. On the side of the pipe that is to be the top, a 6 inch x 9 inch hole was cut, the 9 inch measurement is lengthwise of pipe. Directly across or on the other side of pipe, which is to be the bottom, a 6 inch x 11 inch hole was cut, the 11 inch measurement is lengthwise of pipe. Flanges of $3/8$ inch x 2 inch mild steel were forged by blacksmith to fit around ends of pipe and spaced $12\frac{1}{4}$ inches outside to outside, and were arc welded on the inside of flange or on side toward opening in pipe. Then the short hoppers were fabricated of $1/4$ inch plate to size of openings in pipe at small ends of hoppers and to 10 inches x 10 inches at mouth of top hopper and 10 inches x 11 inches at mouth of bottom hopper, and a rise of 3 inches at the center of opening of pipe to mouth of hopper, the ends of hoppers being cut to radius of pipe. A flange of $1/4$ inch x 2 inches was welded around large ends of hoppers to facilitate bolting to feed spout and conveyor frame. Eight $3/8$ inch machine bolts anchor the feeder to spout at top and eight in bottom flange anchor it to conveyer. The hoppers being arc welded to pipe, the assembly was placed in lathe and bored to $10\frac{1}{4}$ inch diameter and both end flanges were faced to 12 inches in length and faces were scribed for a $12\frac{1}{2}$ inch bolt circle which was laid out for eight $3/8$ inch machine bolts equally spaced. The end flange facing did not cover the entire face of flange but extended to a 7 inch radius leaving about ½ inch of the outside of the flange untouched and forming a shoulder for end plate to fit into, for purpose of centering the head plate and relieving head bolts of responsibility of holding head central. The end heads were cut from ¼ inch plate, being round and 14½ inches in diameter or large enough so they could be machined for a spigot fit into end flange of feeder. In the center, a hole was cut large enough to allow a 2 inch length of 2 inch pipe to enter. The pipe section was welded into plate flush on the inside. Four ribs of ¼ inch x 1½ inch iron were cut and tapered to edge of plate and butt welded to plate and pipe section at 90° around pipe section.

On inside of 2 inch section of pipe several beads were run lengthwise of pipe to hold babbitt. A hole was drilled in pipe section and tapped for ⅛ inch alemite zerk grease fittings for lubrication. The plates were then babbitted solid, placed in lathe and faced, and bearings bored to fit 1½ inch shaft. Outside of head plate was turned for spigot fit into shoulder in feeder flanges.

The rotor or runner that fits into the feeder has four blades that was made by cutting four pieces of ¼ inch plate 6 inches wide and 11½ inches long, being careful to get the ends perfectly square. At 1½ inches from edge of the first plate and lengthwise of plate, the second plate was stood on edge at a 90° angle from first plate and butt welded to first plate on one side only, the side away from the 1½ inch measurement, the ends being flush. On the second plate, the third was placed on edge at a 90° angle from the second plate and at 1½ inches from second plate being sure that ends were flush and butt welded on the side opposite the first plate. And the fourth plate was stood on edge at a 90° angle from third plate and contacted the 1½ inch edge of the first plate and was welded to third and first in the outside corners; thus making a four-bladed rotor with a 1½ inch square hole through center. Two round discs were cut from the same material, 10⅜ inches in diameter, and a 1½ inch square hole was cut in the center of each with square holes lining up with square through the blade assembly. The blades were butt welded on both sides to the discs, one on each end of blade assembly. The assembly was then slipped over a piece of 1½ inch square steel with center in one end, the other end being chucked in lathe and turned to 10⅛ inches in diameter, faced on both ends to 11⅞ inches in length. The shaft on which they are carried is made of 1½ inch square key stock turned on one end to 1½ inches in diameter x 2½ inches long, while the other end is 1½ inches in diameter x 7½ inches in length. The square portion in center or on which the rotor rides is 11⅞ inches, making the total length of shaft 21⅞ inches.

A ⅜ inch x 3/16 inch keyway, 1½ inches long, was milled in long end of shaft and 2¾ inches to center of keyway from end of shaft. The feeders are rotated by an oscillating movement with an overrunning clutch by using a 6 inch diameter x 1½ inch face roller and wedge block; the wedge block being on the oscillating frame and roller on feeder shaft. A 1⅛ inch round x 1½ inch long roller contacts 6 inch roller and wedge block between them. On the back stroke the small roller simply follows the wedge block to end of travel and on forward stroke it grips the 6 inch roller on feeder shaft and rotates it. The oscillating frame was fabricated of ¼ inch plate, cutting two 7 inch diameter discs having two projections on them outside of the radius line. The projections are at a 90° angle to each other, one at the bottom of oscillating or driving frame and one on the side. The side projection is 4½ inches wide and extends to 5¼ inches from center of disc or frame. The end of projection is trimmed to 10° from vertical, or leans out at top, that much forming a seat for wedge block. The wedge block is of 1 inch x 1⅝ inch steel, 4½ inches long, is faced with manganese steel electrode, and has two $33/64$ inch holes drilled through edgewise or through the 1 inch face at 3 inch centers. The projections were drilled likewise, and block bolts in between the projections on the discs of frame. The bottom projection extends 1½ inches outside of the 3½ inch radius line and its purpose is to provide a place on which to bolt the driving arms. On the vertical center line of the lower projections, 2¼ inches from center of driving frame or discs, a ⅜ inch hole was drilled in both discs. 5 inches from the ⅜ inch hole, and on the same center line and toward point of projection, a $5/16$ inch hole was drilled in each disc projection. These last holes are for shear pins. The driving frame rides on babbitted bearings on feeder shaft, straddling the 6 inch diameter x 1½ inch face roller. The bearings were from 2 inch sections of 2 inch extra heavy pipe and welded into holes cut in center of frames; the pipes being flush on one side and welded to frame on opposite side. Three or four beads were run on inside of pipes to hold babbitt.

They were babbitted solid and bored out to fit 1½ inch feeder shaft. Holes were drilled and tapped in pipe bearings for zerk grease fittings. The frames are exactly alike except they are right and left hand or in pairs. The 6 inch diameter x 1½ inch face roller that rides between frames has a forged band of ⅜ inch x 1¾ inch material and, in rough, was 6⅛ inches in diameter. The web of roller is of ⅜ inch sheet steel with hole in center to allow passage of a 1¾ inch section of $27/16$ inch shafting for hub. The hub was welded in plate on both sides of plate and rim or tire was welded to web on both sides; the hub being central with web as well as tire. The roller assembly in the rough was then turned to 6 inch diameter and 1½ inch face and 1½ inch hub length. The hub was bored to 1½ inch, and ⅜ inch x $3/16$ inch keyway was cut. Two, or a pair of driving arms, were made of

Fig. 2. Ring shrunk on turned shoulder. Fig. 3. Welded and turned mill. Fig. 4. Edgewise view of sound head. Fig. 5. The nine rotary feeders after finishing.

¼ inch x 2 inch x 16 inch long flat iron. In one end, a ⅜ inch hole was drilled in each arm; and ¾ inch from end, at 5 inch centers from the ⅜ inch holes, a ⁵⁄₁₆ inch hole was drilled in each arm. The arms are loose riveted to the driving frames through the ⅜ inch holes in arms and ⅜ inch holes in frame.

The ⁵⁄₁₆ inch holes in arms match the ⁵⁄₁₆ inch holes in bottom projection in driving frames where a shear pin is placed as the driving mechanism is positive. A shear pin is necessary as sometimes tramp iron and other hard objects get into the feeder. The arms being riveted on outside of driving frames, the clearance between arms is 2⅛ inches. A 3 inch diameter x 2 inch width roller is carried on a hardened bushing between arms at bottom; a ¾ inch bolt running through arms and bushing. When mounted on top of 16 inch screw conveyor casing the arms, with roller between them, hang down in conveyor trough to within 2 inches of barrel or center tube of conveyor screw. At this point, a section of the screw is cut away with a 90° to center of screw edge. Leading to this straight edge a ½ inch x 2 inch x 3½ inch piece of flat iron is arc welded the long way of the block at 90° from conveyor center tube. As the conveyor screw rotates, the block strikes the roller thus turning the feeder until the block runs out from under the roller, then roller and arms return to the starting point. At top speed of the feeder, the ratio is 6 to 1, 6 revolutions of screw to 1 of feeder. The feeder can be adjusted by a stop screw that can be screwed in to shorten the return of roller and arms. To be certain the arms will return to their starting point, an adjustable weight is made of a 2½ inch section of 2⁷⁄₁₆ inch shafting with a ⅞ inch hole being drilled through lengthwise of shaft section and a ½ inch set screw from side to meet hole. The weights are mounted on a 10 inch section of ¾ inch round rod which has a triangle shaped piece of ¼ inch plate welded to one end of it, wide enough to drill two ¹⁷⁄₃₂ inch holes across end at 3 inch centers. The triangle plate is bolted to driving frame with same bolts that secure wedge block. The assembly of the feeders was to slip the rotor of feeder over the square portion of shaft and then push rotor in to body. Bolt head to body on the side that the short end of shaft projects. Then the other head is bolted on opposite end of body. The driving frame that has projection on left side, as you stand facing long end of shaft, is slipped over shaft with bearing projection first. Then woodruff key is placed in shaft and 6 inch diameter x 1½ inch roller is forced over key, and the remaining driving frame is slipped on. The wedge block is next put in place, two ½ inch x 3 inch machine bolts are passed through driving frames and wedge block and adjustable weight arm plate holes are slipped over bolt ends and secured by hex nuts. The top hopper of feeder is bolted to spout from feed bin and bottom of feeder is bolted to angle frame over conveyor. These feeders work very satisfactory and cost only a fraction of the factory-made cast iron feeders. The material in these feeders is mostly used material. The actual cost of these feeders was $50.45 a piece, or $454.05 for the nine of them, while the price of factory-made feeders that perform the same duty and of equal size cost $290 a piece. We bought two of these feeders in 1927 at a cost of $580.

The third and last subject is an all arc welded, oil-tight, dust-tight, self-lubricated gear train or transmission for an 8½ foot x 125 foot rotary cement kiln. This unit consists of seven gears and four shafts, ten bearings or pillow blocks and two thrust bearings. The shafts range in size as follows: 3¹⁵⁄₁₆ inches in diameter, 4¹⁵⁄₁₆ inches in diameter, 5⁷⁄₁₆ inches in diameter, and 7½ inches in diameter; the bearings, in length from 9 inches to 17 inches. The original setup was a cast iron frame or sole plate set in concrete with bearings or pillow blocks bolted to it. The gears and bearings run in the open; the bearings being lubricated with a hard high temperature block grease while the gear teeth were lubricated with "Coglube" a heavy sticky dope that became very hard when cooled off. There is no way provided to retain gear dope; it or a good part of it found its way to the floor. There is always cement clinker dust present around the kilns and this dust mixed with the gear dope makes an excellent grinding compound, causing very rapid wear to gear teeth and bearings and shafts, necessitating a complete overhaul once a year or oftener. This equipment operates twenty-four hours a day.

In building this unit we used the material at hand including the gears, bearings, etc. Had we been allowed to select our materials, the unit could have been much more compact. Most of the gears and bearings are of a standard and fit most of the kilns, dryers and rotary coolers. The arrangement of the gears and shafts as well as the lengths of shafts were changed to suit our design. The main frame of the gear train case was fabricated of 10 inch I beam sections with $\frac{1}{2}$ inch web. The outside measurements of the main frame were 6 feet 2 inches x 9 feet 6 inches, the 9 feet 6 inches measurement running parallel with kiln. The closed-in compartment does not cover the entire frame 9 feet 6 inches, because the final drive pinion shafts are outside of closed-in portion on account of the pinion meshing with a girth or master gear which encircles the shell or body of kiln and therefore cannot be enclosed with balance of gears. There are two side members of frame, one on each side, cut to 9 feet 6 inches in length, with top and bottom flanges beveled to 45 degrees leaving the ends of web untouched. The end I beam members were beveled at ends the same way so, as the four members were set up corner to corner, the beveled ends fit perfectly. These corners were welded inside and out. The untouched webs offered a 90 degree fillet to be welded in. At a point 6 inches from center of front main members, a 5 inch notch reaching from inside edges to web of side frame I beam, was cut in top and bottom of both side frame members to allow a crossmember of the same material (10 inch I beam) to be dropped in. This member was welded top and bottom and at both ends to flanges on side members as well as being butt welded to web of side members of frame and will be known as No. 1 crossmember. At 14 inches from No. 1 and toward back end of frame similar notches were cut in side frames for a second crossmember. It was also welded to side frame members as No. 1 was. This member will be known as No. 2. At 11 inches from No. 2 crossmember, also toward back or rear end of frame, a third member was fitted in and welded as was Nos. 1 and 2. This member will be known as No. 3. At 7 inches from No. 3 member, a fourth member was welded in place as were the other three, this one will be known as No. 4. 25 inches from No. 4 and toward the rear of frame, No. 5 member is located and anchored the same as the four preceding ones. The sixth member is only 7 inches from the fifth and notched and welded similar to the others. It is known as No. 6. To next and last crossmember is 31 inches which is 8 inch centers from the center of back end member of frame and is known as No. 7. All measurements are from center to center of webs of cross and end members of frame. Between No. 6 and No. 7 crossmembers, a double knee brace of the same material was welded in. The ends of each knee or corner brace intersect in the center of No. 6 crossmember while the other ends are welded in the back corners of frame. This is to stiffen frame at this point as the final drive is located here. From top of frame to top of

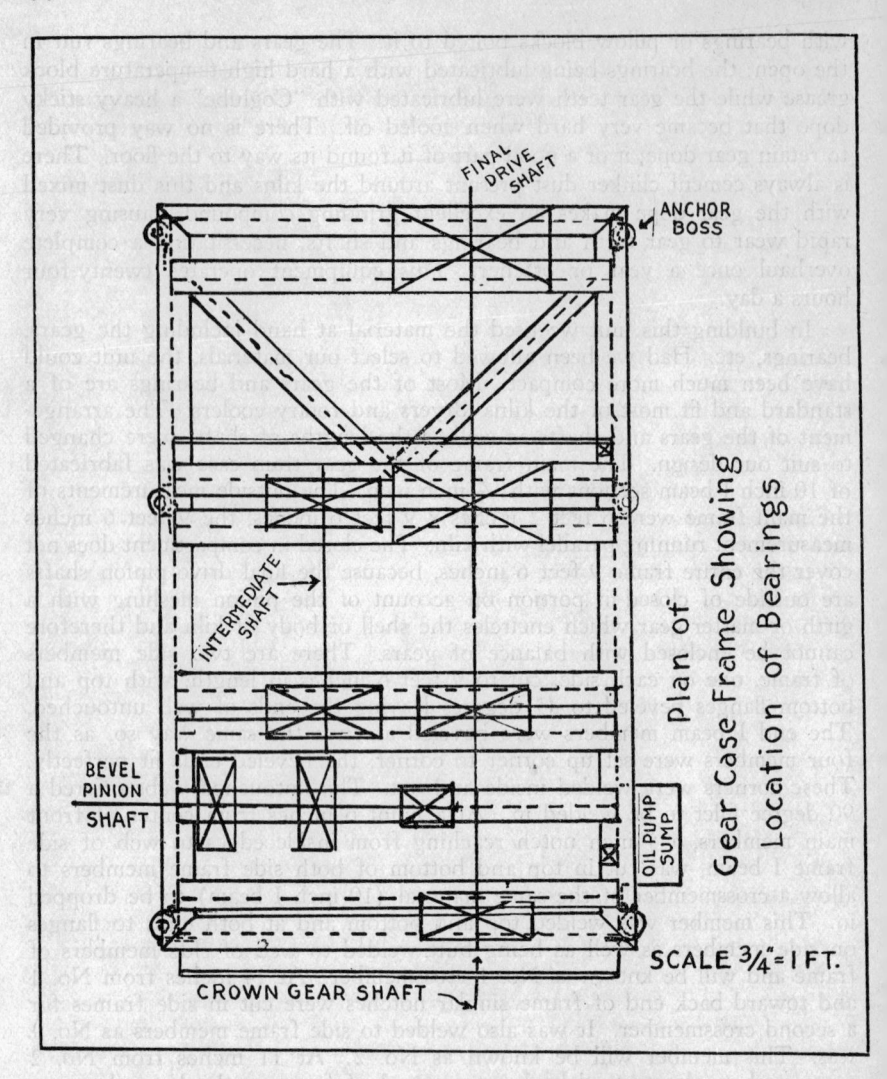

Fig. 6. Gear case frame showing location of bearings.

bearings, base of outboard bearing on final drive is 18 inches. A pedestal 18 inches in height, 12 inches in width, 26 inches in length at top or bearing seat, and 4 feet 9 inches at bottom, was fabricated. The center line of bearing was 19 inches from one end, and 38 inches from the other end. The long end gives the pedestal a brace against drive, as this bearing being on end of final drive shaft has the greatest pressure of all bearings. The side plate is of ¾ inch boiler plate, and the top is of 1 inch plate. The short battered end cover plate is also of ¾ inch plate. The batter at this end amounts to 6 inches. The top of long batter or brace is of ¾ inch plate. At the end of cap piece or bearing seat, and on the end that has long brace, a scotch block of 1 inch material stands up 4 inches above bearing seat; and the length of the width of bearing seat, or 12 inches is welded to seat. Two right angle triangle pieces of $\frac{3}{4}$ inch plates, 4 inches wide at widest end and 10 inches long tapering to 1 inch at narrow end, welded to edges of bearing seat, the 4 inch end is welded to scotch block and narrow end toward center line of bearing rests between the braces. Under the cap piece or bearing seat and $1\frac{1}{4}$ inches on either side of bearing anchor bolts, a rib of $\frac{1}{2}$ inch x 3 inches is welded crosswise of the pedestal, being butt welded to bottom of seat and ends of ribs to inside walls of side plates. These are to stiffen cap piece and hold bolts from turning. These bolts are $1\frac{1}{2}$ inches in diameter and are 22 inches center to center. The scotch block has two $1\frac{5}{8}$ inch holes drilled $2\frac{1}{4}$ inches above bearing seat and 5 inch centers. The bearing has corresponding holes running lengthwise of base through which $1\frac{1}{2}$ inch bolts are passed to hold bearing tight against scotch block. A 7 inch round hole was cut in the short battered end of pedestal to permit bolting bearing to pedestal. The second pedestal for final drive shaft includes a bearing seat for (what we call the intermediate shaft) bearing. This double pedestal is the same length at base as the first one with the same 6 inch batter on the same end as the other. It is 18 inches high from top of main frame crossmembers to top of bearing seat for final drive shaft bearing and only 4 inches from top of main frame crossmembers to top of bearing seat for intermediate shaft bearing. The dimensions of bearing seat for final drive shaft are the same as the first one having the cross ribs under cap plate and welded in the same way.

At the end of the first pedestal that had the long brace, the second pedestal drops vertically at the 26 inch end of cap piece of final drive shaft bearing to a level of 4 inches above the top of main frame crossmembers No. 5 and No. 6. The 4 inch level for the intermediate shaft bearing extends 24 inches, where a $\frac{3}{4}$ inch plate x 10 inches long and $6\frac{1}{2}$ inches wide is welded vertically to cross members No. 5 and No. 6, and stands up against end of intermediate shaft bearing base serving as a scotch block, drilled and tapped for two 1 inch set screws $1\frac{1}{4}$ inches above bearing base and at 5 inch centers. To gain additional thread a 1 inch square nut is welded to plate at each set screw hole. At the other end of intermediate shaft bearing seat a 1 inch plate, 12 inches wide and 18 inches long, is stood vertically against end of final drive shaft bearing and welded to it as well as to the seat of intermediate shaft bearing. The plate serves as a scotch block for final drive shaft bearing and has two $1\frac{5}{8}$ inch holes drilled in it at $2\frac{1}{4}$ inches above final drive shaft bearing seat and 5 inch centers, through which $1\frac{1}{2}$ inch bolts pass into bearing base to secure bearing to scotch block. The intermediate shaft bearing base is drilled for a bearing that has four base bolts of $1\frac{1}{4}$ inches. There are two $\frac{1}{2}$ inch x 2 inch ribs under cap piece running lengthwise of the base and set at $2\frac{1}{2}$ inches apart outside to outside. The holes in base for bearing are $4\frac{1}{2}$ inch centers so the bolt heads contact the ribs on the outside, thereby preventing bolts from turning when nuts are screwed on or off. The bearings used on this shaft are of the angle type, the angle being 30 degrees and are 10 inches in length and fitted with bronze split bushings. A hole was provided in end of base to enter bearing bolts. The opposite end of this double pedestal has a 7 inch round hole to enter final drive shaft bearing bolts. As the driven gear on the final drive shaft overhangs the bearing and pinion, it "lifts" on the gear, causing severe cap strain on the bearing. Four extra bolts were provided to secure cap to bearing. The upper ends of these bolts pass through a special saddle that was made to fit over bearing cap. The lower end or heads of the bolts fit into claws that were welded to side plates of pedestal. The four extra bolts are 1¼ inches x 20 inches and being too long to pass through an eye at the bottom, the claws were designed so the body of bolt could be passed between the fingers of claws and pulled up until heads were secured. The claws were made of 1 inch boiler plate 5¼ inches x 5¼ inches, a notch being cut in one side 1¼ inches wide, 1¾ inches deep with a 2 inch piece of ½ inch x 2 inches welded on the projecting ends on each side of the gap to prevent bolt working out and keep head from turning. The back edge was then butt welded to the ¾ inch side plates of the pedestal. The assembly was then butt welded to cross members No. 5 and No. 6, with final drive shaft bearing in line. Now the third pedestal which is also double was fabricated of the same size material. The cap plates are 1 inch plate and the side and end plates are ¾ inch. One end of this double pedestal is a companion for the intermediate shaft bearing support and is 4 inches high to top of bearing seat from top of main frame crossmembers while the other end is 12 inches high from main frame cross members to top of bearing seat and is 19 inches between scotch blocks. The end plate on the battered end of the 12 inch height stood 2½ inches above the bearing seat and was bent enough so it stood vertically and formed a scotch block at that end, having the regulation set screws to adjust and secure bearing, and having 6 inch round hole in end plate through which the bearing bolts are passed. At other end of this 12 inch height, a ¾ inch x 10 inch x 10½ inch plate runs vertically to 4 inches level, leaving 2½ inches above bearing seat which is the scotch block at this end, having the set screws as does the other end. The 4 inch level is for the lower or front intermediate shaft bearing with the same dimensions as the other one, being 19 inches between scotch blocks. As the 12 inches is for a smaller bearing than the final drive shaft bearing, it is necessary to weld a scotch block on 4 inch level and at 5¾ inches from vertical plate, which divides the 4 inch and 12 inch levels, to back up intermediate shaft bearing. This block is a piece of 2 inch by 2 inch square iron and has no set screws. The shaft that rides the bearing on the 12 inch level is known as the crown gear shaft and is 4$^{15}/_{16}$ inches in diameter while the intermediate shaft is 5$^{7}/_{16}$ inches.

The bearings for these two shafts are identical, the only difference is in the brass bushing which is cast with enough stock to bore to either size. A 15-tooth, 2¼ inch pitch, 8 inch face, spur pinion overhangs the bearing on crown gear shaft on this end. The crown gear shaft and the final drive shaft are in direct line vertically. This assembly is butt welded to main frame crossmembers No. 3 and No. 4. On crossmember No. 2 a combination bracket was fabricated to carry the three 3$^{15}/_{16}$ inch bearings of the bevel pinion shaft, two of the bearings being of the pillow block type and one of the sleeve type. The sleeve type bearing consists of a cast iron bushing 6½ inches outside diameter and 8½ inches long, fitted with a bronze sleeve to fit the shaft. The bevel pinion that meshes with the bevel or crown gear is mounted on this shaft using two keys, one tapered and one gib. The gib, to hold pinion in mesh with gear by putting thrust on shaft, projects 8½ inches beyond small end of pinion. On this projection where sleeve bearing is mounted, the end of pinion shaft clearing the crown gear shaft is ½ inch. A pillow block is located directly behind bevel pinion and sleeve in front of pinion. A bracket had to be designed that would clear pinion teeth between bearings. The sleeve bearings had to be made as small in diameter as possible as the room between pinion shaft and bevel gear is very limited. The bracket that supports the sleeve bearing was built up with ½ inch plates 18 inches long and square on both ends and 12 inches in width. These plates were stood on edge, the 18 inch measurement on the horizontal, spaced $3\frac{1}{2}$ inches inside to inside and located with one end of them $2\frac{3}{4}$ inches to left of center line of crown gear shaft while looking at front end of gear train, from the front of kiln, while the other ends of plates extend from this location still farther to left toward intermediate shaft where they butt up against the right side of the bracket or bearing base of the pillow block that is located directly behind the bevel pinion on the same shaft. The cap piece or bearing seat for sleeve bearing is of 1 inch plate $6\frac{1}{2}$ inches wide and $8\frac{1}{2}$ inches in length, and is welded to tops of the $\frac{1}{2}$ inch plates at extreme right hand corners of vertical plates and flush with vertical plate corners. To the top of cap piece are welded 2 pieces 1 inch x 7 inches x $6\frac{1}{2}$ inches long. These pieces before welding were chucked in lathe and a hole bored in center to $5\frac{1}{2}$ inches after boring, the plates were split lengthwise or the $6\frac{1}{2}$ inch way. The two bottom halves were welded (back down) to the cap piece of sleeve bearing seat at 7 inch centers. The sleeve bearing has grooves turned in the cast iron bushing that pushes down over the semi-circles or rides in the semi-circles as a cradle. The two remaining semi-circles are fabricated to form a saddle to clamp cast iron bushing into place by welding two $\frac{3}{4}$ inch x 2 inch flats 8 inches long to tops of semi-circle plates so they measure 7 inches center and fit grooves in bearing bushing. The outsides of plates are flush with ends of semi-circles and are drilled for four $\frac{3}{4}$ inch machine bolts, center to center or crosswise being $5\frac{1}{2}$ inches and lengthwise the same. Cap bolts are used and pass through slots that are machined in sides of bushing and on into cap plate of bearing bracket which has been drilled and tapped. The top of sleeve bearing bracket is braced sidewise with a $\frac{3}{4}$ inch plate welded between bracket top and top of crown gear shaft pedestal. The sleeve bearing bracket is welded to crossmember No. 2. Directly under this bracket the No. 2 I-beam crossmember was ribbed between top and bottom flanges for stiffness. There are two ribs on each side of $\frac{1}{2}$ inch x 2 inch flat iron and spaced 8 inches apart. The pillow block bracket or pedestal behind bevel pinion is at 90 degrees to sleeve or outboard bearing bracket due to the fact that the base of the pillow block is crosswise to the bore of the pillow block while the bore and base length are parallel to each on the sleeve bearing. The rear end of this bracket butts into center of front side of intermediate shaft bearing bracket and is welded to it standing 8 inches higher than intermediate shaft bearing bracket which is only 4 inches to cap piece from top of main frame. The other end of bevel pinion shaft pillow block bracket rests on No. 1 crossmember and is welded to it.

The end of sleeve bearing support brackets butts into side vertically under center of shaft and is butt welded to it. This bracket is made up of $\frac{3}{4}$ inch plate sides and $\frac{3}{4}$ inch cap piece or bearing seat and is drilled for four $\frac{7}{8}$ inch bearing base bolts at $3\frac{1}{2}$ inch centers across base and 11 inch centers lengthwise of base. There are two scotch blocks welded to cap plate of $\frac{3}{4}$ inch x 2 inch flat iron and they fit both ends of bearing base snug, as the bevel pinion shaft bearings are never shifted. The mesh of the gear teeth being adjusted by end motion on both shafts and thrusts are on shafts, the pinion and gear being keyed to shaft with gib keys. Sixteen inches along shaft from center of last pillow block bracket is a similar bracket for a similar bearing or pillow block. The 16 inch measurement is from center to center of bearing, the bearings being 10 inches in length leaves 6 inches in clear between ends of bearings. This bracket is near or within two inches of vertical case housing, and is welded at back end to No. 3 crossmember, and to No. 2

crossmember at shaft center line and has a sloping end from its 12 inch height down to meet No. 1 crossmember and is welded to all three crossmembers. The last two brackets have two ribs each of $\frac{1}{2}$ inch x $1\frac{1}{2}$ inch flat iron running lengthwise under cap piece and spaced so as to fit against flats or inside of bearing base bolt heads preventing from turning when nuts are screwed on or off. Between these last two bearings is a thrust bearing on bevel pinion shaft with adjusting screws that project through to outside of housing for ease of adjustment. This thrust bearing is of the single ring type, a ring 1 inch thick and $6\frac{3}{4}$ inches in diameter, and bored to shrink fit on the 3 foot $\frac{5}{16}$ inch bevel pinion shaft is located at the center of and between the pillow blocks on shaft. The face or the thrust side of ring was faced with manganese steel electrode and ground smooth. A bronze collar $\frac{1}{2}$ inch thick, $6\frac{3}{4}$ inches in diameter and $3\frac{31}{32}$ inch bore with oil grooves in both faces rides against thrust ring. An elliptic shaped plate 1 inch thick was cut and bored to 4 inches, measuring 8 inches across narrow way and 13 inches from point to point. At 11 inches from center to center and near the points, a 1 inch hole was drilled in each point. One end of a 10 inch section of 1 inch cold rolled round steel was welded in each hole flush on one side. On the flush side a 2 inch section of 7 inch extra heavy pipe was welded central with the bore. The purpose of this pipe is to carry the bronze washer, as I have known loose washers riding shafts to cut shaft nearly in two. In the top of this pipe section a hole was drilled and tapped for $\frac{1}{4}$ inch pipe fitting directly over bronze washer to connect with automatic lubricating system. A section of 2 inch x 2 inch x $\frac{3}{8}$ inch angle iron 10 inches long was drilled to match anchor bolts in base of pillow block, one of these for each side of bearing. On top of the vertical leg and offset enough so to be central with anchor bolts, a 10 inch section of 1 inch heavy tubing was welded to each angle, a 1 inch hex nut was welded on one end of each through which adjusting screws pass. The sections of 1 inch round cold rolled steel welded in the elliptic plate enter these sections of 1 inch tubing and extend to and against ends of adjusting screws. The nuts on ends of tubing are snug against vertical side of housing, a hole being cut in housing to permit screw to pass through. A lock nut can be run up against housing from outside to secure screw and hold adjustment. Located on the front main member and No. 1 crossmember is the bracket or pedestal for the front crown gear outboard bearing. This bearing is at the back of bevel or crown gear. The backing of gear being toward bearing is 12 inches in height from top of main frame to top of cap plate or bearing seat and is 8 inches wide at top and 14 inches long between scotch blocks which are formed by the 1 inch end plates projecting $2\frac{1}{2}$ inches above top of cap plate. The ends of this pedestal are battered so that pedestal measures 24 inches long at base. The end plates are bent at top of cap plate so they stand vertical. The end plates are also battered sidewise, while they are 9 inches wide at top they measure 12 inches wide at bottom or base. This batter is to help take care of the end thrust that is exerted by the crown gear shaft. The side plates are of $\frac{3}{4}$ inch plate and four $\frac{1}{2}$ inch x $1\frac{1}{2}$ inch ribs are run crosswise under cap plate and in such a manner as to hold the bearing anchor bolt heads between them, four $1\frac{1}{4}$ inch bolts being used. The tops of end plates are drilled and tapped for two 1 inch setscrews to secure bearings.

The end plates also have a 6 inch round hole in them to pass the bearing anchor bolts through. The bracket is butt welded to front main member and No. 1 crossmember. The crown gear shaft and the final drive shaft are in line vertically. The final drive shaft pedestals are 18 inches in height while the crown gear shaft bearing bracket is only 12 inches. To front main I-beam member is welded a 4 inch x 4 inch x $3/8$ inch angle running from center web of one side main member to center of web on other side member. One leg of angle is welded to edge of upper flange of front main end member all of its length from side to side, the other leg of angle pointing upward. There are seven ribs between lower flange and upper flange and 4 inches x 4 inches x $3/8$ inch angle to strengthen I-beams and help support the angle. The ribs are butt welded to I-beam flanges and web and to bottom of angle. These ribs are made of $1/2$ inch plate, $6\frac{1}{2}$ inches wide at top and taper to $2\frac{1}{2}$ inches at bottom or lower I-beam flange. The purpose of this angle is twofold, one being to support the bottom half or the vertical end of housing which is fabricated of $1/4$ inch plate to a height of $25\frac{3}{8}$ inches above top of main frame or to the center of final drive shaft. The other purpose is to gain room between housing and outboard crown gear shaft pedestal to place a thrust bearing for crown gear shaft. This thrust is of the step type. Two vertical angles 4 inches x $3\frac{1}{2}$ x $1/2$ inch and 16 inches long are welded leg to leg making a channel. The $3\frac{1}{2}$ inch x $3\frac{1}{2}$ inch legs are welded together and the bottoms of the welded legs are trimmed with torch so the 4 inch legs will slip down in behind the vertical leg of the 4 inch x 4 inch x $3/8$ inch that was welded horizontal to the front main member, and the vertical angles, now a channel, are located in center and in front of outboard crown gear shaft bracket and legs of channel are welded to front side of bracket. At the height of the center of crown gear shaft a hole was drilled through weld and tapped for a $1\frac{3}{8}$ inch set screw. An additional length of thread was secured by welding on a $1\frac{3}{8}$ inch square nut. On the inside of this angle in direct line with shaft, a four inch section of 5 inch extra heavy pipe was butt welded, a piece of 1 inch square key stock being welded lengthwise of pipe and on inside of pipe before pipe was welded in place to angles.

A $3\frac{1}{2}$ inch section of shafting was turned to fit this pipe loosely with a 1 inch keyway milled in it to fit key in pipe. The end of shaft section was counterbored to receive shank of a bronze button $4\frac{7}{8}$ inch in diameter at face and necked down to fit tight in counterbore of shaft, the button having a slot across the face for an oil way. This bearing is oiled through the automatic system. The adjustment is made through the $1\frac{3}{8}$ inch set screw. The $25\frac{3}{8}$ inch high vertical housing is built clear around the main frame from front to No. 6 crossmember except a section directly in front of intermediate shaft assembly which is removable by lifting up. This is to allow the removal of intermediate shaft assembly as this assembly cannot be lifted straight up on account of the pinion on it rides under the pitch circle of the driven gear. The vertical sides of the housing have a $1/4$ inch x 2 inch flat welded edgewise 2 inches below top on the outside, and are used to bolt the housing cover, having $13/32$ inch holes drilled at 8 inch centers and in center of flats for $3/8$ inch bolts. Running along back side of No. 6 crossmember a 4 inch x 4 inch x $3/8$ inch angle is welded, the edge of the horizontal leg is welded to edge of back top flange of No. 6 crossmember with the other leg toward back of frame and standing up in much the same manner as 4 inch x 4 inch x $3/8$ inch angle which was welded to front main member. The 4 inch x 4 inch x $3/8$ inch reaches from center of I-beam web on left side of side member to center of web on right side member. The back housing is carried on and welded to the vertical leg of angle. The angle provides needed space between housing and in the closed final drive shaft bearing pedestal for the extra bolts and claws that reinforce the regular cap bolts. The space is also used for a connecting rod that drives oil pump that lubricates the whole assembly of gears, shafts and bearings. The end of the intermediate shaft is drilled and tapped 2 inches off center for 1 inch N.C. stud. To the stud a connecting rod is attached with an adjustable bronze bushing. The connecting rod reaches from center of intermediate shaft, which is on left side of case, to the opposite corner and behind final drive shaft bearing bracket, and is connected to a vertical arm 10 inches long which is keyed to a horizontal $2\frac{3}{16}$ inch shaft that runs along side of case and on inside of case to front of main frame, where at 18 inches from front end of frame, a horizontal arm is keyed to shaft and projects through side of vertical housing, a slot being provided for travel of arm. From center of pumpshaft to center of eye in arm is 8 inches. An outboard bearing is used on each end of pump shaft. The bearing was made of $2\frac{1}{2}$ inch sections of $2\frac{1}{2}$ inch pipe, babbitt lined and are clamped in frame provided for same by butt welding two $\frac{3}{8}$ inch x 3 inch flats 4 inches long side by side and measuring $1\frac{1}{2}$ inches between them to top of right frame member. The flats were at the ends and stand vertically and have a notch cut from top and into which pipe bearings fit. A saddle or clamp bent to radius of pipe is clamped over pipes and held by two $\frac{1}{2}$ inch bolts that run through top flange of side member I-beam. The kiln that this gear train drives is set out of level $\frac{1}{2}$ inch per lineal foot of kiln section and gear train is set likewise. The front end of gear train frame being lowest is reason for pump in front end. The pump is of our own design and build, has a bore of $3\frac{7}{8}$ inches, a stroke of $3\frac{1}{2}$ inches, plate valve in bottom of cylinder and a plate valve on top of piston, the piston having ten $\frac{3}{8}$ inch holes. A compartment for oil pump was fabricated on outside of housing the center of it being 18 inches from front end of frame. The compartment is 12 inches deep, 16 inches wide and projects from main frame side member 8 inches. The bottom of compartment is flush with bottom of frame side member. The compartment is welded all around. The projecting horizontal arm on pump shaft extends to directly over center of pump piston rod, a short connecting rod between arm and rod to take care of the swing of arm as it reciprocates up and down. The pump is anchored by two $\frac{5}{8}$ inch bolts which pass up through ears that are welded to top cylinder head. The pump rests on a chain in bottom of pump compartment which holds it off bottom 1 inch. The anchor bolt heads slip into claws that are welded to chain.

A dust tight sloping cover for compartment is made so it can be lifted up and taken completely off. The bottom of cover has inside and outside flanges that straddle top edge of oil pump compartment. The pump being on outside of gear case can easily be taken care of. A 1 inch oil line runs from pump to a manifold mounted on front vertical housing and on inside of housing. A $\frac{1}{4}$ inch pipe leads from the various outlets in manifold to every bearing in case and a sight feed drip to final drive shaft bearing that is outside of case. A $\frac{1}{4}$ inch pipe also feeds a reservoir that is under drive pinion on intermediate shaft. All other gears get plenty of oil from splash and bearing drains. The driven gear on intermediate shaft runs directly in the oil in bottom of frame. There is a valve in manifold for each oil line that can be adjusted from outside. On the right side of case when standing in front of it there are three inspection doors, one in front of each bearing pedestal, and are 14 inches wide and 18 inches high. Through these doors minor repairs can be made such as tighten base or cap bolts. These nuts can't work loose for the reason we weld a light strip such as $\frac{1}{4}$ inch x 1 inch flat iron from one nut to the other which can be easily removed with torch if necessary. The covers for these openings are made of $1/4$ inch plate with a $1/8$ inch x $3/4$ inch strip welded edgewise to cover and to just fit the opening and are held in place with two $3/4$ inch round rods, with two eccentrics welded on each rod 1 inch from each end. The rods have a handle welded in center of them and when handle is straight up the short side of eccentrics are next to covers and when handle is down the eccentrics tighten against the covers. The ends of rods fit into holes in $1/2$ inch x 2 inch ribs that are welded vertically on each side of each door. In the front wall of vertical housing there are two 7 inch round inspection doors. These covers are held on the same as the larger ones except have only one rod and handle. In back wall of vertical housing, and directly in front of intermediate shaft bearing where oil pump connecting rod is connected to (out of center) stud a 14 inch x 18 inch inspection door is located. In the top cover plates two 7 inch round inspection doors are present; one over crown gear shaft, and one over intermediate shaft and have (push over) caps. One 7 inch round inspection hole is in front cover plate wall directly over oil manifold. The cover for case is made in four pieces and is made of 14 ga. iron so it would be light to handle. The lower edge of cover has a $1 1/2$ inch x $1 1/2$ inch x $1/4$ inch angle all around and welded to cover to match the $1/4$ inch x 2 inch flat that is butt welded to top of vertical housing, with holes for $3/8$ inch bolts to match holes in $1/4$ inch x 2 inch flat. On inside of cover at the two inch height above the $1/4$ inch x 2 inch flats that are welded to vertical housing a 1 inch x 1 inch x $3/16$ inch angle is welded to cover in such a way as to straddle top of vertical housing plates thereby keeping oil splash from getting outside of case, the cover being over the outside of lower housing keeps the dust out. The gap in the side of vertical housing to remove intermediate shaft assembly was cut on 15° angle on both ends, the bottom being the narrow measurement. Along the top of the main side frame and between the edges of gap a $1/2$ inch x 2 inch flat was butt welded. The filler plate rested on main frame I-beam and on outside of $1/3$ inch x 2 inch flat. On filler at 2 inches from bottom and on the inside a 1 inch x 1 inch x $3/16$ inch angle was welded to form channel to straddle the $1/2$ inch x 3 inch. The 15° ends of filler plate were built the same way to keep dust out and oil in. The top of this filler plate conforms to the balance of vertical housing from one side of case to the other with a semi-circle gap cut out to cover final drive shaft, a similar gap being cut in bottom half. A cone shaped oil deflector is welded over the gap or hole in top cover to deflect any oil to inside, the cone deflector having a trough over the small end so oil will not drain on shaft. The back cover reaches from back of housing to within 1 inch of teeth on driven gear on final drive shaft, and rises to a height of 16 inches in the center of cover above top of vertical housing or high enough to clear cap and saddle on final drive shaft inside bearing. The driven gear on the final drive shaft stands up above this cover 12 inches and is in the right side of case. Over the top of back cover from left side and to within 2 inches of final driven gear, a $1/4$ inch x 1 inch rib is bent edgewise to conform to shape of cover and welded to cover on edge and in the line of 1 inch back of back edge of final gear rim. From the end of this $1/4$ inch x 1 inch rib, a plate of 10 gauge metal was cut to conform with circumference or 2 inches outside of circumference of gear and joined to rib at one end and welded to cover, from that point to other side of case being cut to conform to curvature of inside cover. The cover for front part of case is made in two pieces and the division point is in line lengthwise of case with end $1/4$ inch x 1 inch rib and start of shield back of final driven gear. The right side of front cover reaches from front end of case to within 1 inch of driven gear on final drive shaft where a shield of 10-gauge metal rises 2 inches above and following 2 inches outside of circumference of driven gear from right side of case to point of split or division of front cover. This plate or shield is an exact duplicate of the one behind the gear. The distance between these two plates is 12 inches, as the gear face is 10 inches. The other half of cover extends from front end to the same point as the right side and has a $\frac{1}{4}$ inch x 1 inch rib bent to conform to curvature of cover and welded to end of cover and to edge of shield and reaching the left side of gear case vertical section. At the point where the $\frac{1}{4}$ inch x 1 inch ribs meet the shields on each side of gear, a $\frac{1}{2}$ inch x $2\frac{1}{2}$ inch bolt is welded in both front and back covers with heads down and threaded ends up and measuring 14 inches centers. A section of 14-gauge iron, long enough to reach from one side of case to the other side and over ribs and gear shields, and 14 inches wide was formed to fit the ribs and gear shields and flanged 1 inch on each side and on the bottom so flanges would fit over the outsides of shields and ribs. No channel effect was used here as the motion is so slow there is no oil splash.

At the point where ribs meet shields a $\frac{1}{2}$ inch x 2 inches x 16 inches long was welded on top of 14 inch plate with $1\frac{7}{32}$ inch holes drilled in ends to fit $\frac{1}{2}$ inch x $2\frac{1}{2}$ inch bolts to hold plate down and hold the cover together at this point. The ends of the 14 inch strip had the outside hold down angles and the inside straddle angles. The front covers at division are clamped together with two $\frac{3}{8}$ inch x $1\frac{1}{2}$ inch flats welded edgewise along top of cover and bolted together with $\frac{3}{8}$ inch bolts at 8 inch centers. The vertical end of top cover is also clamped together with the same method. A 75 inch x 72 inch x $\frac{1}{4}$ inch plate forms the bottom of frame and is welded all around to bottom of 10 inch I-beams and to crossmembers at frequent intervals from inside. This makes case oil tight. The cross members have several 2 inch holes cut in them near the bottom to permit the oil to flow from one compartment to another. At oil pump compartment a 2 inch x 4 inch hole was cut in main frame I-beam to allow oil to flow to pump. The bevel pinion shaft projects through the wall of vertical housing on left side of case. On the end of this shaft is mounted a 36 inch diameter, 7 groove pulley for V belts. Where shaft projects through housing a $4\frac{1}{2}$ inch slot was cut from top of housing to shaft to permit the removal of shaft. A bolted-on plate with gasket was used to fill the gap with a semi-circle cone with drain trough at small end welded to it or the inside. On the outside and under the shaft a semi-circle cone was made, the small end fitting shaft closely and welded oil tight to housing, and small end standing out away from housing $\frac{3}{4}$ inch. A hole $\frac{1}{2}$ inch in diameter was cut in housing at the bottom and inside of cone to drain back any oil that might collect. A slightly larger cone covers the bottom cone to keep out the dust. This shaft is fairly high speed and a bearing almost against wall inside with jet of oil on it made it necessary to protect against oil leakage. The method is very satisfactory. The final drive pinion, or the pinion that meshes with the ring gear on kiln shell, being on the outside of case had to have some method of lubrication, so a semi-circle pan was fabricated of $\frac{1}{4}$ inch sheet steel to fit around the bottom side of pinion and within 2 inches of the ends of teeth and welded to back housing of gear case on one side and to outboard final drive shaft bearing pedestal on the other side. The pan is full length between these two points. $2\frac{1}{2}$ inches x $2\frac{1}{2}$ inches x $\frac{1}{4}$ inch angle sections are welded from pedestal to back wall of gear case on each side of pinion.

The inside legs or the legs toward pinion stand vertical while the other legs of angles are facing up and extend away from pinion. Intersecting the ends of these horizontal angles are two verticals, one welded to back wall of housing and one to inside of pedestal with faces out or away from pinion. To this angle assembly a drip trough for each side of ring gears is bolted to catch and drain oil dripping from ring gear back to pan under pinion. The drip troughs are 22 inches in width and taper to six inches at half way up on side of kiln. The troughs conform in shape to the circumference of ring gear. At the bottoms of these troughs a $\frac{1}{8}$ inch plate 22 inches x 12 inches x 10-gauge iron is welded for reinforcement. To the 22 inch x 12 inch x $\frac{1}{8}$ inch plate an angle assembly is fabricated to match the one in the pedestal and back housing wall and the trough assemblies are bolted there too. The angles on the trough have a $\frac{1}{4}$ inch gusset plate connecting the angles to help brace the tough at that point. A heavy gear lube is used to lubricate the teeth in final drive gear. The outboard bearing is lubricated from pump system through a $\frac{1}{4}$ inch pipe and drip sight feed and oil enters the bearing through an end cap. Surplus oil drains into sump under final drive pinion. The prime mover of this gear train is a 40 horsepower, 600 to 1200 variable speed, direct current, 250 volt, motor equipped with a 12 inch pitch diameter, 7 groove V belt sheave for "C" section belts. The V belts drive a 36 inch diameter sheave that is mounted on the bevel pinion shaft which is $3^{15}/_{16}$ inch diameter by 60 inches long. A 14 tooth, $2\frac{1}{4}$ inch pitch, 10.03 inch pitch diameter, $6\frac{1}{8}$ face, bevel tool steel pinion is also mounted on this shaft. The bevel pinion meshes with a 50 tooth, $2\frac{1}{4}$ inch pitch, 35.8 inch pitch diameter, $6\frac{1}{8}$ inch face bevel tool steel gear, mounted on the crown gear shaft which is $4^{15}/_{16}$ inch diameter and 50 inches long.

An outboard bearing carries the shaft behind gear. On the opposite end of the shaft is a 15 tooth, $2\frac{1}{4}$ inch pitch, 10.74 inch pitch diameter, $7\frac{1}{2}$ inch face, tool steel spur pinion overhanging the bearing at this end. This pinion engages a 55 tooth, $2\frac{1}{2}$ inch pitch, 39.39 inch pitch diameter, $7\frac{1}{2}$ inch face, tool steel gear mounted on a $5^{7}/_{16}$ inch shaft known as the intermediate shaft and is 41 inches long. On this same shaft is mounted hub to hub, a 16 tooth, $3\frac{1}{4}$ inch pitch, 16.55 pitch diameter, 10 inch face cast steel spur pinion. This pinion meshes with a 40 tooth, $3\frac{1}{4}$ inch pitch, 41.38 pitch diameter, 10 inch face semi-steel gear, which is mounted on the final drive shaft. This gear overhangs the bearing. The final drive shaft is $7\frac{1}{2}$ inches in diameter and 65 inches long. Also on this shaft is a 16 tooth, 4 inch pitch, 20.37 inch pitch diameter and 14 inch face cast steel pinion known as the bull pinion which is of the spur type. The bull pinion engages the ring gear which encircles the shell of the kiln and has 104 teeth, 4 inch pitch, 132.41 inch pitch diameter and a 14 inch face. The ring or master gear is of semi-steel material.

The frame of gear train is anchored to sole plate with 6, $1\frac{3}{4}$ inch, 10 thread bolts, through lugs or bosses made of 4 inch sections of $3^{15}/_{16}$ inch shafting and bored to two inches. The lugs or bosses are on the lengthwise sides of frame, one at each of the four corners and one on each side at No. 5 and No. 6 crossmembers. The lugs at corners are $2\frac{1}{2}$ inches from corners. At the corners a piece of $\frac{1}{2}$ inch x 4 inch flat iron and long enough in between top to bottom flanges of I-beam frame members, was welded to end frame members and 2 inches projecting out beyond side members. Four inches from this plate, or far enough so $3^{5}/_{16}$ inch boss or lug would fit in between a $2\frac{1}{2}$ inch x $2\frac{1}{2}$ inch x $\frac{1}{2}$ inch angle, was welded to web of I-beam and to top and bottom flanges of I-beam with the leg bearing against the I-beam in opposite direction from plate. The other leg of angle projects outward as a companion to the plate. The lower ends of lugs or bosses were cut to fit the angle of the bottom flange of I-beam.

The bosses rest on bottom flange of I-beam and in between angles and plate and are welded there, a notch being cut out of bottom flange of I-beam to clear the body of bolt. The lugs or bosses at all four corners of frame were identical to this one. At No. 5 and No. 6 crossmembers on both sides of the frame a boss or lug was welded in between two sections of 2½ inch x 2½ inch x ½ inch angles cut to fit in between top and bottom flanges of I-beam frame members and welded in much the same manner as the corner ones. A special socket wrench was made to tighten anchor bolts. At the front end of frame of gear case and running crosswise to frame and central and in line with front lugs or bosses, a 3 inch x 3 inch x ½ inch angle was welded to bottom of frame with down hanging leg toward back end of case, and at rear end of frame a similar angle was welded crosswise of frame with down hanging leg on side toward front end of case, both angles reaching from boss to boss across the frame are used for skids and guides to ride the case from under the kiln when necessary. The angles rest on the tops of 60-pound railroad rails, which form the sole plate. In line with center bosses which are located at No. 5 and No. 6 crossmembers a piece of ½ inch x 3 inch flat iron is welded to bottom of case to level up and this flat is also rested on a 60-pound rail. The sole plate has three rails. The sole plate was fabricated of 7, 60-pound rails, 10 feet long, and 3, 60-pound rails, 8 feet long, and 6, 4 inches x 4 inches x ½ inch angles 8 feet long, and 12, 1 inch plates 8 inches x 8 inches square plus 6 bosses, 4 inches outside diameter x 4 inches long and 2 inches inside diameter. The bosses were made out of 4 inch shafting. 12 bosses were used for under nuts of bolts that extend 24 inches into the concrete. At the center line of gear frame and parallel with kiln, or the long way of gear frame, is a central rail 10 feet long. 17 inches on either side of the central rail another 10 foot rail is located, making three rails, and 17 inches toward outside of frame from the last rails are two more 10 foot rails, one on each side, making five rails.

Two more rails were placed 7 inches outside of the last ones, one on each side, make the 7, 10-foot rails. The two outside pairs measure 2½ inches between the base of rails. The rails are upside down. The base or foot of them on top and the face down. Across these rails or transverse to them are 6, 4 inch x 4 inch x ½ inch angles in pairs with one leg of each angle welded to each rail it crosses. They are 8 feet long and back to back with legs welded to rails projecting out or away from each other and are spaced 4½ inches in clear between them. A pair is located on sole plate to match each pair of bosses and skid angles on bottom of gear case. One pair under front end of case lines vertically with bosses or lugs of gear case frame. One pair is to line up with anchor bosses or lugs at No. 5 and No. 6 cross member of frame and the third pair is directly under bosses that anchor frame to sole plate at rear end. From front to back the measurement is 5 feet 4½ inches from center of front pair to center of second pair and 3 feet 4 inches from center of second pair to center of third and last pair. From inside to inside of gear case frame anchor bosses a 60-pound rail is welded in between tops of the 4 inch x 4 inch x ½ inch angle pairs and bottom or base of rail is ½ inch below the tops of angles. Under the rail bases, spreaders of 1 inch x 3½ inch flat iron were welded vertically in between angles to help support rails and to stablize the angles. The spreaders were at 12 inch centers. These rails carry the gear frame at the three points.

To the ends of these rails an eye was welded to receive the bolts that anchor the frame. The eyes were made from 4 inch sections of 4 inch shafting having a 2 inch hole bored through. Under each eye a 4 inch x 4½ inch x 1 inch plate with 2 inch hole in center is welded ½ inch below flush with tops of the 4 inch x 4 inch x ½ inch angles to make seat on top for eye and seat on bottom for bolt head also filling the gap of ¼ inch on each side of eye to inside of angles. On the right hand side of case and sole plate, a 5 inch section of 60-pound rail continues to end of angle pairs, being welded to eye on end next to eye and in between and ½ inch below flush with angle tops.

On the top of the 5 inch section of rail a scotch block is built up and welded to rail to prevent further movement of gear frame in that direction and to relieve shear strain on anchor bolts. The scotch block is fabricated by using two ½ inch plates, one on each side of rail section the bottoms of which are welded to rail base and to the ball or face where it contacts same and extends 4 inches above top or face of rail sections. The scotch block being 4 inches high above rail where it contacts boss on gear frame tapers to 1 inch high at end of rail, and the two plates of scotch block have a covering of ⅜ inch flat iron. The ends of angle pairs are also covered with a ⅜ inch plate. Now to the other ends of angle pairs, or the left side of case and sole plate, a 13 inch section of 60-pound rail butts against and is welded to anchor bolt eyes and in between ends of and ½ inch below flush tops of angle pairs. These 13 inch sections have three $1\frac{3}{16}$ inch holes drilled through webs to anchor removable scotch block which has adjusting screws. This block was made up by using two ½ inch x 8 inch x 12 inch plates for sides with a ¾ inch x 2½ inch flat iron welded lengthwise at lower edges of them. The 2½ inch sides of flats are vertical when plates are stood against rails and form a clinch between ball and base of rails. Through the 2½ inch flats and plates three $1\frac{3}{16}$ inch holes were drilled to match holes in rail sections. Between the plates at the top of rail sections a ¾ inch x 2¼ inch flat was welded, spacing the plates 2¼ inches in clear and rides on top of rail. Between the plates and flush with the tops of them and toward the anchor boss on the gear frame, a 1⅜ inch square N.C. thread nut was welded to take the adjusting screw. Over the top of the plates a ⅜ x 2½ inch flat is welded starting at 1⅜ inch nut and continuing to opposite end of plates and down the ends to rail. At the point in end that lines with center of nut, a 1⅜ inch hole is drilled to guide the end of adjusting screw. When bolts are taken out, the block can be pulled off over end of rail section. By removing the anchor bolts the entire assembly can be easily pulled out from under kiln for overhaul and can be removed to a cool place if desired.

The room temperature at gear case is often 160°F. A shield of double corrugated iron with corrugations running transverse to each with a sheet of asbestos between keeps the direct heat off motor and V belts. The temperature in the hot zone or the burning zone of kiln is 24 to 27 hundred degrees. There are 12 anchor bolts that anchor sole plate to concrete pier. The bolts are 1½ inches in diameter and 36 inches long with 6 inch hook turned on bottom end, on each side of the skid rails and in line with frame anchor bolts. These bolts are 8½ inches on either side of frame bolts or 17 inches center to center of bolts and fit in between the two outside rails that are in concrete. A 1 inch plate 8 inches square with 2 inch hole in center is welded on top of the two sole plate rails and are offset ½ inch so one edge of the plate rides up over the leg of the 4 inch x 4 inch x ½ inch angle pairs and is welded to rails and legs of angles. There are twelve of these plates, one for each of the sole plate bolts. Note: At each of the six gear frame anchor points the three bolts are in line which prevents any spring in sole plate frame. The anchor bolts for gear frame enter from the bottom by casting slots in concrete pier.

This gear train or transmission without gears, bearings or shafts weighs about 10,000 pounds.

The cost for labor was	$ 543.56
Should the material have been new	600.00
550 pounds 5/32" and 3/16" E6010 Electrodes	44.00
Oxygen and Acetylene about	24.50
The cost of gears and pinions was	1088.89
" " " shafts @ .07¢ per lb	108.50
" " " bearings	60.00
" " " bronze and babbitt	83.00
" " " machining bearings	105.00
" " " misc. machine work	50.00
	$2707.45

A quotation of a few years back on a complete gear set of similar size built with cast iron frame and housing which was considerably heavier was $8000. This gear set probably is a better set as it was equipped with roller bearings, but we never have any bearing trouble.

On a gear train on a kiln of the the same size, that is identical with the one just described and this was installed March 1937, has never had a bearing lining changed. These kilns are on a 24 hour operation and have been for the past 7 years continuously.

As a comparison of operating costs between the old open gear, cast iron frame drive and the drive just described: For lubrication, the old drive used 6 pounds of high temperature grease per day of 24 hours, and 16 pounds of "Coglube" per day. The new gear train just described uses on an average of 2 quarts of heavy mineral cylinder oil per day of 24 hours.

Old train per day, 6 lbs. of high temperature grease @ .14	$ .84
16 lbs. of "coglube" @ .06	.96
Per day	$ 1.80
New train per day, 2 quarts of mineral cylinder oil @ .70	.35
Old train per month	$54.00
New train per month	10.50
Saving	$43.50

General Wear—The old gear set after a year's operation was ready for a complete overhaul. Changing all bearings and shafts and some of the gears especially the cast steel and semi-steel. The tool steel gears will run in the open sometimes for three or five years. In mid-summer or in the hottest part of the summer we often have to go into them and replace bearing brasses and the like. The clinker dust and oil when mixed up make a very good grinding compound.

The gear set described was built in 1940 and installed November of 1940. So far nothing has been changed except some bearing cap bolts.

The set identical with the one described except of the opposite hand and driving an identical kiln was installed March 1937 and so far has had no replacements except minor troubles such as oil lines, etc. The reason for opposite hand drives is that when gear teeth wear on one side they can be changed to a drive of opposite hand and get the wear on opposite side of teeth.

Chapter IV—Ceramic Plant

By CARLMAN MARTIN RINCK,

Chief Engineer, Trenton Potteries Co., Trenton, N. J.

Carlman Martin Rinck

Subject Matter: A considerable portion of the paper is devoted to the place of welding in a plant and its organization. Instances too numerous to discuss separately are cited of repairs, maintenance and new work performed with the arc. A conclusion is given in which is summarized the annual savings effected by welding which on the jobs described amount to $5,315.

Introduction—This paper is a study of some of the welding problems and their solutions and also of the development of welding in a large ceramic sanitary manufacturing plant, the Trenton Potteries Company of Trenton, New Jersey. This company is a subsidiary of Crane Company, Chicago, Illinois. The Trenton plant manufactures all of the vitreous china and porcelain ware to which the Crane Company fittings are affixed.

Scope of Our Maintenance Welding—Our maintenance welding consists of two branches:
 (a) The repairing of broken or worn parts of equipment;
 (b) The construction of special machines and equipment of our own design which, though designed for our own particular plants, are also adaptable to many other ceramic industries, such as pottery, brick, tile, electrical porcelain, terra cotta, and earthenware manufacturing plants.

Though we first purchased welding equipment for the sole purpose of making repairs, it later became evident that the welding equipment was becoming even more valuable to us in the fabrication of special welded machines and equipment. The transition from acetylene repair welding to arc repair and fabrication welding in our plant was a most interesting development.

Development of Our Welding Department—(A) Welding Becomes a Necessity.

Shortly after we installed modern type tunnel kilns in our plant to take the place of inefficient periodic round kilns, it became apparent that speed was of utmost importance in making repairs to the new kilns' auxiliary equipment such as pushes, pullers, fans, oil pumps, steam and oil lines, etc. This was necessary since the kilns were operating on definite schedules that were costly to interrupt.

Since speed was of utmost importance in making repairs, it became apparent that field repairs would save much time by eliminating the necessity of taking apart the equipment and sending the broken part to our blacksmith shop for repairs. This led to our purchase of a portable acetylene welding outfit, which though it served its purpose also had its difficulties. Some of these advantages and disadvantages were as follows:

Advantages—The main advantage of our acetylene equipment was that it could be used not only for welding but also for burning steel. However, we found that by keeping the acetylene equipment solely for cutting work and doing our welding electrically, we secured much better results.

Disadvantages—1. Since our acetylene equipment was purchased from a mill supply house, no special effort was made by them to insure the correct usage and maintenance of the equipment.

2. Improper welding flame due to improper gas pressures at the torch, or by
   (a) Gauges out of calibration.
   (b) Leaky valves or hose lines.
   (c) Conserving gas in a low tank of either acetylene or oxygen.
   (d) Improper welding tip. (On small jobs, a welder does not always bother to change to the proper tip but uses the one he may happen to find in the torch.)
   (e) Clogged holes in the welding tip by sputtering metal.

3. Harmful heating or machine parts adjacent to repairs due to the spreading of the welding flame after impingement on the part to be welded.

4. Fire hazards with field repairs.
   (a) Overheating of adjacent machine parts.
   (b) Difficulty of keeping watch on long flying sputtering sparks.
   (c) Leaky hose line near combustible material being ignited by long flying sparks.

5. Necessity of removing carbon smudge from walls and equipment after the welding job is completed. Much of this was done by allowing the acetylene to burn without oxygen.

6. Distortion of welded members after cooling usually took place because of the useless heating of too much of the machine part at each weld.

7. Non-uniformity of welds due to overheating and the difficulty of controlling the other variables present with acetylene welding.

Selecting Our Arc Welder—After being confronted with the above disadvantages and being aware of the progress being made by the arc welding in general, we decided to try out in our own shops different types of arc welders.

The first electric welders we tried out were very disappointing in their performance. They were of the alternating current transformer type with plugs to obtain the different voltages. The men demonstrating the equipment had particular difficulty in maintaining a continuous arc and also in preventing the electrode rod in the holder from sticking to the weld. The demonstrations were so unsatisfactory that we decided to keep on trying the various arc welding machines until we found a suitable one.

Organizing Our Welding Department—Immediately after the new arc welder arrived, the company representative gave our men who were to be the nucleus of our welding department a thorough lesson on the proper use of the equipment. The next move was to construct a room for welding only with proper exhaust ventilation and shielded from the eyes of passers-by from other departments. The best welder we had in our department was then placed in charge of the equipment, the welding room, and men who were to become his assistants. Accurate time is kept on the welding of each

ARC WELDING

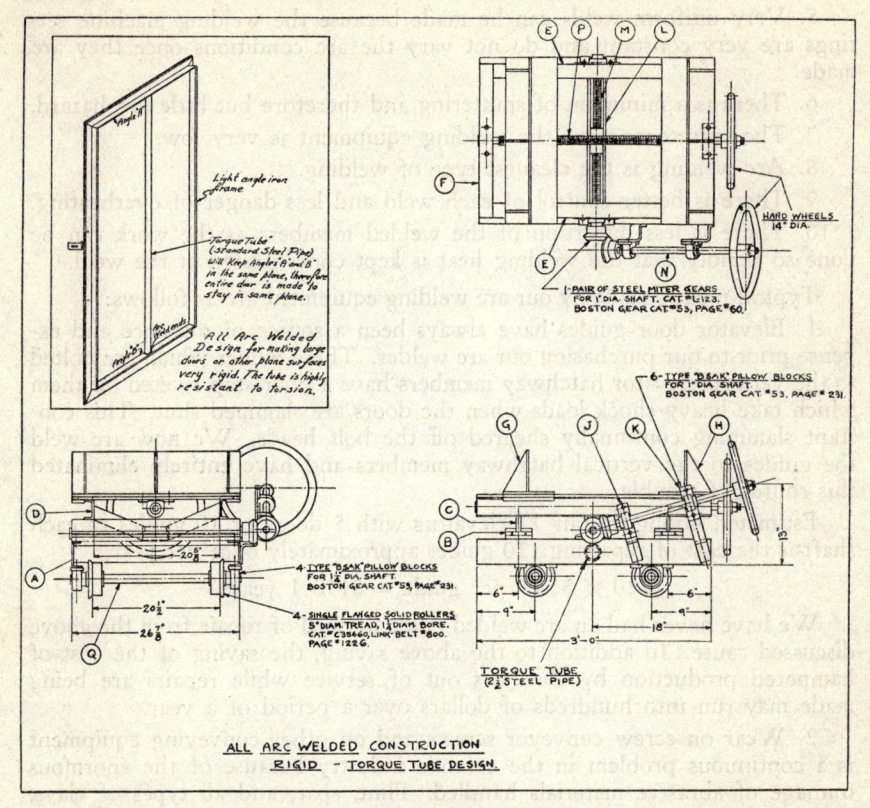

Fig. 1. (Inset) Welded door frame with torque tube. Fig. 2. Assembly drawing of grinding carriage.

job which has a number and this is recorded by the timekeeper who charges it against the respective job number. We are thus able to keep an accurate labor cost on the job. Many of our repair jobs are so small that we do not attempt to keep track of the rod and electricity cost. This cost is spread over the various machines repaired. When fabricating and constructing new equipment, etc., the rods and electrical costs are taken into consideration as there is generally a substantial amount of welding in this type of work.

Arc Welding in Repair Work—Whenever speed is paramount we bring our welding equipment to the machine to make the necessary repairs without disassembling the machine. We find that the arc welder is particularly adapted to this type of work.

Some of the apparent advantages that we have found in the shop and field of the arc welding of ceramic equipment are:

1. The welding equipment is portable and is easily moved to the machinery to be repaired.

2. The welding is so rapid that with most jobs the welding is completed before the heat can be conducted to adjacent machine parts.

3. The welder by using long, short, or bent welding rods can weld in very inaccessible places.

4. So little heat is developed other than that coming from the arc that the welder can work in comparative comfort.

5. Very uniform welds can be made because the welding machine settings are very constant and do not vary the arc conditions once they are made.

6. There is a minimum of sputtering and therefore but little fire hazard.

7. The maintenance of the welding equipment is very low.

8. Arc welding is the cleanest type of welding.

9. There is better control of each weld and less danger of overheating.

10. There is less distortion of the welded members as the work can be done so rapidly that the welding heat is kept concentrated at the weld.

Typical repairs made by our arc welding equipment are as follows:

1. Elevator door guides have always been a source of nuisance and expense prior to our purchasing our arc welder. These guides which are bolted to the vertical elevator hatchway members have a door stop riveted on them which take heavy shock loads when the doors are slammed shut. This constant slamming continually sheared off the bolt heads. We now arc weld the guides to the vertical hatchway members and have entirely eliminated this source of trouble.

Estimated saving on our 12 elevators with 5 doors or 10 guides to each shaft is the cost of repairing 120 guides approximately once per year.

$$120 \times \$1.25 \text{ per guide} = \$150 \text{ 1 year}$$

We have never had an arc welded guide in need of repair from the above discussed cause. In addition to the above saving, the saving of the cost of hampered production by elevators out of service while repairs are being made may run into hundreds of dollars over a period of a year.

2. Wear on screw conveyor screws and on other conveying equipment is a continuous problem in the ceramic industry because of the enormous tonnage of abrasive materials handled. Flint, spar, and all types of clays, grog, etc., continually wear down the toughest steels. Arc welding has permitted us to reinforce wearing edges and surfaces with "Stellite" and other alloy steels, thereby greatly extending the useful life of much equipment.

Estimated savings on arc welding alloy steel edges on wearing edges of equipment is difficult to estimate as we have never been able to satisfactorily weld alloys prior to purchasing our arc welder. We can safely state, however, that the alloy wearing surfaces seem to outlast the regular steel repaired surfaces at least three times. The cost of repairing the screws, etc., used to be approximately $1870 per year. On this basis, it is safe to say that alloy steel arc welding saves us approximately $1246 per year for these repairs alone.

3. Puller chain channel guides on the floors of the exit ends of our tunnel kilns always presented a problem because of the presence of ware placing sand which dropped down from the kiln cars on to the guides. This acted as an abrasive between the links of the puller chain and chain guide. The puller chain being made of special alloy steel easily outwore the comparatively soft structural steel guide. Arc welding enabled us to reinforce the worn grooves in the guide with alloy steel and thus minimize this trouble.

Estimated savings on our six tunnel kilns is approximately $240 per year. This is based on the alloy reinforcement increasing the span of repair from two to four years at the cost of $160 per repair for a complete set of guides per kiln every other year.

160×3 sets per year $= \$480$ former cost per year

Half of yearly repairs $\dfrac{480}{2} = \$240$ saving per year

Since the kiln cars have to be moved over the track once every hour even while the repairs are being made, repairs to the chain guides are a costly operation.

4. The installing of nipples in steam and water mains by arc welding has saved us much time and money. Instead of cutting the main line, taking down a section of it, threading the ends, installing a tee and then a union after it, we merely weld a nipple into the main line and screw a valve on it. This can be done very rapidly with a minimum of shut down time.

Our savings of fittings and time by arc welding this past year for insertion of nipples was $148.

5. The bending and arc welding of mould reinforcement rods for our plaster moulds results in considerable savings for us. Heretofore, these rods were bent cold and hammered haphazardly into shape with the result that no two were alike. Sometimes they were so bent that they did not perform the function for which they were intended. We now make jigs for the various shapes and arc weld corner braces where additional support is needed.

The saving involved in this item is approximately $246 per year. In addition, we have a much more substantial reinforcement.

Arc Welding in Our Machinery Construction and Fabrication—New designs of bathtubs, lavatories, surgeons' sinks, etc., present problems of manufacturing equipment which must be designed by our own engineering department. Most of our new plumbing designs are made by Mr. Henry Dreyfuss, the famed industrial designer. It is up to our engineering department to design the moulds, lifting rigs, and mechanical means for producing the newly designed ware.

Of greatest importance in "green" or plastic ware handling before the ware is fired is the necessity of eliminating any possible strain in the piece

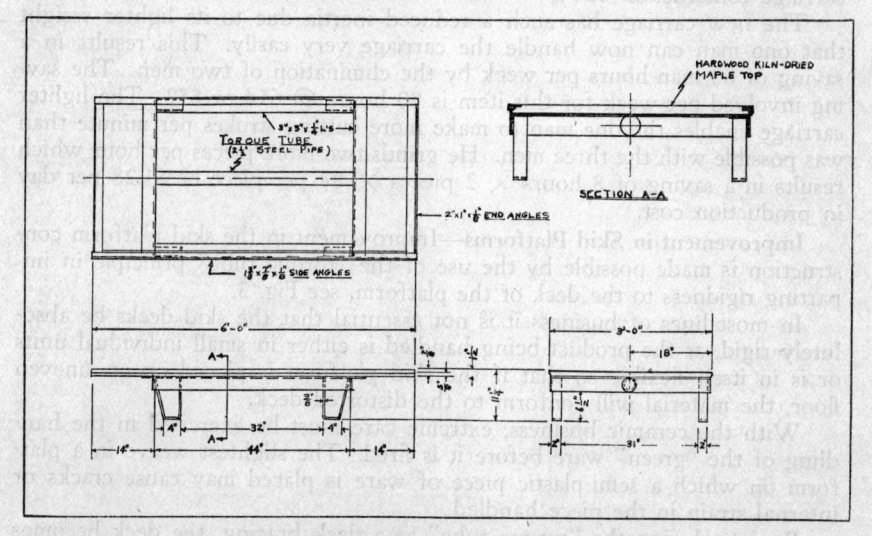

Fig. 3. Arc welded torque tube design of skid platform.

while handling. After much studying and experimental work with welding, we are able to produce ware setters and skid platforms capable of supporting one ton loads without perceptable deck deflection, also all kinds of special machinery and appliances.

Improvement in Grinding Carriage Construction—For many years the ceramic industry has been using large 42-inch vertical wheel grinders whose carriages have been extremely heavy. These carriages, which were made rugged to resist distortion, require three men to move them back and forth across the face of the grinding wheel. Apparently overlooked, however, was the consideration of the inertia in the heavy cast iron design. This inertia had to be overcome at each stroke of the carriage.

This past year we studied the number of grinding strokes and the speed of the ware across the grinding wheel face and decided that a light weight all arc welded carriage made of structural steel and carefully designed would have far less inertia to overcome, see Fig. 2. This would not only permit a faster grinding stroke but would also permit a greater number of grinding strokes per minute. As we wanted rigidity with lightness, we incorporated a "torque tube" as a cross member which gave the carriage rigidness beyond our expectations.

The "torque tube" is a section of common steel pipe welded to the channel side members. This pipe is very resistant to twisting or to a torsion load. This, therefore, tends to keep any member welded to its ends in its original plane. We have found that this tube will produce a far greater rigidness to a plane than is possible with any other kind of simple bracing having equal weight of metal in it. Where weight is a factor, we use this tube design wherever possible. Since designing the carriage, we have used this tube as a means of making rigid many other pieces of equipment such as steel doors, lift truck platforms, hand trucks, pallet boards, etc.

The weight of the new arc welded carriage is 630 pounds. The weight of the original cast iron carriage was 1740 pounds.

The cost of constructing the new arc welded carriage was $540 and the cost of the original cast iron carriage was $784, making the saving in the carriage construction $244.

The new carriage has such a reduced inertia due to its lighter weight that one man can now handle the carriage very easily. This results in a saving of 80 man-hours per week by the elimination of two men. The saving involved per week for this item is 80 hours @ 65¢ or $52. The lighter carriage enables the one man to make more cutting strokes per minute than was possible with the three men. He grinds two more pieces per hour which results in a saving of 8 hours × 2 pieces × 8¢ per piece or $1.28 per day in production cost.

Improvement in Skid Platforms—Improvement in the skid platform construction is made possible by the use of the "torque tube" principle in imparting rigidity to the deck of the platform, see Fig. 3.

In most lines of business it is not essential that the skid decks be absolutely rigid, as the product being handled is either in small individual units or is in itself flexible so that if the skid platform is placed on an uneven floor, the material will conform to the distorted deck.

With the ceramic business, extreme care must be exercised in the handling of the "green" ware before it is fired. The slightest weave in a platform on which a semi-plastic piece of ware is placed may cause cracks or internal strain in the piece handled.

By introducing the "torque tube" as a deck bracing, the deck becomes

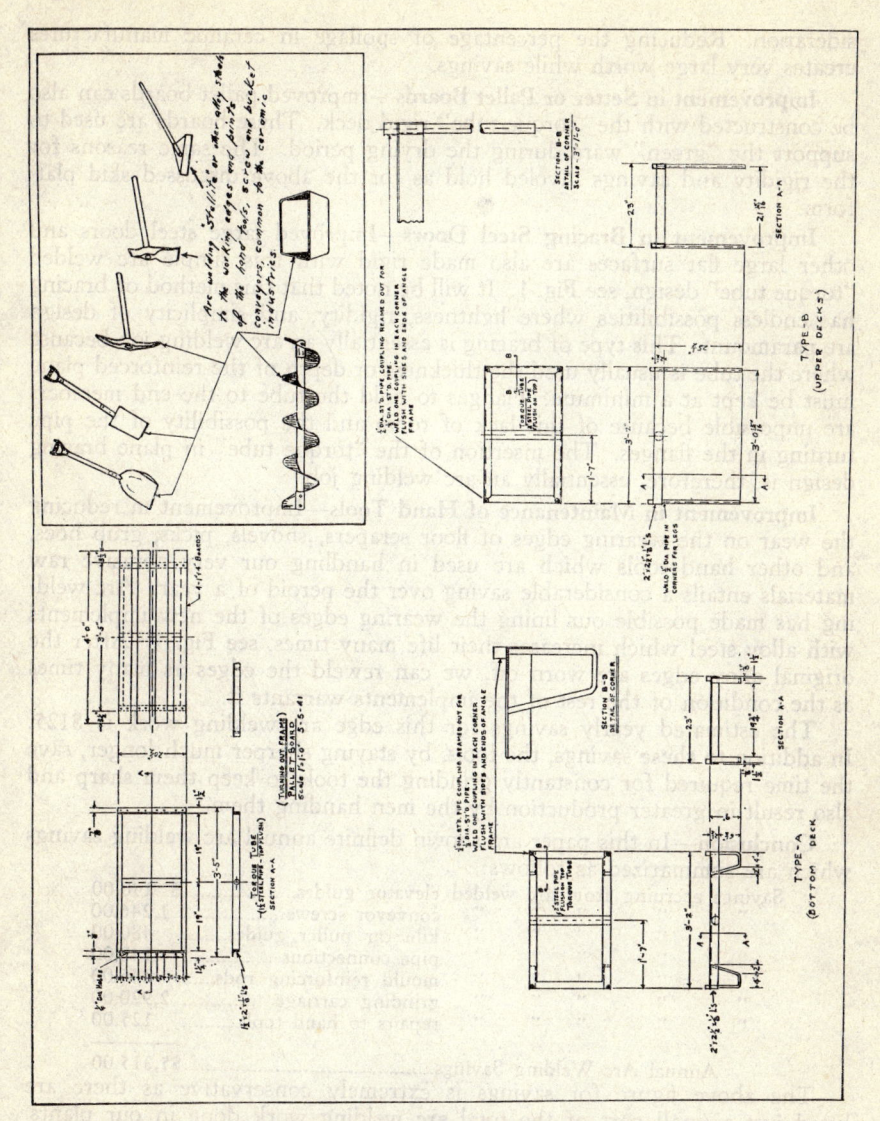

Fig. 4. Arc welded multi-deck special skid platform. Fig. 5 (Inset) Arc welded wearing edges of tools and equipment.

extremely rigid, so much so that a twenty-five hundred pound load spread uniformly over the deck does not cause any noticeable deck distortion when the skid is placed on an uneven floor where only three of the four legs are in contact with the floor, see Fig. 4.

Estimated savings of this improvement is in the reduced handling cost and in the reduced percentage of "green" ware breakage. The new type skid platform costs approximately the same as the conventional skid platform, perhaps a dollar or two more as it is special. The savings in better ware however, though intangible, runs into a few thousand dollars per year when the mould cost and general overhead, etc., are taken into consideration. Reducing the percentage of spoilage in ceramic manufactures creates very large worth while savings.

Improvement in Setter or Pallet Boards—Improved pallet boards can also be constructed with the "torque tube" rigid deck. These boards are used to support the "green" ware during the drying period. The same reasons for the rigidity and savings involed hold as for the above discussed skid platform.

Improvement in Bracing Steel Doors—Improved large steel doors and other large flat surfaces are also made rigid with this simple arc welded "torque tube" design, see Fig. 1. It will be noted that this method of bracing has endless possibilities where lightness, rigidity, and simplicity of design are paramount. This type of bracing is essentially an arc welding job because where the tube is usually used the thickness or depth of the reinforced plane must be kept at a minimum. Flanges to hold the tube to the end members are impossible because of this lack of room and the possibility of the pipe turning in the flanges. The insertion of the "torque tube" in plane bracing design is, therefore, essentially an arc welding job.

Improvement in Maintenance of Hand Tools—Improvement in reducing the wear on the wearing edges of floor scrapers, shovels, picks, grub hoes, and other hand tools which are used in handling our very abrasive raw materials entails a considerable saving over the peroid of a year. Arc welding has made possible our lining the wearing edges of the new implements with alloy steel which increases their life many times, see Fig. 5. After the original alloy edges are worn off, we can reweld the edges as many times as the condition of the rest of the implements warrants it.

The estimated yearly savings for this edge arc welding work is $125. In addition to these savings, the tools, by staying sharper much longer, save the time required for constantly grinding the tools to keep them sharp and also result in greater production by the men handing them.

Conclusion—In this paper are shown definite annual arc welding savings which are summarized as follows:

Savings accruing from arc welded elevator guides	$ 150.00
" " " " " conveyor screws	1,246.00
" " " " " kiln car puller guides	480.00
" " " " " pipe connections	148.00
" " " " " mould reinforcing rods	246.00
" " " " " grinding carriage	2,920.00
" " " " " repairs to hand tools	125.00
Annual Arc Welding Savings	$5,315.00

The above figure for savings is extremely conservative as there are listed just a small part of the total arc welding work done in our plants. Very large additional savings have been made on the innumerable small repair and construction jobs which can be done only by arc welding. The intangible savings resulting from use of our arc welder are in reality far greater than the tangible savings. The very nature of the ceramic industry, the continuity of manufacture, accounts for the huge intangible savings involved. This industry as a whole is an extremely fertile field for the use of arc welding because of the speed, quality, ease, economy, and safety of making repairs, and for the vast new avenues of special machinery and equipment fabrication and construction which are now opened up by the developments in the use of arc welding equipment. It may be safely said that no other one piece of equipment has been such a boon to the ceramic industry as the arc welding machine.

Chapter V—Chemical Plant

By J. E. Gurvin,

Plant Engineer, Monsanto Chemical Co., Columbia, Tenn.

Subject Matter: Rotary coke dryer 6 feet, 6 inches by 45 feet long had lines which wore out too fast from abrasive coke requiring expenditure of about $600 per year. Carbon steel bars 0.40-0.50% carbon were welded in lengthwise. They filled with coke and prevented wear on lining. Over six years saving estimated at $3,200.

A roll crusher was remodeled so as to leave more wear resistance by hard surfacing beads lengthwise about 2½ inches apart onto two rolled half sole abrasive resisting steel plates. Saving estimated at $336.42 per year with less time out.

A 48-inch by 10-foot pug mill had its rods hard surfaced with an estimated saving of $1,938.97 for handling 423,563 tons of product.

J. E. Gurvin

Cutting Maintenance Cost by Arc Welding

The task of maintaining machinery to give maximum production at minimum cost is the prime function of the Maintenance Department, which the writer supervises.

A more or less standard piece of equipment is installed somewhere along the flow line with the expectation that it will do the job for which it was installed economically and well. Too often it turns out to be the beginning of new headaches. The "bugs" must be taken out of it, and the cure often calls for welding, which did not exist in the machine as it was furnished by the manufacturer. The following are some instances which we engineered here.

A rotary dryer for coke came provided with half-inch thick bolted-on alloy steel wear plates for liners. The dryer is 6 feet 6 inches in diameter and 45 feet long. Coke is very abrasive. After only a year of service, the wear plates in the 15 foot long front section wore out. We replaced these plates with cast alloy plates of various compositons, but a year's service or approximately such was about all cast plates gave us.

It so happens at this plant that we use a great many inch and a quarter round bars 16 feet long. These are 0.40 to 0.50 carbon content. The short ends find their way to the scrap pile. The writer conceived of a method of using these bars, instead of the conventional wear plates in the manner depicted in Fig. 1, attached. The bars were welded around the surface to the inner shell at a 3 inch center to center spacing, the bars running lengthwise of the dryer. This allows a 1¾ inch minimum space between bars which key up with caked coke. The caked coke thus becomes the wearing surface, and the steel shell is protected from abrasive action.

New plates were costing us about $600 a year. This bar idea was installed in January 1940. After two years of service, the bars show but little wear, and it is estimated will give about four years of service. Plates over

55

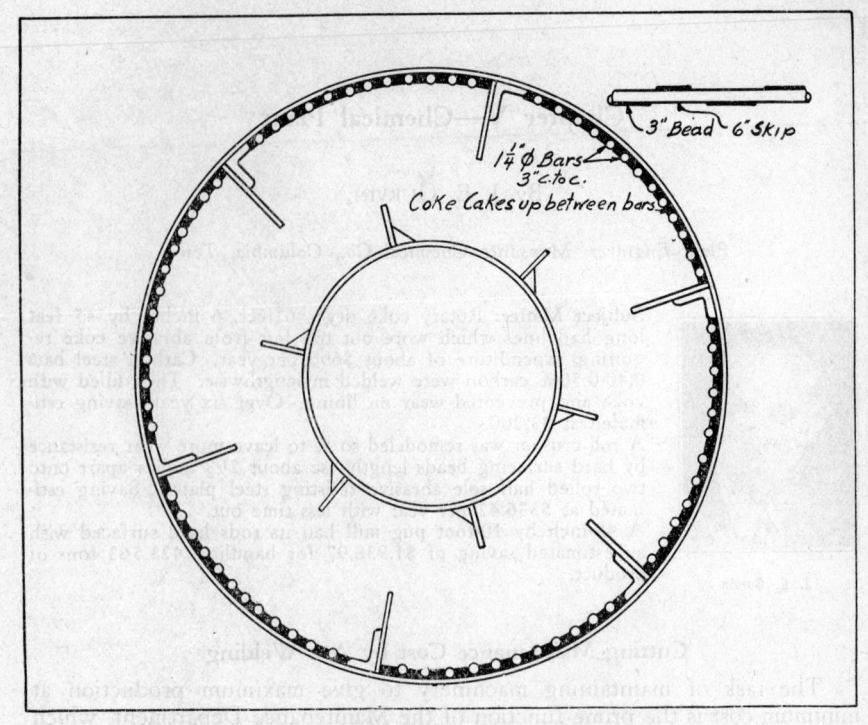

Fig. 1. Cross section through dryer showing bars welded to shell.

a six year period would cost $3,600. The bars, if new, would have cost about $250, but being short ends they were only worth a scrap value of about $20. The cost to install the bars, including labor and welding rod, was about $380. Over a six year period this is a total saving of $3,200. Fig. 2 shows the cross section assembly.

A conventional roll crusher equipped by the manufacturer with cast segment wear plates was installed in September 1936. Each roll required six plates. We soon found that these cast plates broke at times when a stray piece of metal went through the crusher, a happening which is now and then inevitable in a plant like this. The average cost of these cast plates was $16.74 each.

Our records show for an average twelve month period that 23 plates were replaced, which cost $385 for the plates alone.

On September 18, 1939, we installed on one roll, two rolled half sole abrasive resisting steel plates, welding together where the halves met. These were one inch thick. On lines 2½ inches center to center across these steel plates we welded hard surface beads. This cost as follows:

Abrasive resisting steel plates	$210.00
Labor applying plates and running beads	19.20
Welding rods and miscellaneous supplies	22.00
Total	$251.20

The roll described above stood up splendidly and with no maintenance, but we wished to try a design which would be as good and cheaper. On

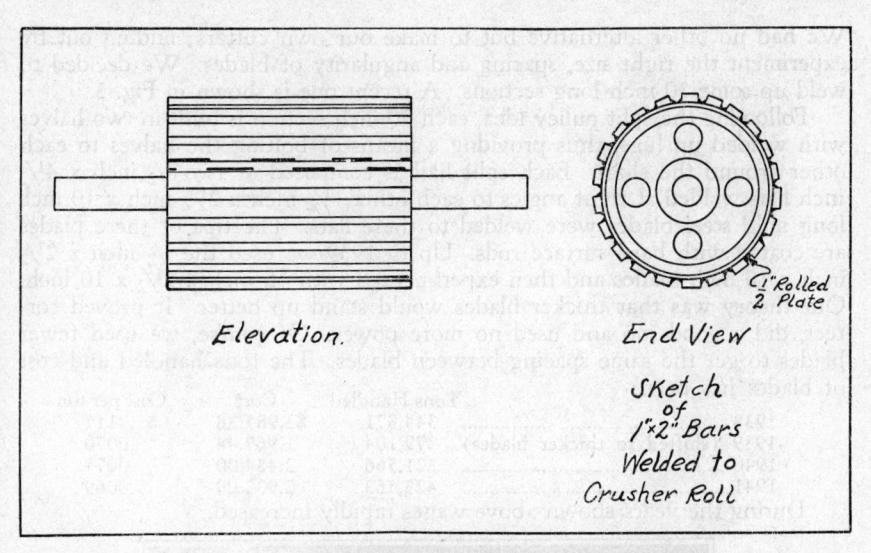

Fig. 2. End view showing bars welded to crusher roll.

March 3, 1941, we installed on the other roll, two ½ inch thick half sole mild steel plates, and across these skip welded abrasive steel bars. These were 1 inch x 2 inches, layed flat with 1½ inch spaces between. This cost as follows:

Rolled steel plates	$ 49.00
1 inch x 2 inch abrasive steel bars	23.86
Labor applying plates and bars	15.80
Welding rods and miscellaneous supplies	8.50
Total	$ 97.16

We stopped buying cast plates. For six months, or until September 5, 1941, these two rolls operated together in the crusher with little sign of wear on either. On September 5, 1941, the first mentioned roll had to be removed because of a bent shaft. We were forced to replace it wth a spare roll, and for expediency used some cast plates which were on hand. As of March 1, 1942, the 1 inch x 2 inch bar roll is still going strong and showing negligible wear. We estimate it will last four years with no maintenance.

If a second 1 inch x 2 inch bar roll had been made and used, the total cost of the two rolls would total $194.32. As their life is four years, the annual cost would be $48.58 per year as compared with cast plates costing $385. Therefore, the 1 inch x 2 inch bar roll saves $336.42 per year. There rightfully could be claimed still further, other savings because cast plate breakage cut down production and, of course, there were labor costs of the replacements.

A print of this 1 inch x 2 inch bar roll follows.

The following is a description of efforts showing how the maintenance ton cost has been gradually decreased in spite of the gradual increase in wages of late years.

A 48 inch x 10 foot pug mill was installed, but the conventional cast blades with which it came equipped did not satisfactorily chew up the material. In addition, cast blades were subjected to breakage from shock.

We had no other alternative but to make our own cutters; finding out by experiment the right size, spacing and angularity of blades. We decided to weld up some 30 inch long sections. A recent one is shown in Fig. 3.

Following the split pulley idea, each 30 inch section is built in two halves with welded up lugs, thus providng a means of bolting the halves to each other around the shaft. Each split half is composed of two $1/2$ inch x $4 1/2$ inch flats welded at right angles to each other. $1/2$ inch x $2 1/2$ inch x 10 inch long mild steel blades were welded to these flats. The tips of these blades are coated with hard surface rods. Up to 1939 we used the $1/2$ inch x $2 1/2$ inch x 10 inch blades and then experimented with $3/4$ inch x $2 1/2$ x 10 inch. Our theory was that thicker blades would stand up better. It proved correct, did a good job and used no more power. Of course, we used fewer blades to get the same spacing between blades. The tons handled and cost of blades has been:

	Tons Handled	Cost	Cost per ton
1938	344,871	$3,985.38	$ .0115
1939 (shifted to thicker blades)	279,104	1,967.44	.0070
1940	321,566	2,434.00	.0075
1941	423,563	2,932.00	.0069

During the years shown above wages rapidly increased.

Fig. 3. Weld-fabricated blades for pug mill.

Previous to 1941 we did nothing to the cutters once we installed them, except to move them towards the discharge end as they wore, and when a new cutter was installed. During 1941 we began the practice of touching up with hard surface all blades in place during the weekly shut-downs. We thus were able to continue cutting the cost down during 1941. We believe that one inch thick blades would be still cheaper, but that they would not give us the fine cutting necessary in addition to probably pulling increased horsepower.

We have tried a great number of different hard surface rods, and the data given above is based, in the main, on a rod costing about $2.25 per pound. As 1942 swings into being, and as this paper is written, we believe we have found another stunt that is going to still further cut down our costs. In an endeavor to find substitutes for the higher priced hard surface rods we first coated the blades with a cast iron rod, and chilled them. After this, we applied one coat only of the higher priced hard surface rods, where we formerly used two coats. It is too early at this writing to be sure, but so far the results have been promising.

We cannot state what savings over cast cutters, our welded steel cutters have provided. However, we can point out that the development on the item of cutters alone based on 1941 costs has saved us over 1938 costs as follows:

```
423,563 tons @ .0115..................................................$4,870.97
Actual cost in 1941.................................................... 2,932.00
                                                                        ─────────
Annual saving ........................................................$1,938.97
```

We plan to cut the ton costs down and obtain greater savings.

Chapter VI—Coke Oven Doors

By H. A. Immisch,

Master Mechanic, Columbia Steel Co., Ironton Works, Provo, Utah.

Subject Matter: In this paper the author describes in detail the construction by arc welding of steel coke oven doors to replace cast iron ones. No new features are brought out in the design. Only innovation is a method of rotating unit so all welding is performed in flat position and enabling more than one man to work simultaneously. Pre-bonding to offset warpage is described and worked successfully. Substantial economies are claimed for doors assembled in the plant over those purchased.

H. A. Immisch

The Ironton Works of the Columbia Steel Company was put into operation in 1924. It consists of one 600-ton blast furnace and two batteries of coke ovens. Because of the limited size of operations of this plant, a separate welding department has never been deemed necessary. Therefore, the welding which has been done at this plant has become a side function of the mechanical department. At present the welding equipment consists of three electric welding machines, and several sets of oxy-acetylene welding torches.

As master mechanic it is my responsibility to keep all operating machinery in good repair, and to do all the planning and supervising on any new or emergency installation or repair work which is to be undertaken.

I have made several observations as to the effect of heat on the cast iron coke oven doors. This type of door seems prone to warp and crack under the high degree of heat to which it is subjected. In many instances it has become necessary to remove the cast iron doors, straighten them by cold working, and then fill the cracks by welding. Because of the constantly increasing amount of repairs and excessive cost necessary to maintain the doors in a satisfactory operating condition, the management decided to purchase a considerable number of new coke oven doors; so we experimented with a pair of steel welded coke oven doors and decided to install them. After observing these doors closely for several months, keeping a record of their service qualifications such as warpage, cracking, etc., it was found that the steel doors did not have a tendency to warp, thus reducing the breaking, cracking, and repairing that was found prominent in the cast iron doors. The steel doors also were lighter and constructed so as to provide greater heat radiation. It was for these reasons that the management decided to purchase welded steel doors in preference to the present cast iron doors.

I made a study to determine the type and the amount of additional help which would be necessary to begin construction on the doors. From the

ARC WELDING 61

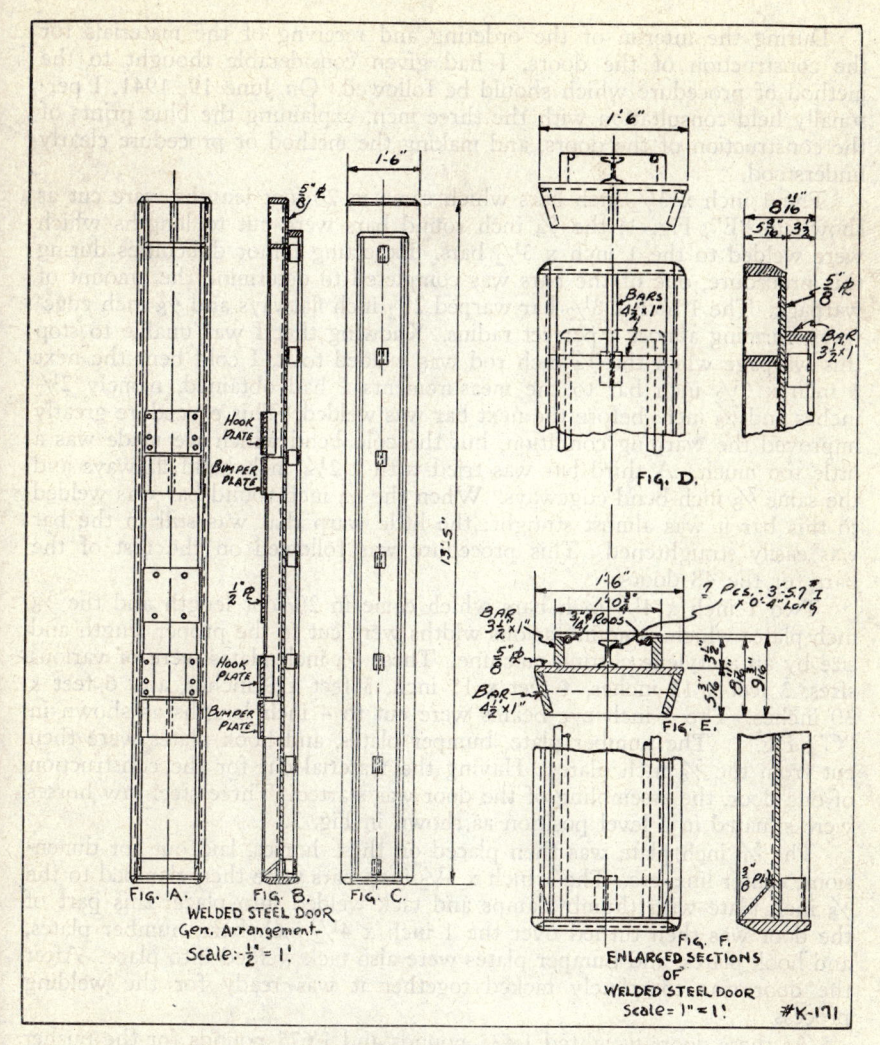

Fig. 1. Detailed drawing of welded coke oven door.

study made it was found that the undertaking would necessitate the full time services of one boilermaker and two electric welders. As the mechanical crew we maintain at our plant is for maintenance work only, I had to seek the additional help from other sources. A boilermaker was hired but no experienced electric welders could be found.

Coincidentally, an instructor of an electric welding class in our locality approached one of the officials of the company and recommended one of the students, who at that time had about 500 electric welding class-hours to his credit. The majority of these class-hours had been spent on a 300-ampere electric welding machine. This student welder was employed. An employee from the yard department was advanced to the mechanical department as boilermaker helper. These three men made up the foundation of the crew.

During the interim of the ordering and receivng of the materials for the construction of the doors, I had given considerable thought to the method of procedure which should be followed. On June 19, 1941, I personally held consultation with the three men, explaining the blue prints of the construction of the doors, and making the method or procedure clearly understood.

The 1 inch x $3\frac{1}{2}$ inch bars which came in 20-foot lengths were cut as shown in "E", Fig. 1; the $\frac{3}{4}$ inch round bars were cut to lengths which were welded to the 1 inch x $3\frac{1}{2}$ bars. Expecting minor difficulties during this procedure, one of the bars was completed to determine the amount of warpage. The 1 inch x $3\frac{1}{2}$ bar warped $2\frac{1}{2}$ inch flatways and $\frac{7}{8}$ inch edgeways, forming almost a perfect radius. Knowing that I was unable to stop this warpage when the $\frac{3}{4}$ inch rod was welded to it, I cold bent the next 1 inch x $3\frac{1}{2}$ inch bar to the measurements I had obtained, namely $2\frac{1}{2}$ inches and $\frac{7}{8}$ inch, before the next bar was welded. This procedure greatly improved the warping condition, but the cold bend which we made was a little too much. A third bar was tried with a $2\frac{1}{4}$ inch bend flatways and the same $\frac{7}{8}$ inch bend edgeways. When the $\frac{3}{4}$ inch round bar was welded to this bar it was almost straight; the little warp that was still in the bar was easily straightened. This procedure was followed on the rest of the bars for the 48 doors.

Two 1 inch x $4\frac{1}{2}$ inch bars which came in 20-foot length and the $\frac{5}{8}$ inch plates which came in various widths were cut to the proper length and size by an acetylene cutting machine. These $\frac{5}{8}$ inch plates were of various sizes, 3 feet x 12 inches, 4 feet x 15 inch, 3 feet x 8 inches, and 6 feet x 30 inches. The 3 inch eye beams were cut to 4 inch lengths as shown in "C", Fig. 1. The number plate, bumper plates, and hook plates were then cut from the $\frac{5}{8}$ inch plates. Having the material cut for the construction of one door, the assembling of the door was started. Three steel saw horses were situated in a level position as shown in Fig. 2.

The $\frac{5}{8}$ inch plate was then placed on these horses, laid out for dimensions, center line, etc. The 1 inch x $3\frac{1}{2}$ inch bars were then clamped to the $\frac{5}{8}$ inch plate with thumb clamps and tack welded into place; this part of the door was then turned over the 1 inch x $4\frac{1}{2}$ inch bars, number plates, and hook plates, and bumper plates were also tack welded into place. After the door was completely tacked together it was ready for the welding process.

As these doors weighted 1,435 pounds and 1,675 pounds for the pusher side and coke side respectively, it was my desire to plan some device whereby they could be handled with the minimum amount of trouble. Outside the machine shop there is a chain block and a small jib crane (shown in Fig. 2), which I thought would be ideal for handling the doors; thus the cost of installing any additional hoisting devices was eliminated. It was now my desire to arrange a set-up so that a desirable position for welding could be obtained. The following procedure was my original idea wherein lies the whole crux of this report. I obtained two circular $\frac{3}{8}$ inch plates 22 inches in diameter to be used for the pusher side door which is 16 inches in width. From the center of these circular plates the shape of the door was cut out, thus allowing the plates to slip over each end of the door. With the use of steel wedges the plate was wedged tight against the door as shown in Fig. 3.

The width of the coke side doors was 18 inches; so we were required to use another set of plates for these doors.

Fig. 2. (A) Arrangement of steel saw horses to facilitate door assembly. (B) Method of slipping circular plates over each end of door and utilizing wedges to hold plates tightly. (C) Profile of completed door.

Blocks and railroad ties were then set and spaced to conform with the distance between the circular plates which had been placed over the ends of the door. Two pieces of 3 inch eye beam of sufficient length to allow complete turn of the $3/8$ inch circular plates were used to act as a track or guide, making the manipulation of the door very easy and also making it convenient for two or more welders to be working at the same time.

The operation of the welding setup proved to me that two welders could work simultaneously and with notable success. It was my plan to start in the center of the door—welding towards the ends in the "step weld" method —that is to weld for two inches, then leave a 6 inch space, and then weld for two inches again—working on both sides of the door at the same time. I was confident that with this procedure the doors could be welded without warping and without clamping the door to a massive face plate, thus allowing the expansion and contraction to take care of itself.

To carry out the above stated procedure it was necessary at this time to find another welder. Another student welder who also had about 500 class-hours to his credit was employed.

At the completion of the first door the welder who was first hired became so enthusiastic over the success which we had obtained with the unique welding arrangement and the ease with which we handled the heavy doors that he immediately began investigating the various methods which other concerns were using in fabricating these doors. He found to his own satisfaction, that the method we were using in welding and handling the doors, namely, that of inserting the ends of the door into the center of a circular plate and placing such on a track so as to provide a complete revolution of the door, as well as enabling two welders to work simultaneously, one welding on the inside of the bottom 1 inch x $4\frac{1}{2}$ inch bar, was more efficient than any other method now in use. In his investigation he found a photograph in the "Procedure Handbook of Arc Welding Design and Practice", 6th edition. This photograph on page 101, Fig. 163 of the above book was of a coke oven door clamped to a massive face plate with one man working on it; further, this picture showed the heavy crane which was necessary to handle the doors. It seemed quite a coincidence to me that on this same date I should receive an invitation to enter your Foundation Award Program.

After studying the above mentioned photograph, I decided to enter your contest hoping that my method of fabricating coke oven doors was superior to those now in use.

With the two welders working so successfully together, and my simple device for handling the doors operating far beyond my expectation, it was natural that my next thoughts were of methods by which we could expedite the welding process and increase production. As previously mentioned, we have three electric welding machines; however, two of the machines are in continual use for repair and maintenance work, allowing only one to be used in the welding of the doors. Therefore, to increase production, it was necessary either to purchase more machines or hire more welders and operate on the 4:00 P.M. to 12:00 midnight shift. I decided on the latter. By this time, the news of the manufacturing of these doors and the success which we were having in their construction was being discussed in the various welding classes in this locality. This increased interest in the work which we were doing on the doors was shown when several student welders with 400 to 500 class-hours to their credit, made application at the Industrial Relations Office and expressed their desire to obtain work in the welding of the coke oven doors. Three such student welders were hired.

These men were put to work welding the doors on the 8:00 A.M.–4:00 P.M. shift where they welded intermittently in order to determine their ability as welders and at the same time acquaint them with the working conditions and surroundings. As soon as their welding was satisfactory I put these welders on the afternoon shift, 4:00 P.M. to 12:00 midnight.

This arrangement allowed a separate welding machine for each welder without interference from maintenance welding. Two welders were used in the welding of these doors, while the third welder was used for welding the $\frac{3}{4}$ inch round bars to the 1 inch x $3\frac{1}{2}$ inch bars. This third welder also took charge of the assembling and welding of the bumper plates, which you will note from Fig. 1, consist of two $\frac{1}{2}$ inch plates welded together with a 1 inch bar in the back which acts as a stiffener for these plates when welded to the door. This welder also assisted in welding number plates and ends on the doors.

With these seven men, a boilermaker, a boilermaker helper, and 5 welders, working the doors two shifts per day; the production of these doors increased steadily until we were averaging two completed doors per day. The schedule of production for the 48 doors is as follows:

June 19 to June 20, 1941, inclusive—none
June 23 to June 27, 1941, inclusive—three
June 30 to July 3, 1941, inclusive—four
July 7 to July 11, 1941, inclusive—five
July 14 to July 18, 1941, inclusive—six
July 21 to July 25, 1941, inclusive—eight
July 28 to August 1, 1941, inclusive—nine
August 4 to August 8, 1941, inclusive—ten
August 11 to August 12, 1941, inclusive—three (completing the 48 doors)

The amount and size of the welding rod used per door is as follows: 20 pounds of $\frac{5}{32}$ inch coated electric welding rod, No. E 6010, and 30 pounds of $\frac{3}{16}$ inch coated electric welding rod, No. E 6010.

In conclusion, I would like to summarize and emphasize the points in my report which seem to be the most significant. First is the possibility of using successfully relatively inexperienced welders on this type of project,

ARC WELDING

Production Chart

Date	Number of Welders	Welders' Daily Hours	Welders' Daily Rate	Number of Boiler-Makers	Boiler-Makers' Daily Hours	Boiler-Makers' Daily Rate	Number of Boiler Makers' Helpers	Boiler-Makers' Helpers' Daily Hours	Boiler-Makers' Helpers' Daily Rate	Total Labor Cost per Period	Labor Cost per Day	Number of Doors Completed	Labor Cost per Door
June 19 to June 20 Incl.	1	8	7.08	1	8	7.60	1	8	5.96	41.28	20.64	None	
June 23 to June 24 Incl.	2	16	14.16	1	8	7.60	1	8	5.96	55.44	27.72	1	96.72
June 25 to June 27 Incl.	5	40	35.40	1	8	7.60	1	8	5.96	146.88	48.96	2	73.44
June 30 to July 3 Incl.	5	40	35.40	1	8	7.60	1	8	5.96	195.84	48.96	4	48.96
July 7 to July 11 Incl.	5	40	35.40	1	8	7.60	1	8	5.96	244.80	48.96	5	48.96
July 14 to July 18 Incl.	5	40	35.40	1	8	7.60	1	8	5.96	244.80	48.96	6	40.60
July 21 to July 25 Incl.	5	40	35.40	1	8	7.60	1	8	5.96	244.80	48.96	8	30.60
July 28 to Aug. 1 Incl.	5	40	35.40	1	8	7.60	1	8	5.96	244.80	48.96	9	27.20
Aug. 4 to Aug. 8 Incl.	5	40	35.40	1	8	7.60	1	8	5.96	244.80	48.96	10	24.48
August 11	5	40	35.40	1	8	7.60	1	8	5.96	48.96	48.96	2	24.48
August 12 4:30 P.M.	2	16	14.16	1	8	7.60	1	8	5.96	27.72	27.72	1	27.72

Total Cost for Labor.................. $1740.12
Average Cost per Door.................. 36.25

which, under previous practices, necessitated the use of experienced welders. The second point, and that which makes the first possible, is the simple arrangement for handling the doors. This arrangement allows two or more welders to work together, and at all times to weld in a natural horizontal position, thus greatly simplifying the welding process. The third and final point has to do with the percentage of saving in time, money, and labor.

We received bids of $9600—jobsite; $6720—F. O. B., Johnstown, Pa.; and $12,480—F. O. B., Los Angeles, for the 48 coke oven doors. The freight charge from Johnstown, Pa., is $1.43 per hundredweight, making a total freight charge of $1,067.35 which would bring the total cost for the 48 oven doors to $7,787.35. The freight charge from Los Angeles is 66¢ per hundredweight, making a total freight charge of $492.62 and bringing the total cost for the 48 coke oven doors to $12,972.62.

The production chart, shown herewith, illustrates the cost of labor for each worker, and the total cost of labor for all the workmen who participated in the construction of the doors. The total labor cost as shown was $1,740.12, and the cost of material was approximately $75 per door, or $3,600 for the 48 doors, making a total cost of $5,340.12 for the 48 coke oven doors manufactured at this plant. The nearest bid was $7,787.35 jobsite. The difference between this cost and our cost was $2,447.23, which shows a saving of 31.43 percent. I sincerely believe that this large percentage of saving was made possible only by the unique arrangement which I devised for handling the doors while they were being welded. In stating the above percentage saving I am fully cognizant of the rules and conditions which state, "Extravagant claims must not be made since they will create, in the mind of the jury, uncertainty and doubt as to the authenticity and accuracy of other data and thus affect the rating of the paper," however, the facts stated above are true and can be substantiated in every respect.

Our average cost per fabricated steel coke oven door was $110.25. This cost compares very favorably with the cost of the cast iron coke oven door which this company purchased in 1936. The cost of these purchased was $179.44 per coke side door and $262 per pusher side door. As these values were given in 1936, it is fair to assume that the cost of labor and materials have increased 20 percent since that time. This would bring the cost of the doors to $215.33 and $315.60, respectively. Using the above figures, the percentage of saving is 94.4 percent and 186 percent, respectively.

The accompanying production chart also shows the total labor cost per completed door. It can be seen that the labor cost for the first completed door was $96.72. This makes the total cost for the first completed door approximately $171.72. The high labor cost for the first day was due to the lack of welding experience of the men, and also to the new type of work which they were performing. It is shown that as the men become better acquainted with their work, the labor cost took a decided drop; and as more men were employed to allow the operation of two shifts, this drop continued until the labor cost per door was decreased to $24.48. This drop in labor cost reduced the cost per completed door from $171.72 to $99.48, a reduction of $72.24 or 42 percent per door.

During this period of 5 days—August 4th to August 8th, 1941—ten (10) coke oven doors were completed at a cost for labor of $244.80. The average labor cost per door for the 48 doors was $36.25. After observing the results which were obtained in manufacturing the fabricated steel coke oven doors by our procedure, I believe it is safe to say that our method is more efficient, and more economical, than many methods now in use.

Chapter VII—Copper Plant

By Gordon B. Forbes,

Mechanical Superintendent, American Smelting and Refining Company, Garfield, Utah

Subject Matter: Instances of the substitution of welding for former methods of fabrication with consequent economy and longer life. Comparative costs and savings are given for several of the jobs undertaken. Mention is also made of maintenance and reclamation of several parts used in connection with copper smelting and refining.

Gordon B. Forbes

It is said that there is nothing new under the sun, and so it is. It just remains for someone through experimentation, or by accident if you please, to discover the things that go to make up our way of life.

Of electricity we know this to be true, Benjamin Franklin, Thomas Edison and many others discovered ways and means of utilizing this mighty force as we know it today. The electric arc as a tool lay dormant until by accident, shall we say, it was discovered that here was a tool that could be utilized to good advantage in the joining of metals.

Within the past few years, remarkable strides have been made in the improvement of welding rod and welding machines, with the result that we now have a tool, if properly utilized, the potentiality of which is just beginning to be realized.

With the above in mind, it can be said that today the method of joining metal with the electric arc is not new, and no matter what you may undertake to weld, someone else has already welded something similar, but this I do say, that the potentialities of the electric arc are not fully appreciated by many in the maintenance of their plants. Competition has forced many to adopt the electric arc in the manufacture of a product for sale, but many, many plants are not aware of additional profits available through the use of the electric arc in the maintenance of their plants, or if aware of them, do not have any one in their organization capable of developing the use of this tool as an aid to greater profits.

If, by the presentation of this paper, I am able to call to the attention of some of these plants referred to, the possibilities of the electric arc as an aid to a better operating plant which in turn results in greater profits, then I shall feel greatly rewarded regardless of any other considerations. Back in 1935 the author started missionary work with his company towards utilizing the electric arc more in the maintenance work in the plant, at which time we had one 200-ampere machine used for light patch work only, with the result that one 400-ampere machine was purchased, and a real effort was started towards using the electric arc in maintenance.

It also was the author's good fortune to have work with him, the chief engineer of the company, who was a very aggressive engineer, and with his aid we soon had new design work in his office coming out with welding, included in the design, with the result that each year from 1935 on it was necessary to increase our welding capacity in the shops. By the end of 1939 we had 12 welding machines, one large mechanical flame cutting machine, a 10-foot x 10-foot x 14-foot stress relieving furnace, a set of bending breaks, a squaring shear, a complete ventilating system to take welding fumes out of shops for operators' protection, and other miscellaneous equipment that would facilitate welding to the fullest extent—and we now have on order two 6000-pound welding positioners.

Along with the above equipment, we had 18 very good operators and all concerned had attained the necessary confidence in the electric arc, with the result that it was the natural course of events that we would consider welded design more than ever, and in all design work and maintenance work the first thought that now comes to our minds is, "can it be welded?"

Fig. 1. Welded slag pot, view from above.

During the last two years we have accomplished things with the electric arc that 4-years ago we would have considered impossible or should I say welding would not have even entered the picture.

In this treatise, the author will, with the aid of pictures and descriptions show how several problems were overcome through welded construction, in most cases a redesign and in some a new design of a piece of equipment required to do necessary processing in our plant. In most every case, costs of welded design were ignored for the reason that we know by experience, that on the average piece of equipment it will cost us so much to make it of cast iron or cast steel, and by experience we know how much welded design will cost. And in each design submitted in this paper the first consideration, with one exception, was will it increase the continuity of plant operations, and in some instances the safety of the employee was the main consideration. From the author's experience, it can be said others can profit by application of the electric arc in their own problems.

ARC WELDING

Fig. 2. Welded slag pot, bottom view.

Item 1, Welded Slag Pot Built to Handle Slag from a Lead Plant Blast Furnace—It was desired to have a slag pot of greater capacity to serve the blast furnace due to increased tonnage through the furnace. On analysis of the design it was found impossible to increase the height of original design due to lack of head room. It was then decided to build an elliptical-shaped bowl to obtain the capacity required, and through the author prevailing on the engineering department, welded construction was decided upon, and in Figs. 1 and 2 it will be noted that welding was utilized to the fullest extent.

The bowl proper is 1½-inch plate with 1¼-inch ribs and presented quite a problem of forming with the tools available. The conical sections for each end were heated in an improvised furnace adjacent to a set of rolls built to roll ½-inch plate cold. Each plate was heated to about 1600-degree F. and formed in the rolls with a single heat with remarkable accuracy as will be noted by observing alignment of the welded joints, and it was very necessary that this alignment be accurate as it would interfere with the slag shell releasing properly when emptying the pot.

The spherical sections presented another problem, this was solved by casting a half section sphere of cast iron, machining to proper radii. A ring was then provided to set disc on, all of this was then taken to blacksmith shop, the disc heated and placed under a 2500-pound steam hammer and 4 blows of the hammer formed the half sphere required, when cut in half gave us the proper quarter section to complete the ends of the bowl.

The center section of the bowl, it will be noted, is in one piece thereby permitting a minimum of welded joints, of which there are four.

All of the material in this bowl was laid out on one sheet of steel and then flame cut on a flame cutting machine.

In Fig. 2 the method of applying the trunnions will be noted. In order to secure good alignment of these trunnions, a layout was made on each end, then a hole large enough to permit a four-inch boring bar to enter was flame cut. The bowl was then placed upside down on a 42-inch lathe and the hole bored to size required. The trunnion shafts were then made up on a piece of 6-inch extra heavy pipe. The bored holes were then scarfed both inside and out for welding, and shaft was inserted and welded outside and reinforcing ribs attached, then shafts were cut off inside and welding was completed. This method was then checked on surface plate and it was found that perfect alignment had been maintained. The welds were then ground flush on the inside to permit easy shelling of slag shells. The completed bowl was then stress relieved at 1400-degree F. in a 10-foot x 10-foot x 14-foot gas fired furnace, built for stress relieving all types of welded work, which we feel is necessary on equipment similar to this.

The underslung frame is a welded section, made up of stock bar iron, and flame cut section for the corners of the offset. This corner section is a thicker section than the adjoining pieces that make up the web. With this construction we were able to develop the strength required, which could not be obtained in any of the H-beams of the depth required for this frame.

Further observation will show that the brake beam, spring cradles, worm shaft supports, etc., are all of welded construction. This slag pot was built complete in our shop, the only parts not fabricated by us being the wheels, axles, springs and couplers, and as stated before, costs were not even considered when we started this design. However, we know that using welded design insofar as possible, and that with six to build, we could build these pots much cheaper than by the conventional methods of making all the patterns required and having cast steel castings made.

Accurate costs were kept during the construction of these slag cars and we were rather pleased to find we had built them for $1485.65 each. We did not break down the costs, just the cost of total material and labor. Overhead, insurance, etc. being included in the above costs.

Item 2, Welded End Bells for 100 Horsepower Electric Motor—At our plant we have four 100 horsepower motors which for some time had been giving trouble due to operators operating with drive belt too tight, with the resultant burning out of sleeve bearing. We of the mechanical department decided that the proper bearing to eliminate this trouble was an antifriction bearing and in considering the problem, it was decided that welded construction would be the most economical due to the fact that

Fig. 3. Welded end bell for electric motor, outside view.

these motors were direct current motors, with their necessarily large end bells, and patterns would be very expensive to make.

As will be observed in Figs. 3 and 4, the welded end bells were made up of standard bar iron sections, plate and one forging. In assembling, 1/8-inch machining stock was allowed where required, after welding, stress relieving was applied.

Figs. 5 and 6 show the completed construction, and these motors are operating as we expected them to, not having been out of service after 13-months of operation. Here again costs were not considered, nor did we keep account of costs. The main consideration being continuity of operation. However, the savings effected by this type of redesign are numerous, in that all operations stop when failures occur, which results in lost time never to be regained to say nothing of an operating force standing idle waiting on repairs to equipment, and in this particular instance $21.00 per hour in labor was idle waiting on these repairs.

Fig. 4. Welded end bell for electric motor, inside view.

Item 3, Bosh Plates for Blister Copper Cooling Sump—In casting bars of blister copper, the bars are dumped into a cooling sump in which these Bosh plates are supported, over which a bar type elevator or conveyor runs to bring copper bars up out of sump. These copper bars weigh 500-pounds each and fall 3-feet 6-inches onto the Bosh plates at the rate of 6 bars per minute. Being made of cast iron and weighing some 7000-pounds each, they would eventually break in two. Here again continuity of operation would be interfered with, and with present operations of some 800-tons of copper production per day being interfered with, the management wanted to know what could be done in a hurry about this condition.

Welded construction was suggested and accepted. It so happened that necessary material was on hand and work was started Dec. 11, 1941 and completed Dec. 20 and placed in operation Dec. 24, requiring 4 days to install.

In the construction of these weldments the drawings as used for cast iron were used to fabricate from using plate on hand nearest to dimensions called for on drawing, this happened to be 2-inch plate for the top and 1¼-inch and 1½-inch for all ribs, etc.

Figs. 7 and 8 are top views and Figs. 9 and 10 are bottom views. It will be noted from these pictures the massiveness of these two weldments also that all support brackets were machined.

Here is a splendid example of the utility of the electric arc with the aid of a flame cutting machine. In 13-days after it was decided to do this job it was in operation, and I know of no other way such speed could be attained. If cast steel had been the only out it would require more time than above just to make patterns, and under present conditions it would have taken that long at least to get the proper priority to get the speed required in this instance.

As to costs, we did keep accurate cost of material and labor and found them to be as follows:

Steel plate 9800-lbs. at 6-cents	$ 588.00
Welding rod 550-lbs. at 9-cents	49.50
Labor	538.50
	$1176.00

Cast iron plates cost $700 per set and average one replacement per year at a total cost of $1250 to replace, it cost approximately $550 to install them each time. These steel weldments should last for quite a number of years and will more than repay for themselves in the first year of service.

Item 4, Copper Casting Machine Upper and Lower Track Rings—In casting blister copper bars, moulds are supported by arms, that in turn hang from the rim of upper track ring. Conical rolls fit between upper and lower rings. The upper ring is rotated through a driving mechanism. These, too, were made of cast iron and due to explosions of blister copper under certain conditions, the upper ring would break, a patch would be placed over break, and this would continue until it was impossible to patch again. Then a new wheel body would be installed and the above process repeated.

Fig. 5, (left). Welded end bells, finished construction, commutator end. Fig. 6, (right). Welded end bells, finished construction, pulley end.

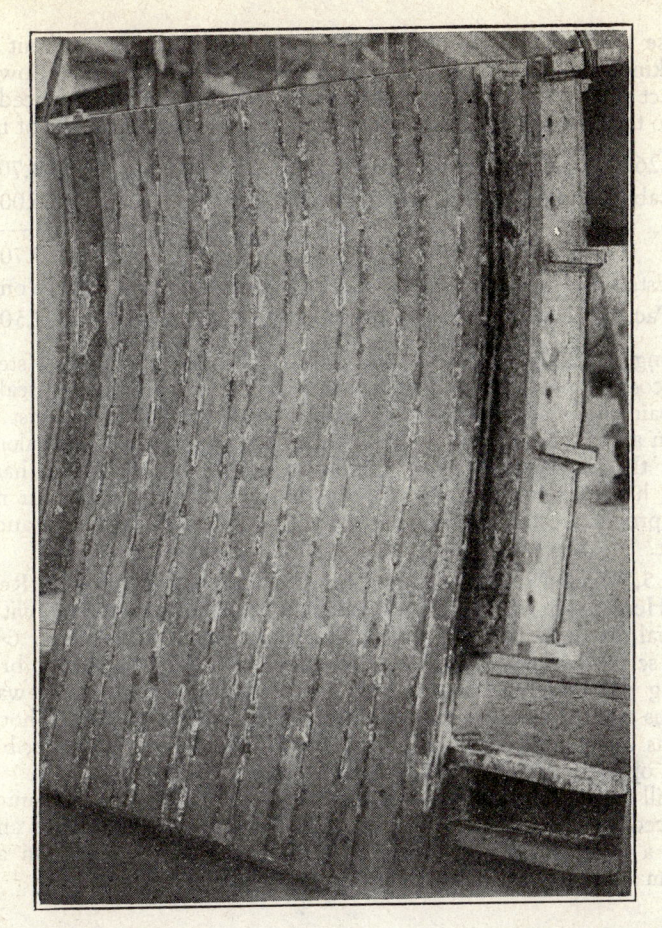

Fig. 7. Bosh plates for blister copper cooling sump, top view, upper section.

Depending on operations this replacement would vary but would average one per year.

These castings cost $2311 in place divided as follows:

27220-lbs. castings at 5-cents	$1361.00
Machining, installation, etc.	950.00
	$2311.00

Some 18-months ago a failure at a critical time in production raised the question about replacing these castings with steel castings. The author again suggested welding and Figs. 11, 12 and 13 are the result of this suggestion. It will be noted from these pictures that welding was held to a minimum by the use of large plate sections and flame cutting to shape. The bottom ring on top section is of $2\frac{1}{2}$-inch plate as is the corresponding plate on bottom section. These were formed to required taper to accommodate the conical rolls. The ring on the upper ring is 1-inch plate as is the spider, all ribs were cut from sections cut out to form spider. The top edge of ring was reinforced with 2-inch square bar.

These weldments have now been in service 16-months without trouble of any kind and ultimate life now appears to be how long the lower ring in contact with rolls will wear, this can then be cut off and replaced.

As to the cost of this construction the following figures will be of interest:

22620-lbs. of plate at 3.5 cents..$ 791.70
Labor, misc. material, machining installation.................. 1676.00
$2467.70
Estimated cost of cast steel castings submitted by company on Pacific Coast including pattern cost.............................$4675.50

Net saving of $2207.80 effected through welded design over cast steel, and due to cost of patching and delays due to cast iron castings breaking, it can be said the welded design cost less by at least $500 for the first year of operation and is now making a real return on the changeover, this along with the fact that the continuity of operation which this weldment has made possible, has enabled us to keep production at a maximum for our national defense program, is something that cannot be measured in dollars and cents, or can it?

Item 5, Welded Ladle Used to Pour Copper into Moulds from Receiving Ladle—Here again is a typical weldment replacing cast iron with very substantial savings. The cast iron ladles would break in two after 6- to 10-days of service, if not watched closely and changed out before breaking. Changing out could be determined by the length of crack. It was very dangerous to the operator working around it, and being full of hot metal, there was a potential accident present at all times, with the possibility of burning operator if a failure occurred while in operation.

It will be noted in Fig. 14 that weight was kept to a minimum with well placed ribs. It will also be noted that trunnions are forgings and here again is a unit that was completely flame cut from templates on a flame cutting machine.

Fig. 8. Bosh plates for blister copper cooling sum, top view, lower section.

Fig. 9. Bosh plates for blister copper cooling sump, bottom view, upper section.

The 3 units illustrated in Fig. 14 have now been in service 14-months and good for an indefinite period yet. Using an average of $3\frac{1}{2}$ cast iron units per month, the life to date of weldments is 16 to 1.

The comparative costs will be of interest:

	Weldment		Cast Iron Unit
938-lbs. at .035	$32.83		
Labor, welding rod forgings, etc.	37.52	Casting 1640-lbs. at .05	$82.00
		No labor & machining	
	$70.35		$82.00

Savings per original weldment unit.................$ 11.65
Net saving for the 14-months:
  49 cast iron units...$4018.00
   3 weldment units 210.05

     Net saving $3807.95

This saving, added to the making of this operation 100 percent safe for the operator, which is of inestimable value, clearly demonstrates what can be done with weldments if only we will look over our plants with the thought in mind, what can I do with this piece of equipment with weldments that will increase continuity of operation, and in general the result savings, which need not be considered in the original changeover, will soon become obvious.

Item 6, Sinter Machine Pallets for Lead Ore Sintering—The sintering machine has been in use for years in lead practice to sinter fine lead ores to be smelted in a blast furnace, this sintering is done to hold dusting down to a minimum in the furnace. It had been the practice to use cast iron pallets and still is in some lead smelters, but due to excessive breakage of these units as they drop over bull wheel to shake sinter off, it was decided to use cast steel instead of the cast iron and here is one of the exceptions where cost was considered, and in considering cost, welded design was brought into the picture.

Estimates were made on the weld design and obtained from local representative of Pacific Coast steel foundries on cast steel design, and from our estimates it was found we could expect to make the welded construction at a net saving of $9.35 per pallet. Actual savings were $10.98 per pallet on the first 100 completed.

In designing this pallet for welded construction, it developed that standard bar sizes could be used throughout, which in turn simplified all flame cutting, it being necessary to cut to length only all sections required in the design. It will be noted in Fig. 15 that the heavy bosses on ends were flame cut also, from $3\frac{1}{2}$-inch x $5\frac{1}{2}$-inch bar.

The pallet was assembled in a jig on fitting up floor, tack welded, then delivered to welding floor where they were placed in a special built positioner, permitting all welds to be made in a down hand position. This, of course, speeded up the welding and permitted the use of $\frac{1}{4}$-inch electrode throughout the weldment. Jump welding, as we call it, that is welding a little on one end and then a little on opposite end held warpage to a minimum and permitted the allowance of just $\frac{1}{8}$-inch for machining stock where required.

Of the first 200 completed, which have now been in service nearly 2-

Fig. 10. Bosh plates for blister copper cooling sump, bottom view, lower section.

ARC WELDING

Fig. 11, (left). Upper section of wheel body. Fig. 12, (center). Bottom view, upper section, wheel body. Fig. 13, (right). Top view, bottom section, lower track ring.

years, there has not been a single failure which has fully justified our selection of the welded design, and the continuity of operation of the machine on which these units are used, has been very satisfying to the operators, as it is very disrupting to operations when it becomes necessary to shut a machine down to change out broken pallets.

The following costs are of interest in this particular instance:

	Weldments	Cast Steel
520-lbs. material	16.66	46.80
Flame cutting	2.80	
50-lbs. welding rod	5.00	
Labor	7.70	
	32.16	46.80
Overhead at 15%	4.82	
Total cost each	36.98	36.98
Net saving each		$ 9.82

From the above it will be seen that a net saving of $1964 was effected on the first 200 pallets made and 300 more have since been made.

Item 7, Bell Grinder Used to Grind Ore Samples—The sampling department desired a larger bell grinder, as increased receipts of ore samples demanded more equipment of the size in use, which was 12-inches, or a larger machine.

Upon making inquiries for a larger machine it was found that none were made, so it was decided to design a unit and built it in our own shops. Of course, as will be noted from Figs. 16 and 17, welding was used to the fullest extent.

It will be noted that the design made for a very compact machine, which would not have been possible had it been necessary to use castings for this design, and from observation it will be noted that some very intricate pattern work would have been required to accomplish what was required of this machine. The only castings used on this machine being the bowl and grinding bell.

This machine performed perfectly when placed in operation, and two more have been built for two of our other plants because of its performance at our plant.

From the design drawings it was estimated that it would cost $1560 to build this machine utilizing welded construction, actual cost was $1385.40. No attempt was made to figure cost of any other method of construction as we felt quite sure that the weldment design would be considerably cheaper.

The foregoing descriptions are just a few concrete examples of what can be accomplished with the aid of the electric arc on the heavier items required in most plants. At our plant, we have used an average of 75,000-pounds of welding rod per year for the last 2-years and this rod was used for every conceivable thing that goes to keep a large copper smelter operating.

Fig. 14. Spoon ladles of welded construction.

We make all of our steel gears, up to as large as a No. 5 milling machine will handle, by rolling a rim of S.A.E. 1035 steel, a piece of plate for the web, and most generally a piece of old shafting for a hub. The weldment is then stress relieved and normalized before machining. By this method of gear making warehouse carry is down to a minimum, as we can always start making a new gear whenever it is decided that one is about worn out, and depending on size a new gear can be made within 10-days.

Bearings of all descriptions are made with a piece of shafting, a piece of I beam for a base and a brass bushing.

There are many plants that have salvage departments in which there are untold feet of pipe of various lengths which with the aid of the electric arc can be made up into standard 20-foot lengths again, odds and ends of angle iron, I beams, etc. that can be welded into desired lengths which when welded by good operators is just as strong as parent metal, and in these days of steel shortages and priorities is something to be considered.

Incidentally, during the last 10-months our plant has not had a single piece of new plate, but with the aid of the electric arc and secondhand plate obtained in junk yards, we have been able to keep our plant at full produc-

Fig. 15. Sinter machine pallets.

tion, even though some of the jobs looked like a crazy patch quilt when completed.

Another item of considerable importance maintained with the electric arc is our cast steel hot metal ladles, of which we have 40 weighing over 15000-pounds each. These ladles develop cracks and frequently have metal washed out due to impingement of hot metal on sides, in which we have deposited as much as 1200-pounds of metal in order to restore them to service again. In welding such ladles we have found by experience that it is necessary to stress relieve before and after welding as they are very heavily stressed due to the service they are in, due to being first hot and then cold in handling hot metal, and being of a medium carbon steel, which requires normalizing after welding to obtain proper grain structure in an adjacent to the weld. These ladles cost approximately $2000 each, and before the advent of the electric arc in our plant were scrapped whenever these defects developed, which we now repair at an average cost of $250 per ladle.

Crusher jaw plates are reclaimed as are grinding roll cheek plates, which are of manganese steel. Clam shell buckets are maintained, electric locomotive tire flanges are built up, and incidentally these tires are normalized before machining. All grizzlies are built up with a hard surfacing rod and maintained with hard surface rod from then on.

From the foregoing descriptions and pictures it will be noted that quite a variety of weldments and maintenance jobs have been and are being performed at this plant, and to say the least, only a small part of what we are doing has been described.

Management—Volumes have been written on the best way to organize welding departments, and the author has been able to use the information gained from these volumes to a very good advantage and would suggest that anyone interested could do likewise by utilizing the information that is now available, with special reference by the author to read Mr. Gibson's paper on commercial welders, Grand Award Winner of the 1938 Lincoln Foundation Award Program, and which was published by the Foundation in the book titled "Arc Welding in Design, Manufacture and Construction", with particular reference to his conception of management, operator training and qualification, equipment required, cost data, etc., and select from this data that which could be utilized to best advantage in their particular plants.

In addition to the above suggestions, the author has the following to offer. To anyone contemplating the increased use or starting the use of the electric arc, they should first select an aggressive energetic young man who had demonstrated his practical ability as a welder, who has shown his aggressiveness by his attitude toward substituting welding for other types of construction, his ability to get along with men and his salesmanship. Then with this type of man send him on a plant visitation trip where welding is used to the utmost, have him observe the tools used, the methods used to obtain the results desired, have him note the jigs and fixtures used throughout the industry to simplify the procedure of welding, have him talk to production men how to control warpage and stress in welded structures of all kinds, have him pick up all the points he can on stress relieving, normalizing, etc. and the finer points in working with alloy steels, and observe the various methods of fume control for operator protection. During this plant visitation trip have him visit plants wherein the electric arc is used primarily as a maintenance tool, and plants wherein it is used as a manufacturing tool.

We should now have a man who is going to be more enthusiastic than he ever thought he could be about electric welding, a man who is now ready to put the process to work for his company. He will now start asking for the necessary equipment to start this process. He will no doubt want one or more 400-ampere welding machines, a portable flame cutter, one or more well ventilated welding booths, pneumatic flux scalers, etc. and herein lies the success of the whole plan.

This man has been selected because of his characteristics and because of these he will be very conservative in his request for new equipment in order to get the process started, and management must see that his requests are granted when made; it must support him in organization of operator

Fig. 16. Bell grinder, side view.

ARC WELDING 81

Fig. 17. Bell grinder, end view.

training, for it will be found that if you can train your own men from within your organization, you are promoting an incentive for the lower paid to want to develop up to the point of future operators, also you will have operators who will be more loyal.

After the preliminaries are over and the organization is functioning, it will be found that a natural growth will take place which again will want full support of management, and a part of this natural growth will be the desire to utilize this process in new design and this will require the very closest of cooperation between the engineering and production departments, and here with the inspiration, imagination and creative thinking required, the process will grow by leaps and bounds, so to speak.

Conclusion—In this short paper the author has endeavored, with the aid of pictures, to show what can be done with the aid of the electric arc when properly applied, and when it is considered that we are but a small part of the industries who, like our plant, have realized the full benefits of the use of this process, it can be said that the electric arc has contributed more to the industrial progress in recent years than any other one factor. This can also be verified by the fact that boats are now being launched every day that are completely welded, and at rates never conceived of, with the use of less material, which at a time like the present surely demonstrates its value to the country as a whole.

Chapter VIII—Cracking Still Charging Pump

By GEORGE M. HEATH,

Mechanic, Pure Oil Company, Toledo, Ohio.

Subject Matter: Paper describes the surfacing with stainless steel of a pump in a refinery which had become corroded. The method of preparing for the welding and the fabrication by welding of a 5' cutter head boring tool for finishing the weld are discussed. Drawings of the job are furnished as are also relative costs of doing the work with shop machinery and the tool made by welding for machining.

George M. Heath

Perhaps few people have the opportunity of knowing nor do they realize the tremendous array of tanks, furnaces, fractionating towers, pumps, machinery, control equipment, and the miles of piping that makes the modern oil refinery of today.

Little do they realize as they drive up to the filling station pump the vast amount of research and engineering, the construction, and the continuous operation entailed to bring to them this clear, delicately tinted fluid which performs miracles in the engines of their automobiles.

Today, as never before, is our country so dependent on the oil industry for transportation, farming, heating, and for adequate petroleum supplies to keep rolling our highly mechanized war machine.

To us, whose task it is to keep a modern refinery in working order, and to those who come in daily contact with the numerous problems of refinery maintenance, or to anyone who has had the privilege of observing the complicated maze of piping and equipment necessary to carry on its work, the vital importance of arc welding is made apparent. Through the medium of arc welding the engineers are enabled to execute their designs, the builder to construct in a safe and efficient manner, and the resultant equipment is maintained at a minmum cost, so that the general public may enjoy the benefits of petroleum products at the lowest possible price. The construction of the tanks, pressure vessels, and pipe-work, carrying working pressures ranging up to 2000 pounds and temperatures sometimes over 900 degrees, is almost entirely dependent upon arc welding. Therefore, knowing the possibilities of this modern tool in the hands of a master craftsman, I welcome this opportunity of extolling its merits and hope to show one of the practical applications to which it has been put in maintaining the machinery in the plant at which I am employed.

During the semi-annual inspection of one of the refinery units, which inspection was carried out in April, 1942, it was discovered that the walls of the valve chambers of one of the Wilson Snyder pumps charging the

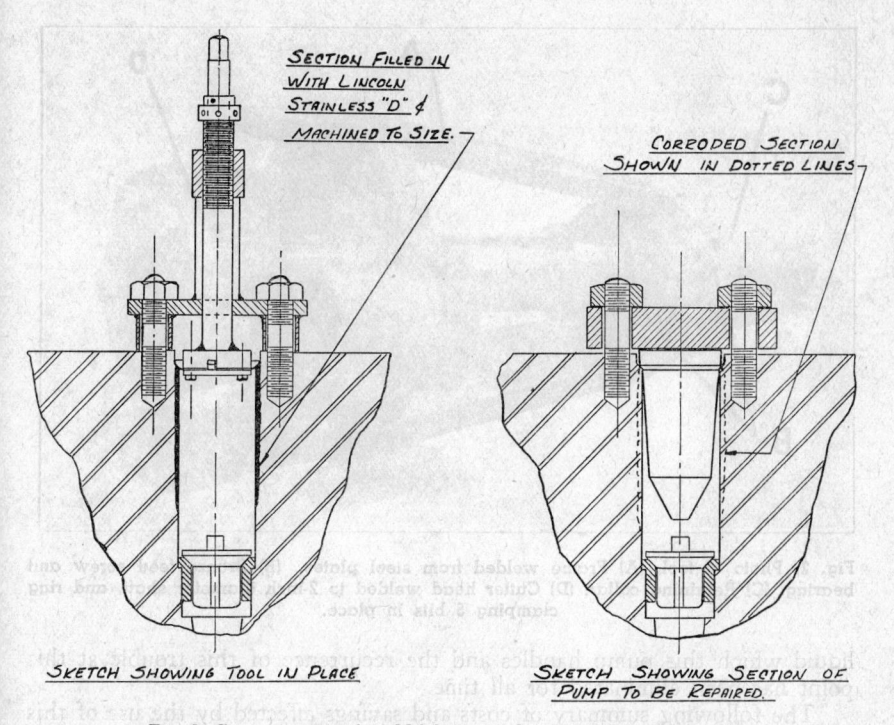

Fig. 1. Cross section of weld-fabricated boring and seating tool.

(Labels on figure: SECTION FILLED IN WITH LINCOLN STAINLESS "D" & MACHINED TO SIZE. — CORRODED SECTION SHOWN IN DOTTED LINES — SKETCH SHOWING TOOL IN PLACE — SKETCH SHOWING SECTION OF PUMP TO BE REPAIRED.)

cracking stills, were cut away as shown by the dotted line on the attached sketch. This cutting was the result of corrosion, probably accelerated by turbulence. This pump is of the horizontal duplex forged steel type, pumping heavy gas oil at the rate of 250 gallons per minute at 800 pounds pressure and approximately 700 degrees temperature. Since time is always at a premium in all oil refineries, and in these days of steel shortages, rationing, and priorites, the replacing of this steel forging was out of the question. Since the problem was one of repairing the forging, we had the choice of sending it to a local shop for machining or to do the work in place. As the latter course was decided upon it fell to my lot to device a tool capable of doing the work in a suitable manner. The tool shown in Fig. 1 was the result. This boring and seating tool was fabricated of steel plate salvaged from scrap. Its main requirements were that it had to be rigid enough to withstand the stress of machining the 6-inch diameter seat, which had been coated with stainless steel, without chatter and in the least possible time. It required approximately $4\frac{1}{2}$ man hours cutting and welding time and a general purpose electrode for mild steel was used in fabrication. The shaft is 2 inches in diameter, turns in bronze bearings, has a cutting head 5 inches in diameter, and carries five inserted tool bits as cutters. The use of the odd number of cutters insured the machining of the seat without chatter. An excellent job was obtained and a perfect seal made without lapping.

The pump body was first machined or ground to a depth of $\frac{1}{8}$-inch from orignal dimensions. A coating of corrosion and impact resisting weld metal was applied and the hole was rebored and reseated to original dimensions. The weld metal used resists the corrosion and cutting action of the particular

Fig. 2. Photo of tool. (A) Frame welded from steel plates. (B) Bronze feed screw and bearing. (C) Retaining collar. (D) Cutter head welded to 2-inch diameter shaft, and ring clamping 5 bits in place.

liquid which this pump handles and the recurrence of this trouble at this point has been eliminated for all time.

The following summary of costs and savings effected by the use of this tool are submitted to indicate some of the advantages of arc welding in a maintenance program. To replace this large forging would have cost several hundred dollars which indicates the advisability of repairing the old forging.

Cost of Performing Job With Shop Machinery

Removing forging from place..........................	64 man hrs. @ $1.30 per hr.	$ 83.20
Machining 6 holes at local shop....................	10 man hrs. @ $3.00 per hr.	30.00
Reassembling pump	96 man hrs. @ $1.30 per hr.	124.80
Total	170 man hrs.	$238.00

Cost of Making Tool and Machining Forging in Place

Making tool—

Welding	4½ man hrs. @ $1.40 per hr.	$ 6.30
Machining	20 man hrs. @ $1.30 per hr.	26.00
Machining six holes..	5 man hrs. @ $1.30 per hr.	9.00
Total	29½ man hrs.	$41.30

Analysis of the above figures indicate that the savings in time as well as in cost by using the arc welded tool amounted to approximately 83 percent when compared with the shop job.

Since we have a number of these pumps, this tool can be used for any futures valve seat repairs which may be required. It can also be adapted to making similar repairs such as boring, reaming, or valve seating in almost any type of similar equipment by changing the base used for securing the tool to the part to be machined, or by changing the cutter head in form, size or number of cutters for the best results in the particular job.

I am convinced that given the steel plate and round stock and the services of a competent welder we can duplicate most any machine part or tool and thus keep our plant in operating condition indefinitely.

Chapter IX—Drill Pipe of Integral-Joint Construction

By H. N. KEENER and C. F. UNDERWOOD,

Development and Metallurgical Engineers, respectively, Jones & Laughlin Steel Corp., Tubular Product & Research Div., Pittsburgh, Pa.

Subject Matter: Integral-joint drill pipe should be rebuilt before it is critically weakened by wear. The most economical method of retarding upset wear of integral-joint drill pipe is by the application of a solid band of abrasive resistant material about the pin-end upset. Advantages of re-building: 1, total expenditure is less; 2, rebuilding cost may be varied through a wide range by the selection of the proper hand electrode; 3, pin-end wearing pad can be applied at mill site by any competent welder; 4, no danger of damaging threads as integral-joint feature remains intact; 5, rebuilding consumes only 10 to 25 per cent of steel required for tool joints.

H. N. Keener

C. F. Underwood

I. The Rebuilding Problems—Until quite recently drill pipe was available only with a tool joint assembly which was removable from the pipe proper. Until then it was common practice to drill with the pipe until the tool joints were worn nearly to destruction, at which time the old joints were removed and replaced with new ones, providing, of course, that fatigue failure was not already becoming too common.

With the introduction of alloy steel drill pipe, structurally improved by forging the tool joint integral with the pipe body, came the problem of rebuilding or hard facing. In order to reach the optimum in performance the joint upset (tool joint) must resist wear sufficiently to equal the added endurance built into the improved structure. Under some conditions we find the various endurance limits well balanced, but in abrasive drilling formations it becomes necessary to prolong the joint life by rebuilding the upsets, or protecting them from destructive wear.

Study of drilling conditions in the field combined with laboratory investigation and development established the following facts:

a. Joint wear is dependent upon the types of formation being penetrated.
b. The rate of wear is greatly affected by drilling practice such as: size and straightness of hole, amount of drill collar used, etc.
c. Tool joint rebuilding by various methods is becoming common field practice, and is an established economic procedure.
d. Integral-joint type drill pipe being free of threaded connections possesses a very favorable section for various rebuilding procedures.
e. The degree of joint wear previous to rebuilding is a factor of vital importance.

Integral-joint drill pipe eliminates the critical threaded connections between tool joints and pipe by forging. Thus the heavy pin and box ends of this drill pipe are the only remaining critical sections. The design of tool joints is such that the strength of the pin-end is not reduced by abrasive wear, therefore the problem resolves itself into one factor, namely; the protection of the box end to maintain a safe margin of structural superiority over the pin. It should be borne in mind that rebuilding by any method does not materially increase the joint strength; it merely protects the joint from wearing to the point of destruction. Integral-joint drill pipe, like most other equipment, should be rebuilt before it is critically weakened by wear. Thus it becomes apparent that the joint must be rebuilt before the box-end has worn dangerously thin.

II. Selecting the Proper Type of Rebuild. A. The most economical method of retarding upset wear of Integral-joint drill pipe is by the application of a solid band of abrasive resistant material about the pin-end upset as illustrated in Fig. 1. The most common procedure is to deposit hard surfacing material by the electric arc, since it is conducive to shallow heat penetration, fast welding speed, and in general is the most readily available economic method. This rebuilding method is adaptable to field application as no re-threading or machining is necessary. Rotative wear is absorbed by the oversize pin, whose action is not unlike an oversize sub. (A sub is

REBUILDING OF INTEGRAL-JOINT DRILL PIPE
SOLID PIN END WEARING PAD

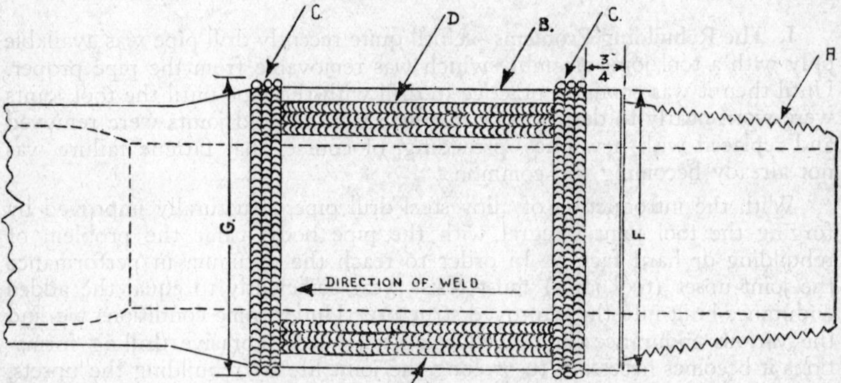

TABLE OF RECOMMENDED MINIMUM DIAMETERS "F" FOR REBUILDING			
SIZE OF PIPE	TYPE	ORIGINAL DIAMETER	MINIMUM DIAMETER "F"
2 7/8	INT. FLUSH	4 1/8	3 7/8
3 1/2	INT. FLUSH	4 3/4	4 17/32
3 1/2	FULL HOLE	4 5/8	4 15/32
4 1/2	INT. FLUSH	6 1/8	5 3/4
4 1/2	FULL HOLE	5 3/4	5 5/16
5 9/16	FULL HOLE	7	6 3/8

A. Protect threads with metal protector, asbestos or other suitable means.

B. Preheat upset to 350°-450° F.

C. Deposit hard facing material circumferentially at ends to desired thickness.

D. Fill in with hard facing material between circumferential deposits with longitudinal beads. The best results are obtained by starting the longitudinal deposit at three points on the periphery. Lay two or three beads at alternate locations and peen between passes. This reduces depth of heat penetration and gives a more uniform thermal condition.

F. The diameter before rebuilding should not be less than shown in the table.

G. Finished diameter depends upon drilling practice.

Fig. 1. View showing solid band of abrasive resistant weld metal about the pin-end upset.

REBUILDING OF INTEGRAL-JOINT DRILL PIPE
PIN END HARD FACING INLAYS

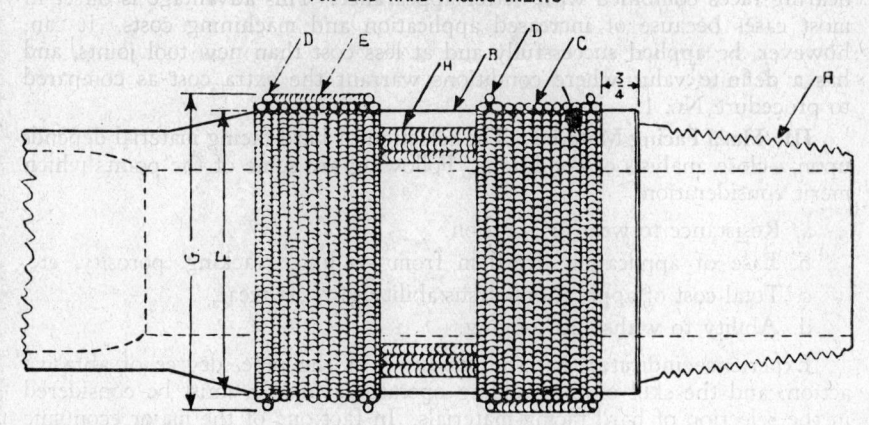

A. Protect threads with metal protector, asbestos or other suitable means.
B. Preheat upset to 350°-450° F. Section B, Sketch 1.
C. Weld circumferentially at both ends of pin upset 2" to 3" wide as a base for hard facing inlay. Maximum electrode size 1/8" diameter. Medium carbon grade recommended. Work from threaded end to shoulder in all cases.
D. Single circumferential bead at each edge of deposits of same grade as "C" to form groove for inlay.
E. While work is still preheated from previous welding, deposit hard facing inlays of highly abrasive resistant material. Use welding electrode of such diameter that one longitudinal pass will give a finished O.D., "G" desired in drilling practice.
F. Same as Fig. 1.
G. Same as Fig. 1.
H. Fill in between inlays to diameter "G" by longitudinal beads using same grade electrode as "C" and "D" above. This can be done in one pass, probably requiring a 1/4" electrode.
I. Beneficial results may be obtained by retarding the rate of cooling by wrapping in asbestos cloth or similar means.

Fig. 2. Extremely hard inlays of weld metal deposited at pin-ends over softer base metals.

a short member approximately one foot long which is connected between tool joints to protect them from wear). It is, therefore, possible to obtain wear protection equivalent to a sub without increasing the number of threaded connections or the initial cost. Fig. 1 illustrates:

a. The heavy pin-end section where the abrasive resistant metal is applied.
b. Integral-joint construction develops a section at this point much thicker than the pipe body, even when worn.
c. There are no threads between pipe and tool joint to warp from welding heat.

The hard facing should be applied before the box-end has become dangerously weakened by wear. The maximum wear limits are given in Fig. 1.

B. Fig. 2 illustrates a similar type of rebuild to that above except that in this case extremely hard inlays are deposited at the ends over softer base metals. The hard inlays are placed at the ends of the pin-upset so as to present a softer surface between inlays for tonging, when assembling or breaking down the joints. The inlays are placed over softer base materials to minimize alloy metal cost as well as to prevent cracking and spalling.

C. Figs. 3 and 4 illustrate a method of rebuilding both pin and box. Due to welding over the female thread this type of rebuilding requires closely controlled welding conditions. It has the advantage of renewing the bearing faces combined with better appearance. This advantage is offset in most cases because of increased application and machining costs. It can, however, be applied successfully and at less cost than new tool joints, and has a definite value where conditions warrant the extra cost as compared to procedure No. 1.

III. Hard Facing Material—The selection of hard facing material depends upon a close analysis of conditions. Following are some of the points which merit consideration:

a. Resistance to wear or abrasion.
b. Ease of application, freedom from spalling, cracking, porosity, etc.
c. Total cost of application versus ability to resist wear.
d. Ability to withstand tonging.

Experience indicates that the condition of the pipe, degree of abrasive action, and the skill of the welding operator available, must be considered in the selection of hard facing materials. In fact one of the major economic advantages of rebuilding tool joints by welding lies in the fact that the rebuilding cost can be adjusted to meet the estimated service life remaining in the pipe. Thus a string of pipe which might be good for only a few

REBUILDING INTEGRAL-JOINT DRILL PIPE
BOX END SOLID WEARING PAD

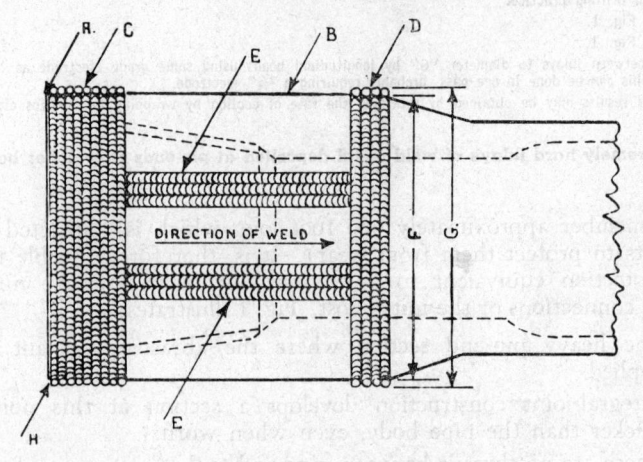

A. Locate steel ring as shown for pin end bearing face. The plug used for this should fit threads and recess tightly to minimize distortion.
B. Preheat to 350°-450° F.
C. Circumferentially welded with ⅛" or 3/32" rod of machinable grade. Deposit in two layers approximately 2" wide, cleaning first pad before depositing second. Heat of welding must be held to absolute minimum.
D. Circumferentially welded with ¼" electrode of machinable grade to desired thickness.
E. Refer to Fig. 1 "D".
F. See table Fig. 1.
G. Finished diameter depends upon drilling practice.
H. Machine bearing face and sloping shoulder.
I. Threads, bearing face and recess should be closely inspected and gaged. Weld checks or excessive distortion must be removed by machining.

Fig. 3. Method of rebuilding box end of integral-joint pipe.

REBUILDING INTEGRAL-JOINT DRILL PIPE
PIN END SOLID WEARING PAD

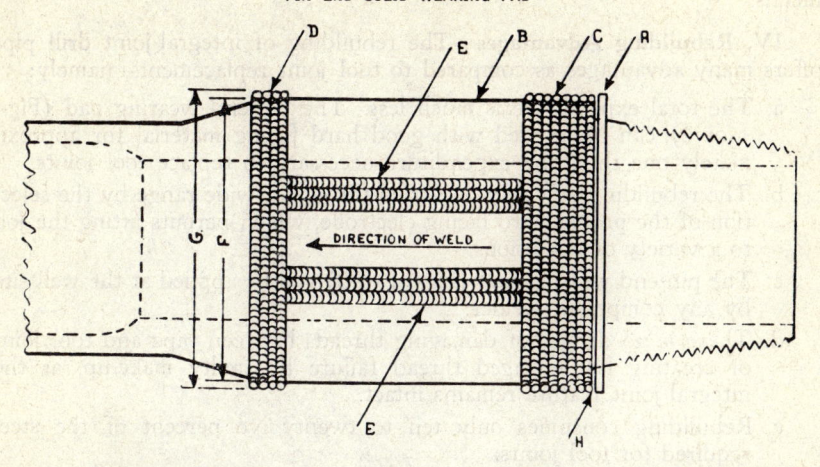

A. Soft steel ring held against bearing face of pin to act as gage for metal deposit and minimize refacing time. The ring is held in place by a short section cut from a discarded box.
B. Preheat to 350°-450° F.
C. Circumferential weld deposit of machinable rod. Build to the desired diameter with a small rod, 5/32" maximum; use least possible welding heat. Peen and clean.
D. Circumferential deposit same as "C" Fig. 1.
E. Deposit longitudinal beads same as "D" Fig. 1.
F. See table Fig. 1.
G. Finished diameter depends upon drilling practice.
H. Machine bearing face to correct stand-off.

Fig. 4. Method of rebuilding pin-end.

thousand more feet of drilling could be rebuilt with a light deposit of inexpensive hard facing electrodes, whereas tool joints are equally expensive whether applied to good or badly worn pipe. We do not, therefore, consider any one type of material adequate to meet all conditions. In areas where drilling is of a mildly abrasive nature and the pipe has already performed the major part of its service, a straight high carbon rod may be used. Highly abrasive resistant hard facing electrodes are more economical under average conditions. Deposits of the carbon, manganese, nickel type have been found highly satisfactory. They offer good abrasion resistance, can be easily applied by the average welder and are sufficiently inexpensive to permit their use for the entire rebuilding job. The more expensive electrodes of the carbide and borium class are of course more wear resistant. The high cost of these alloys, however, limits their use to an inlay over cheaper materials. The inlays should be from $1\frac{1}{2}$ to 3 inches in width; located near the ends of the build-up as illustrated in Fig. 2. The hard inlays are placed near the ends of the build-up to prevent it from rounding off in service and thus afford greater protection to the box and pin-end shoulders. This method also presents an area of softer material for tonging. A welder experienced in the application of hard facing materials should be employed, otherwise difficulty may be encountered from spalling and checking. The use of these premium metals appears to have value only when rebuilding a very good string of pipe or in extremely abrasive territory where the added material cost is offset by the repeated labor charge for the application of cheaper metals.

IV. Rebuilding Advantages—The rebuilding of integral-joint drill pipe offers many advantages as compared to tool joint replacements, namely:

- a. The total expenditure is much less. The pin-end wearing pad (Figs. 1 or 2) can be applied with good hard facing material for approximately one third the expenditure necessary to replace tool joints.
- b. The rebuilding cost may be varied through a wide range by the selection of the proper hard facing electrode, which permits fitting the job to a variety of conditions.
- c. The pin-end wearing pad (Figs. 1 or 2) can be applied at the well site by any competent welder.
- d. There is no danger of damaging threads between pipe and tool joint or creating last engaged thread failure by faulty make-up, as the integral-joint feature remains intact.
- e. Rebuilding consumes only ten to twenty-five percent of the steel required for tool joints.
- f. Rebuilding by method No. 1 has been obtained on a contract basis ranging in price from $9 to $12 per end for 4½-inch full hole joints. Tool joints for this size cost approximately $39 installed.

V. Conclusion—Rebuilding of drill pipe joints appears to be taking a definite place in the economic structure of drilling oil and gas wells. The present need for conservation of material and equipment will doubtless do much to develop this practice.

Chapter X—Farm Machinery

By Leslie Swick,

Mechanic, H. G. Glantz and Son, La Crosse, Kansas.

Subject Matter: Paper is devoted to a description of the various repairs which the author has made with the use of the arc welder. A part of the jobs completed include: 1, remodeling a manifold and installing a new muffler on a rebuilt tractor; 2, removing broken studs with the arc welder; 3, removing sprockets or wheels from their shafts; 4, wheel cut-down jobs; 5, welding cracked motor blocks; 6, charging batteries with direct current battery charger.

Leslie Swick

I will try and relate some of my previous experiences with arc welding. I formerly lived at the edge of a small town in Nebraska where there was no welding of any kind done.

This is where I saw great possibilities and profits in the arc welding business and I thought I would try my skill. I was not able to buy a welder and I knew very little of how they were made. But being determined I set in to make one from the material which I had on hand. This consisted of a large set of light plant batteries (32 volts 200 amps.) and a 32 volt 2000 watt D.C. generator with a speed of 600 R.P.M. I mounted this in a Model T chassis and powered it direct coupled with a Model T Ford motor.

I did not know where to buy welding rods and supplies. So I started my welding with the carbon arc process using carbons from worn out flashlight batteries and old radio B batteries. My welding rods consisted of bailing wire and copper wire for brazing. This was a rather crude way of starting out but I gained a lot of knowledge and experience from it. Later I purchased a supply of about every kind of welding rod that was made at that time. The ones that I could not use satisfactorily I still have on hand. I did a lot of arc welding later of which I have gained a lot of experience, profits and a good reputation.

Later, another mechanic saw my welder and wanted to buy it so I sold it to him for a fair price.

Then I accepted a job here in Kansas with a tractor and implement dealer. I started here in Feb. 1941 and have been here ever since. We sell and service the McCormick Deering line of tractors and farm machinery. We have a lot of trade-ins to rebuild and repair, consisting of tractors, combines, plows, cultivators, drills, pulverizers, discs, etc.

When I started working here we had in the shop as equipment and tools such as vale refacers and reseaters, hard seat grinders, magneto tester, also a set of special tractor tools, electric drills and power grinders, wheel jigs for welding on rims for rubber tires, acetylene welder, etc. We were minus the arc welder which I had been used to using for all of the hundred and one jobs that one has for the arc. There wasn't a day that went by that we did not have some job for the use of the arc and by not having one we were forced to send them to our competitors. This in a few months' time would amount to enough to buy a good welder.

I had asked the boss several times why he did not buy one, and his answer was that we would not have time to do a lot of welding. I mentioned the fact that electric welding would make our business a lot more profitable than to try and run a shop without it. Trying to run a maintenance shop without an electric welder is about like a boat without a sail.

A few months before we had mentioned arc welders I had bought a house but had not moved in it yet. Later I had a chance to trade it for a portable arc welder which I thought would be more profitable to me than a house. The welder has already proven more profitable for it more than takes care of my rent and a nice profit besides.

My welder is a 400 amp. 40 volt D.C. machine and powered by a Buick six motor, built on a four wheel trailer. Since my boss has seen the many possibilities and profits of the arc welder he has wanted to buy it from me. But as I work for him at a straight salary per week I decided to give him a share of the welding to make up for the time that I use for welding. We notice at the end of the week that we both have a nice salary as a result of the welding.

Most of the farmers in this territory burn gasoline in their tractors. Most of these tractors were originally designed for burning kerosene and distillate, therefore they have too hot a manifold for burning gas. I have fixed a way to cut off the preheating construction of these manifolds and weld on a pipe which takes the exhaust upward, keeping the heat which is created by the exhaust away from the intake manifold as you can see in Fig. 1. There is about two feet of cast iron to cut on this job including a round hole in the top where the pipe is welded on. This I cut with the arc welder using a small carbon from a flashlight battery which is about 1/4-inch in diameter and I use about 350 amps. With the right polarity and a little practice this can be done very quickly, neatly and economically. The pipe which I weld on is 12 in. long and of 2½ in. in diameter. This is just the right size to fit a large tractor muffler that the firm has for sale. The remodeled manifold and a new muffler installed on a rebuilt tractor brings it more up to date and makes it sell for a lot more money therefore putting extra dollars in the boss's pocket as well as mine. I get $5.00 for changing one of these manifolds which takes about an hours time and 30 cents worth of rods and 2 gal. of gas. This still leaves me a very nice profit that would otherwise be lost had it not been for the arc welder. I also change several of these manifolds for customers and most of them buy mufflers to fit these remodeled manifolds. This not only makes more profits in the cash register but still adds more satisfied customers which later bring in other things to be welded, such as broken wheels, sprockets, and numerous castings. I always manage to be doing some welding when we have the most customers in the shop. I find this is very good advertising for I do not know of anything that will attract more attention in the shop than the arc welder. This also reminds them that they have several things at home they will bring in the next time they come to town. I also find it very profitable to discuss the fundamentals and ability of my arc welder with my customers as I find them very much interested in its performance and its capability of doing a good job of joining metals. I find that they appreciate a few demonstrations such as running beads penetration of the weld. There are some

ARC WELDING 93

Fig. 1. (A) Remodeling tractor manifold by arc welding. Fig. 2. (B) Removing sprockets from wheel of farm implement. Fig. 3. (C) Typical examples of arc welded repair jobs on farm equipment parts. Fig. 4. (D) Typical wheel change-over jobs made possible by the electric arc. Fig. 5. (E) Welding the rims on wheel converted for rubber tire use. Fig. 6. (F) Cutting out spokes of large tractor wheel for rubber tire conversion job. Fig. 7. (G) Fractured motor block prior to weld repairing.

that are very eager to try their skill at striking an arc which I let them try. This not only gives them a great thrill but it gives them more confidence in our ability as they soon find out that it takes a little practice and skill.

I find it very practical and economical to remove broken studs with the arc welder. To do this quickly and successfully I take a nut just a little larger than the stud, and place it over the end of it and weld it on. The welding will cause the nut to get almost white hot. The heat from the nut will penetrate down the bolt causing it to expand and will help to loosen it. The nut makes it handy for using any kind of a wrench for screwing heat which will help to loosen it. If one gets a good weld on it the bolt it out. If the nut twists off, weld on another nut as this will make stilll more will come out bright and clean and free from rust in the threads. I also find the arc welder very handy and profitable when removing sprockets or wheels from their shafts. I found that by tack welding the straight keys to the wheel or sprocket, which ever it might be, the key will come along with the wheel or sprocket. There are times when I have to tack weld the key to the shaft instead of the wheels so that I can move the wheels or sprockets without moving the keys. I use this method quite often and find that the arc welder is a great time saver as we have a lot of this kind of work to do in this line of business.

I also use the arc welder to weld a bolt of the desired size to these keys for the purpose of making it easier to remove the key itself. This is done by welding the bolt opposite the head on to the key leaving the head for driving with a punch or hammer. This is a great labor and time saver, and using this method it saves breaking many castings, sprockets, and wheels which otherwise would be broken by too much pressing and pounding.

We do a considerable lot of wheel cut-down jobs, that is, changing lug type tractors to rubber tires. This is done by cutting off the spokes of the original wheel to the exact length and welding the spokes on the tire rims. The hub and stub spokes of the original wheel are placed in the jig for welding on the tire rims. After the centering and truing of the rim and hub the welding is quickly done with the arc welder. The spokes of these wheels should be welded opposite each other to prevent warping. By welding these in this manner it saves about half the time over the acetylene welder as there is considerable heat lost by the welds being made opposite each other.

This is where my direct current arc welder of 400 amp. capacity makes another saving as I use it for cutting off the spokes by using a $5/16$ battery carbon 3 in. long. One of these carbons will usually cut about 10 spokes. These spokes are usually $1\frac{1}{4}$-in. wide by $7/16$-in. thick. This is done in about the same time as it would take with the torch method. Although the carbon cutting isn't quite as smooth as the acetylene it is considerably cheaper. The carbon arc also cuts away more metal but with a little practice and plenty of current of about 350 amperes and 140 volts this can be done very smoothly and is fast and economical.

I use the arc welder for most all cutting except where the cutting away of too much of the metal prohibits its use. I also use this method of cutting off old rusty lug bolts as this saves time and is very inexpensive. Most of the old bolts are usually badly worn and it is hard to make a wrench hold them.

By being in the maintenance business we get several tractor motor blocks that have been frozen and cracked. These if bought new would cost at least $100, but by the use of the arc welder we can successfully weld these blocks for a cost of about $6. The price, of course, depends on the size of the breaks as the actual welding cost is not so great, but this kind of welding takes lots of time, as only about an inch should be welded at one run. Each bead should be well peened as quickly as possible after being run. I do these jobs very successfully by using fast, easy flowing electrodes for cast welding. I also find that by using a good pin hole filler paste, any possible leaks from pin holes or small cracks can be eliminated. The uses I have mentioned for the arc welder are only a small drop in the bucket compared to what can be done with it.

I have also found that anyone can use a direct current arc welder for a high rate battery charger. This is done by turning down the voltage and amperage to the desired amount, this depending on the number of batteries that are being charged at one time. With the modern welder one can charge from 1 to 6 six-volt batteries in series by using good connecting wires of heavy duty type. In other words, wire and sufficient current-carrying capacity to carry the desired amount of amperage. The connections must be good and tight to prevent any arching while batteries are charging or after they have been charged. A battery that is being charged at a high rate of amperage will boil very rapidly, and while the batteries are boiling, they will give off a gas that is very explosive when it comes in contact with a spark or flame. If it is desirable to use this charging method, 1 or 6 more six-volt batteries can be charged by connecting these in series and then connecting these with the first group in parallel.

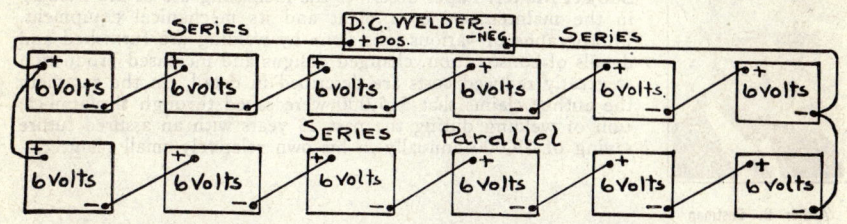

Fig. 8. Wiring diagram for connecting batteries in parallel for charging.

This method of battery charging with the D.C. electric welder can be done very easily and economically, for one has a selection of most any rate of charge. I believe there are hundreds of other profitable uses for the electric welder that have not been discovered yet. In this day and age it seems that the arc welding has done more to speed up production in war work than any other single unit. This is not only true in the huge war plants but also in the farm maintenance shops where it has made it possible to reclaim many broken castings, shafts, and hundreds of other parts which would have to be junked without the arc welder.

In conclusion, I wish to state that it is the author's belief that we in the maintenance and war work, should keep our hoods down and the arc welders running more to produce more and better welds for the duration of the war.

Chapter XI—Fibre and Plastics Plant

By Arthur B. Eastman,

Assistant Plant Manager, Continental-Diamond Fibre Co., Newark, Delaware.

Subject Matter: Paper describes the increasing use of arc welding in the maintenance of a plant and its mechanical equipment. Photographs of various jobs done by welding are furnished and details of construction, changed designs and increased production at greatly reduced costs are described in detail. In the summary the author claims that $15,000 were saved through the application of welding during the past 2½ years with an assured future saving of $9,000 annually in his own relatively small plant.

Arthur B. Eastman

Our Newark, Delaware plant is comparatively small, employing about 500 men in normal times and 900 under the present expanded program of war work.

We became interested in the possibilities of welding several years ago but the first outfit which we purchased was not of the electric type and while it was useful for many purposes, it did not satisfactorily fill our requirements, which covered a miscellaneous variety of jobs, many of which called for a mechanically strong weld and quite often jobs which could not be heated as required.

It was then that we began to investigate the possibilities of electric arc welding, but before investing in the necessary equipment, we decided to first design some of our jobs for electric arc welding, and have the work done by a local weldery, to convince ourselves of its value to our particular problem. This problem concerned only maintenance and repair work and the making up of equipment used in manufacturing our product, which covers non-metallic insulating materials such as vulcanized fibre and laminated plastics.

Within a year's time, the results were so eminently satisfactory, that we felt safe in purchasing our own electric arc welding outfit.

Our anxiety to show some real results to justify our purchase no doubt provided the urge that led to what seems now, on looking back over the last two and one-half years, rather surprising and startling results.

As day after day and week after week passed, all sorts of possibilities opened up, where savings in time and material, as well as increased efficiency, could be made by designing to suit electric arc welding.

In the following pages will be shown a few of the most interesting cases where this type of welding proved very advantageous, and examples of some of the projects that have been developed here during the period covering the two and one-half years ending in May, 1942.

ARC WELDING

Forming Moulds for Fibre Plates—When the railroads of this country began their rehabilitation program after the depression, we were faced with the necessity of increasing our production on "U" shaped formed fibre plates, used by the railroads for track insulation, as shown in the upper part of Fig. 1.

We had been forming these plates in a heavy cast iron mould $16\frac{1}{2}$ inches wide, consisting of an upper or male form, with tongue and flattening elements, and a lower or femal form, with grooved portions to match the tongue, and matching flattening elements, so arranged as to be adjustable for the various sizes required.

This mould was used in a steam heated hydraulic press, just wide enough to accommodate it easily. We had only one other press available for this work, which was slightly wider than the press in use, but not quite wide enough to take two moulds similar to the old one.

We had been instructed to make provision for an increase to five times our present production and, since the two available presses would only accommodate two moulds of the size we were using, it looked offhand as if we would have to work three shifts on this job. This was undesirable, since there would be only one man working alone on the second and third

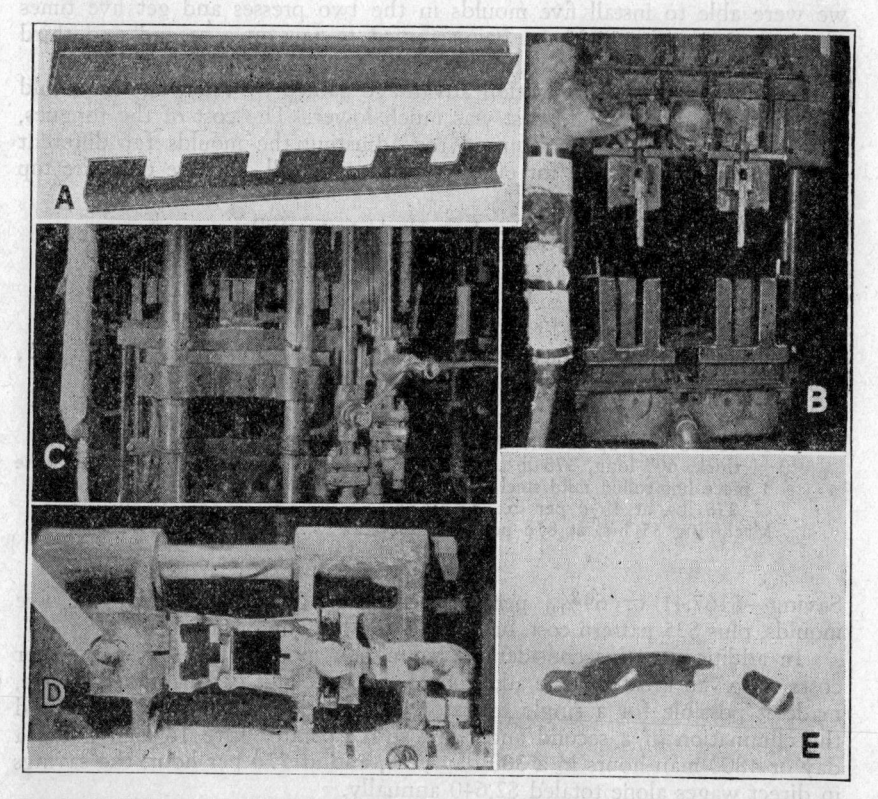

Fig. 1. (A) U-shaped or continuous fibre insulation. (lower) Fibre angle head plate insulation. Fig. 2. (B) Two arc welded moulds in hydraulic press. Fig. 3. (C) Three arc welded moulds in hydraulic press. Fig. 4. (D) Double straightening mould for fibre angle plates. Fig. 5. (E) Clutch pin and throw-out repaired by arc welding.

shifts. The only other recourse was to devise some means of getting more moulds in each press.

After giving this matter considerable thought and study, the writer designed a mould, to be made from standard cold rolled steel bars, electrically welded. By taking advantage of the increased strength of steel and the strength of the welded joints, it was found possible to cut down the width from 16½ inches to 7 inches, so that two moulds could be used in the space occupied by our one old mould.

The new design looked so much smaller than the massive cast iron blocks we had been using, that some doubt was expressed as to whether we would have sufficient strength, but confidence in the proposed design won out and the two moulds were made up and installed as shown in Fig. 2.

Before a week had passed, the new moulds were voted highly satisfactory and had become popular with the operators, since they were less clumsy and much easier to set up. A device had been added to pull the finished plates from the mould as the press opened and this also appealed to the operators, as it had been necessary to pry the plates from the old mould with a bar. After a thorough trial convinced us there were no faults in the design, three more moulds were made up and installed in the other press, as shown in Fig. 3, with just enough room to fit in comfortably. Thanks to the decreased width of the electrically welded steel moulds, we were able to install five moulds in the two presses and get five times our past production, without being forced to put on a second and third shift operator.

In addition to the production advantage gained by reducing the mould sizes, we found the mould cost was much lower. The cost of the tongues, fillers and radius formers required for adjusting the moulds for different sizes was about the same for either type, so we will compare only the top and bottom holders.

Cost of Cast Iron Mould (estimated)

3160 lbs. cast iron at 5½¢ lb.	$173.80
85 hrs. machining at 85¢ per hr.	68.00
	$241.80

In addition there would have been a pattern charge of approximately $35, since the old pattern has been lost or destroyed.

Cost of Electrically Welded Steel Mould

1 Welded built up channel 7" wide x 6⅝" high x 1¼" thick, 60" long, 378 lbs.	$32.15 *complete
1 piece hot rolled mild steel 4" x 4" x 62" long, 278 lbs. at 4½¢ per lb.	12.49
Machining 35 hrs. at 85¢ per hr.	29.75
	$74.39

Saving—$167.41 or 69²⁄₁₀ percent per mould and $837.05 for the five moulds, plus $35 pattern cost, or $872.05 total saving on moulds.

In addition to this considerable saving on moulds, the saving in labor costs was even greater. The addition of the knockout bar mentioned above, made it possible for a single operator to take care of all five moulds and the elimination of a second and third shift operator save 16 man hours a day or 4800 man hours in a 300 day year, and at 55¢ per hour, the savings in direct wages alone totaled $2,640 annually.

*Note—The channel was welded to our specification by the supplier and sent to us, ready for machining.

In addition, there was also considerable saving of light and power, saving of possible lost time due to jobs running out during the night with no one to assist in making changes and the probable saving of defective work due to lack of supervision and inspection. Adding the $872.05 saved in the mould cost to the $2,640 saving in labor, we have a total saving for the first year of over $3,500 with future savings exceeding $2,500 annually.

Another forming mould which the writer designed, is shown in Fig. 4. Some of our long fibre head plates with a single bend, shown in the lower part of Fig. 1, had a habit of warping from end to end which was objectionable when it exceeded allowable limits. When the plates were placed two at a time in the lower mould, and held under heat and pressure for a few minutes by closing the press, the objectionable bow was eliminated.

This mould was 9 feet long and 8 inches wide and cost as follows:

Material—1076 lbs. cold rolled steel at 8½¢ lb.................$ 91.46
Machining—80 hrs. at 85¢ per hr....................................... 68.00
Welding—15 hrs. at 80¢ per hr.. 12.00

$171.46

If this mould had been planed from machine steel, the estimated cost is as follows:

Material— 438 lbs. cold rolled steel at 8½¢ per lb..............$ 37.14
          1440 lbs. machine steel at 9½¢ per lb.................. 136.80
          215 hrs. planing
          15 hrs. assembling cold rolled steel
               locating lugs and spacers

          230 hrs. at 85¢ per hr... 195.50

$369.44

Estimated savings—$197.98 or 53½ percent.

Salvaging Punch Press Clutch Parts—Another example of savings made by electric welding, which at first seemed rather insignificant, has grown to quite an item.

We have over fifty punch presses at this plant and owing to the nature of our work, about one-third of them are used on stepping or second operation work, requiring tripping of the clutch mechanism for each stroke. This is hard on both the clutch pins and the throwouts. When operating normally, these would last for two or three years; but with the speeded up production, increased hours, and breaking in green help, their life was materially shortened.

The white areas in Fig. 5 show where wear occurs. By a little experimenting, we found that this cavity could be dressed out with an abrasive wheel and filled in with hard metal, High Speed Tool Steel, drawn slightly to prevent brittleness, dressed up to proper shape with an abrasive wheel and made good as new.

We were paying from $7 to $22 each for renewals on clutch pins, according to size and make of press, and from $14 to $25 a piece for throwouts. At an average of $15 for clutch pins and $20 for throwouts, a set of renewals averaged $35. It required less than an hour to repair a set of these parts, with a cost of not over a dollar, including the metal. During the last two years, thirty-nine sets were repaired and put back into service, and at an average saving of $34 per set, the total annual saving amounts to $618.

Racks for Bar Steel—We keep in stock a large variety of steel bars, rounds and flats, for use in our tool room, machine shop, and blacksmith and repair shops. As long as we had room to spread this around over the floor of our stock room, it was easy to handle, but as excess space was absorbed by increased defense production, it was found necessary to provide some means of conserving space by using tiers or racks of some kind.

We purchased a couple sets of steel castings, manufactured for this purpose, but while they were fairly satisfactory for holding round stock, they were not suitable for flats and had too small capacity, besides being rather expensive and later on, almost impossible to obtain.

When it became necessary to add additional racks, the author decided to design them from standard sections assembled by arc welding, and the completed rack is shown in Fig. 6.

The uprights were made from 6-inch x 2½-inch x ⅜-inch channels, 5-ft. long, and while a single column may have been strong enough, we decided to play safe and use the double-V column shown. The two bottom cross pieces, were made from 3-inch x 3-inch x ⅜-inch angles, the middle two, from 2½-inch x 2½-inch x 5/16-inch angles, and the upper two, from 2-inch x 2-inch x ¼-inch angles.

The cost of two complete uprights (one pair) was as follows:

434¾ lbs. of angle and channel iron at $3.95 per hundred lbs.	$17.17
8 hrs. welding at 80c per hr.	6.40
2½ hrs. cutting to size at 45¢ per hr.	1.12
Per pair	$24.69

The steel castings cost $25 each or $50 a pair, so that we saved $25 or 50 percent on each pair by electric arc welding, besides having racks suitable for either flat or round stock and with at least 50 percent greater capacity. Lugs could be welded on the ends of the arms, to prevent round stock from rolling off and still not interfere with storage for flat stock.

In addition to the greater safety in handling stock placed neatly in racks instead of being piled all over the floor, we find it easier to check our inventory and avoid running out of any particular size, as often happened in the past.

Arc Welded Steel Plate Bending Brakes—A very striking example of the advantages that can be obtained by the use of welded steel construction, is found in our fibre bending department. For over thirty years we have been forming our fibre in steam heated power bending brakes and we had four of them in operation. While they made a very satisfactory job, it was impossible to keep them tight and the leaking steam made life miserable for the thirty-five employees in that department, especially in summer, by increasing the already high humidity we experience in Delaware. The hoses used to carry steam to the moveable leaf were always breaking or coming loose, the gaskets on the steam chambers always needed replacing, as did the packing used around the trunnions. In addition to the leaking steam, there were always puddles of water over the floor, from dripping condensed steam. Altogether, these brakes were a source of continual headaches.

We considered the installation of electrical heating units on the old brakes, to eliminate the nuisance of the leaking steam and water, but their construction was such that the points requiring heating could not be segregated and the mass of metal in the castings was so great, that electrical heating was deemed impractical.

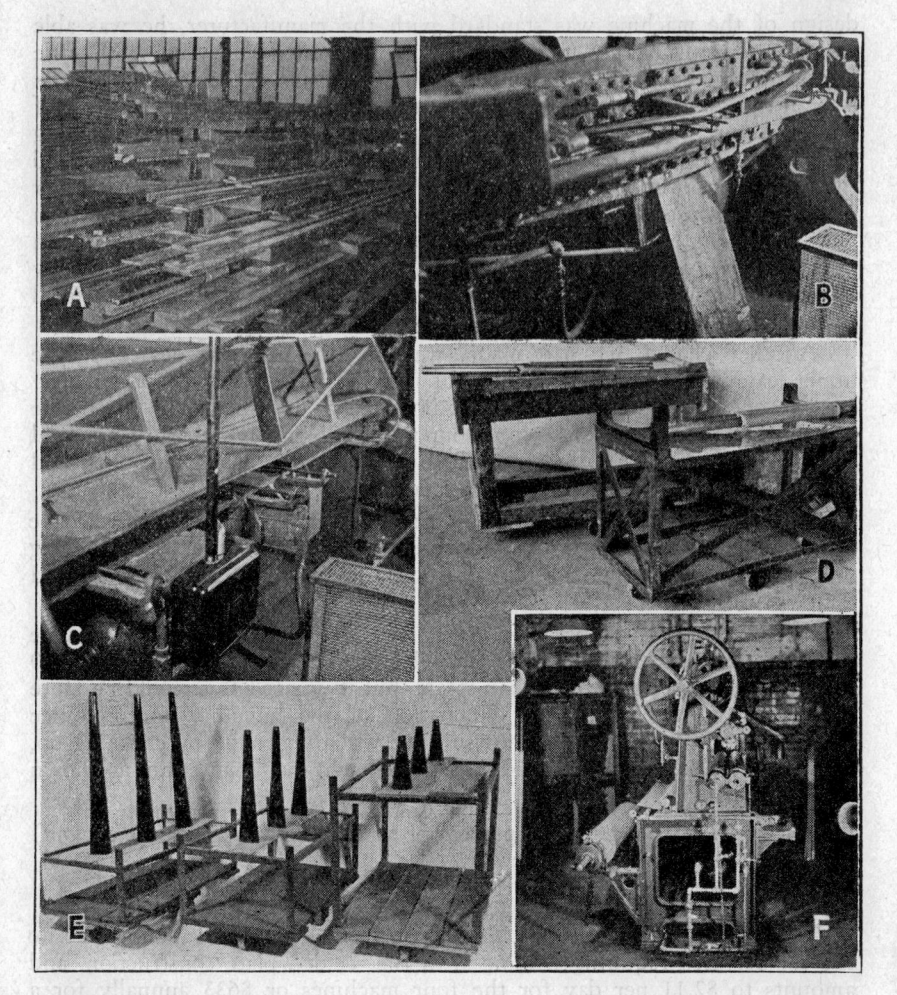

Fig. 6. (A) Arc welded rack for bar steel. Fig. 7. (B) Brake made from machine castings. Fig. 8. (C) Brake made from arc welded steel plates. Fig. 9. (D) Old wooden truck and new arc welded truck. Fig. 10. (E) Oven trucks. Fig. 11. (F) Standard tube machine—cast frame.

When it became necessary to replace these wornout brakes, the writer recommended trying a brake employing arc welded steel construction made by a well-known manufacturer in the middle West, changing over to electrical heat and making other slight changes in design to suit our particular problems. In Fig. 7 is shown the back view of the old steam brake, with hoses, valves, plates and puddles of water, as compared to the neat appearance of the welded steel plate brake, Fig. 8, without these objectionable features. The board shown in the photo of the old style brake was placed there by the operator to keep escaping steam from annoying him.

This brake proved so successful that we replaced two more of the old steam brakes, and a fourth one has been ordered, so that we are looking forward to the most comfortable summer ever experienced in this department.

One thing that appealed to us was the fact that although the general design of the machine was standard with the manufacturer, he was able to make several changes in design which the writer suggested, with little or no additional expense. One of these changes was in the length, which was 8-ft. in the standard machine, but we wanted it two inches longer. Most of our places are cut 24¼ inches long, to allow for shrinkage after steaming and drying. With our old 8-ft. cast iron steam brake, we could only bend three plates at a time, whereas the two extra inches enabled us to bend four plates at a time and gave us a 33⅓ percent increase in production, which with two operators on each shift amounts to an annual saving of 4800 man hours in a 300 day year. This change in length would have been very costly or practically impossible on the old type machines, as it would have involved expensive pattern and core changes.

Another change we had made, was on the clamping device of the upper leaf. The standard machine was made for heavy metal work, requiring two operators, and the clamp took both men, one at each end, to operate it. Since one operator runs two of our machines, this wasn't very practical so we had a pneumatic device installed to enable the operator to open and close the clamp merely by moving a small lever.

We also had the angle of the nose made sharper to enable us to make 60 degree bends sometimes required, and had the necessary electrical heating units installed, with thermostatic control, which could be set at any desired temperature.

As to the relative operating costs, we were given an extra agreeable surprise. It was at first thought that electrical heating would be from 10 to 15 percent more expensive than steam, but it was felt this would be more than compensated for by the elimination of the humidity and nuisance from the steam heat. Imagine our surprise when we found by checking up, that the electric heat was actually 25 percent cheaper than steam as shown by the following figures:

Electricity—11250 watts on 55 percent of time (due to thermostatic cut out) at 1¢ per K.W. = 6.2¢ per hr.

Steam—300 lbs. per hr. at 28¢ per thousand pounds = 8.4¢ per hr.

This saving of 2²⁄₁₀¢ per hr. or 26 percent was no doubt due to the smaller area requiring heating with the welded plate construction, and amounts to $2.11 per day for the four machines or $633 annually for a 300 day year.

Figuring the 4800 man hours saved at 55¢ per hour and equalling $2,640 plus the $633, brings a total annual saving of $3,273 from the installation of these machines; not counting the increased efficiency and added comfort and satisfaction, from the elimination of the nuisance value of the old steam heated machines as well as the additional savings of the time lost replacing wornout hoses and gaskets.

Welded Steel Mandrel Trucks—A continual source of complaint in one of our departments was due to the constant necessity of repairs to a couple dozen wooden trucks used by our tube makers, to move heavy steel mandrels between the making machines, mandrel ovens, mandrel racks, pushers, and cooking ovens. These trucks were subjected to hard usage and, with the recent stepped up production with three shifts running six days a week, constant breakdowns and time out for repairs became so annoying and caused so many delays and complaints, it was decided that something must be done to remedy the trouble.

ARC WELDING

The addition of braces and reinforcements was considered but it was finally decided to make up a trial all metal arc welded truck, which the writer designed as shown in Fig. 9, beside one of the old style wooden trucks.

This trial truck met with such prompt and hearty approval that six more were made up. After these were put into service, complaints about the old wooden trucks seemed to quadruple and ten more all metal trucks were made up. It was figured that these seventeen trucks in constant use would easily replace the two dozen wooden trucks continually needing repairs, and future results amply bore out this prediction.

These metal trucks, as can be seen, were made from standard angle and channel iron and plain iron strips. The only non-metal parts were the hardwood buffers at each end of the top deck, installed for the double purpose of stopping the mandrels from rolling off and to prevent scoring or scratching from metal to metal contact.

A comparison of the respective costs of the two types of trucks, shows some interesting facts. The figures below do not include cost of wheels, since the same type was used on both trucks.

Cost of Wooden Trucks

10 ft. 4" x 4" lumber at 6¼¢ per board ft.	$ .83
8 ft. 6" x 2" lumber at 6¢ per board ft.	.48
30 ft. 1" x 8" x 9½¢ per board ft.	2.85
4 hrs. labor at 80¢ per hr.	3.20
1½ hrs. repair time every 6 weeks, approx. 12 hrs. annually	9.60
Lumber for repairs—approx. $1.00 every 6 weeks	8.00 annually
	$24.96

The life of one of these trucks did not exceed one year, so the annual cost was approximately $25, or $600 for the 24 trucks required to service this department.

It was conservatively estimated that the ten men working on each shift in this department, averaged one-half hour's lost time daily with the old trucks, due to shortages from breakdowns, time taken up for repairs, transporting tubes manually, hunting for an available truck, etc. This seemingly insignificant daily loss, adds up to the surprising total of 90 man hours per week and, at 60 cents per hour, amounts to $2,700 annually.

This brings the total cost of this old type of truck well over $3,000 annually.

Cost of All Metal Arc Welded Trucks

Total cost of angle, channel, and strip iron in the welded type truck, including charge of cutting to size, freight, etc. was	$ 6.30 ea.
5 ft. 2" x 4" oak at 18¢ board ft.	.60
6 hrs. welding at 80¢ per hr.	4.80
Saving $13.26 or 53 percent	$11.70 ea.

No repairs have been made after a year's use and it is conservatively estimated that the life of these trucks will be at least five years.

Figuring 20 percent annual depreciation	2.34
Annual cost per truck	$14.04

and for the 17 trucks $238.68

Thus an annual saving of over $2,800 can be credited to what might appear at first glance to be a relatively insigficant item.

Oven Truck for Baking Enameled Rods and Tubes—Another type of truck in which arc welding played an important part is shown in Fig. 10 and is used for transporting racks filled with enameled rods and tubes from the spray booth to the baking ovens.

For a good many years, we have used for this purpose, standard fibre warehouse cars made by another of our plants because we had a number of them available. The high temperature used in baking (300° to 350°) finally charred the fibre sides of these cars, which were never intended for any such purpose, and made it necessary to replace them. At first it was planned to order new trucks of the same style although they were not entirely satisfactory for such use. For one thing, their height was standard and we could not make any adjustment for different length tubes to centralize them in the oven to get uniform baking. This centering was important because the temperature of our ovens varied slightly from top to bottom. Then too, it was realized that in a short time, it would be necessary to again replace them.

Recalling the success obtained by the electric welded trucks shown in Fig. 9, it was decided to try a similar construction to solve this problem. Inasmuch as the bottoms and wheels of the fibre cars were still perfectly good, the required framework was built up on them as shown in Fig. 10. By making the framework in three different heights, it was possible to centralize short, medium, or long tubes in the baking ovens. The open framework permitted us to place small miscellaneous items requiring baking directly on the platform of the truck, without interfering with the tubes overhead, thus conserving valuable oven space. Most of our painting is on small tubes which are placed upright on racks, which were not shown as their size would hide the truck's construction. The three different length articles were placed on the trucks to illustrate the manner in which the various heights of frame centered the work vertically in our ovens.

In addition to these advantages, and the longer life we anticipate, there was considerable saving in cost as shown by the figures below:

Cost of metal uprights and angle irons	$ 2.04
Blacksmithing and assembly—1½ hrs. at 80¢	1.20
Welding ¾ hr. at 80¢	.60
Cost of hardwood platform and wheels (if bought separately)	9.50
Total cost of new design	$13.34
Cost price to our mill, of standard fibre warehouse cars previously used	$25.75 ea.

Saving $12.41 per truck equals $86.87 for 7 trucks

Electric Arc Welded Machine Frame—A large defense order of small size tubing, urgently required for airplane engines and carrying a high priority, made it necessary to build additional equipment quickly, in order to meet the required delivery.

In Fig. 11 is shown one of our standard machines for making tubes of all sizes. It was realized that to duplicate the cast frame design would require considerable time which was not available, not to speak of the high costs involved. The patterns originally used in these machines were no longer available, and the delay in making up new patterns, getting castings made and the additional machining time that would be required was so prohibitive that we decided on simplifying the design through arc welding.

In Fig. 12 is shown this new design with an arc welded frame, the first one of which was made from 3 inch x 3 inch x ½ inch angle irons within three days after the design was approved. Since this machine was intended for small tubing, we were able to reduce the size considerably and make it much easier and faster to operate.

In addition to valuable time gained and the increase in production due to its smaller size, the cost of the frame was considerably cheapened.

Cost of arc welded frame for tube machine (actual)—

451 lbs. 3" x 3" x 1/2" angle iron	$ 23.45
10 hrs. cutting angle irons to length and shape at 65¢ per hr	6.50
Welding—Welder 6 hrs. at 80¢	4.80
Helper 6 hrs. at 45¢	2.70
Total cost of frame	$ 37.45

Cost of cast frame for tube machine (estimated)—

Pattern $75.00 for 3 machines or cost per machine	$ 25.00
650 lbs. casting at 5½¢ per lb	35.75
Planer time, 65 hrs. at 85¢	55.25
Drill and assembling, 16 hrs. at 60¢	9.60
	$125.60

Savings $88.15 per machine or 70%; $264.45 for 3 machines.

Arc Welded Mandrel Oven—We had an important defense job on which we were running 3 shifts seven days a week, and were asked if it was at all possible to increase production. This job was rolled up on a heated metal mandrel and cooked in moulds in heated hydraulic presses. No more moulds or presses were available and the only chance to increase production was to get more production from the moulds. A time study showed quite a gap in the actual cooking time due to the interval required to open the press, remove the finished part, pull the mandrel, make up a new build-up, place same back in the moulds and close the press. It was decided that an extra mandrel for each mould would enable the operator to make a build-up just prior to opening the press, which would allow him to put the new build-up in the press immediately after taking out the cooked part and save the idle time resulting from pulling the mandrel, and making the new build-up.

In order to put this plan into operation, it was necessary to have some means of keeping the twelve extra mandrels hot during the cooking cycle and, as they weighed about 60 lbs. each, it was important to have a small compact heating arrangement close to the presses, where space was limited.

The writer designed the oven shown in Fig. 13. There are three decks to the oven, each deck holding four mandrels. It was important to keep the surface of these mandrels from being marred or scratched by contact with the metal frame and, since each mandrel was about four feet long, some means of supporting the end was necessary when inserting them into the oven. This problem was solved by the use of trolleys carrying a grooved block in which the ends of the mandrels were placed. The trolleys traveled on parallel tracks made from angle irons and it was important that these tracks did not shift out of alignment when under constant use and increased temperature.

Electric arc welding solved this problem by making sure there would be no shifting, and the framework itself was welded to a cored steam platen, which supplied the heat to the oven. If this platen had been drilled and tapped for holding the frame, there would have been danger of drilling into the core with resulting steam leakage.

The result was a permanent leakproof job which proved very satisfactory and we are planning to make up a duplicate oven for another group of presses on the same job.

Fig. 12. (A) New design of tube machine—arc welded frame. Fig. 13. (B) Mandrel heating oven. Fig. 14. (C) Large and small size frames. Fig. 15. (D) Double groove arc welded mould and double groove machined mould.

Sizing Frames for Pressing Plastic Sheets—Our laboratory had developed a plastic sheet made from molding powder, for which there was a demand in large quantities of various thicknesses, from $\frac{1}{8}$ inch up to 1 inch. In order to maintain a uniform thickness, it was necessary to prevent the material from flowing laterally after heat and pressure had been applied. For experimental purposes we made up a metal frame cut from a sheet of soft steel, for use in a small 12 inch x 12 inch hydraulic platen press. The inside dimensions of the frame controlled the size of the sheet to be made, and the thickness of the metal used determined the thickness of the finished material. The width of the metal frame had to be sufficient to withstand the strain built up by the pressure of 1400 lbs. per square inch applied to the powder placed inside the frame for molding.

When this job was turned over to the production department, it was necessary to make up a large number of metal frames of the different thicknesses required. The sheets were to be made in two sizes, one requiring a frame 41 inches x 41 inches outside, and 33 inches x 33 inches inside and a smaller frame 18 inches x 40 inches outside, 14 inches x 33 inches inside. It was realized that to make these frames from solid sheets would be very expensive and several methods were tried by using flat bar stock. The

ARC WELDING

problem was to get the sides joined at the corners so as to withstand the pressure. Screwed joints stripped easily and a locked type of joint proved equally unsatisfactory.

Finally electric arc welding was tried and a successful joint was worked out and adopted. Seven of the large frames were made up, using 4 inch width of cold rolled steel, in thicknesses from $5/16$ inch up to 1 inch and 65 of the smaller frames, using 2 inch cold rolled steel, from $1/8$ inch to $5/8$ inch thick. Fig. 14 illustrates a large and a small size frame.

The cost of a large size frame, 1/2 inch thick, taken as an average, was as follows:
3 hrs. cutting steel and squaring ends, at 85¢ per hr.....................$ 2.55
1 hr. preparing joints and welding at 80¢...................................... .80
85 lbs. cold rolled steel at 8½¢ lb.. 7.23
                                                                                    ───────
                                                                                    $10.58

If this frame had been made from boiler plate, the estimated cost would be as follows:
Plane both sides, saw out center
Mill inside edge and file corners, 20 hrs. at 85¢..........................$17.00
354 lbs. ¾" boiler plate at 4½¢ lb... 15.93
                                                                                    ───────
                                                                                    $32.93

Savings—$22.35 or 67%

The cost of a ¼-inch frame, small size, taken as an average, was as follows:
1¼ hrs. cutting steel and squaring ends at 85¢............................$ 1.07
½ hr. preparing joints and welding at 80¢.................................... .40
16 lbs. cold rolled steel at 8½¢ lb.. 1.36
                                                                                    ───────
                                                                                    $ 2.83

If this frame had been made from a solid plate, the estimated cost would be as follows:
2 hrs. grind both sides at 85¢...$ 1.70
7 hrs. saw out inside, mill and file at 85¢..................................... 5.95
80 lbs. ⅜" steel plate at 4½¢ lb.. 3.60
                                                                                    ───────
                                                                                    $11.25

Savings—$8.42 or 74%
Estimated savings on 7 large frames $156.45 and on 65 small frames $547.30, or a total savings of $703.75.

Arc Welded Mould For Angles—Still another case where electric arc welding not only helped our company out of a serious predicament, but greatly aided an important defense item, is illustrated in the double groove mould shown on the right side of the press in Fig. 15.

We had received a large order for fibre angles used in connection with some auxiliary equipment used on bombers for long range flying. Since fibre is only half as heavy as aluminum, it proved an ideal material for the purpose and fast delivery was urgently required. This order tied up all our available equipment for bending such angles, which included steam heated bending brakes and solid machined moulds as shown on the left side of the press in Fig. 15.

On top of the first order, we received another urgent order covering other sizes of fibre angles for the same purpose, with the insistence that delivery must start within one week's time.

Since all our available equipment was tied up, we advised them it would take several weeks to make up the necessary moulds, but were advised again that deliveries must be started the following week, regardless.

In the emergency, we turned to electric arc welding for a solution. Fortunately we had on hand some 2½ inches x 2½ inches x ¼ inch steel angles and some bars of cold rolled steel 8 inches wide. The writer designed the mould shown above, which was ready to put in the press six hours after the design was given to the shop.

As far as we could see, this arc welded mould performed as well as the machined mould, and the shop was instructed to make up four additional moulds all of which could be used in the one press shown and which increased our capacity 500 percent, enabling us to meet the delivery requested.

In addition to the feeling of satisfaction at being able to help the war effort by saving a long delay in shipments of war planes, the savings in material and valuable man hours was equally pleasing.

If we had attempted to machine these moulds as had been our practice, the estimated cost would have been as follows:

1560 lbs. cast iron at 9½¢ lb.	$148.20
90 hrs. machining at $1.05 per hr.	94.50
	$242.70

The cost of the arc welded mould was as follows:

120 lbs. 2½" x 2½" x ¼" angle iron at $4.15 C.	$ 4.98
245 lbs. cold rolled steel at $5.85 C.	14.41
Cutting steel, 1 hr. at 55¢.	.55
Assembling and clamping and tack welding, 1¼ hrs. at 95¢.	1.18
Helper, 1¼ hrs. at 55¢.	.69
Grinding, drilling, etc., 1 hr. at 85¢.	.85
	$ 22.66

Saving $219.94 or 91 percent for each mould or over $1,000 for the 5 moulds.

In addition to the special items that have been described in some detail, we have used arc welding for a large number of miscellaneous temporary and permanent jobs, such as every plant requires in the ordinary processes of manufacture and maintenance, but more especially under the high pressure of expanded war production. A few examples that occur to the writer were repairs to broken parts such as gear teeth, housings, machine frames, connecting rods and support clamp straps; repairs to moulds, dies, rolls, hanger clamps; leaking steam pipes, platens, pumps, and tank outlets; and filling in and building up worn parts in bearing housings, fan housings, pulverizer bearings, as well as making up a number of miscellaneous jobs such as carrier frames, motor brackets, braces, stays, etc.

The savings in jobs such as enumerated above, could be divided into two classes. First, the saving from being able to repair the old part over the cost of a new replacing part, which is especially important now, with scarcity of materials and priority requirements. Secondly and often much more important, the saving in time required to get the equipment back into operation, with resulting low production losses and valuable man hours saved. It would be impossible to estimate the value of these savings, but it would be a conservative guess that in 2½ years time, the total dollars salvaged would run into the thousands.

SUMMARY

During the last two and one-half years, electric arc welding has saved us over $15,000, with assured future savings of over $9,000 annually, from the several items alone which have been described in detail, in the foregoing pages. Since we started from scratch and feel we have not begun to utilize all the possibilities in arc welding, future savings should increase far beyond this figure.

These savings are, in addition to many advantages that have been pointed out, in bettered working conditions, increased production and efficiency, reduction of lost time and replacement costs by repairs, and such other items the value of which can only be surmised, but which would no doubt add considerably to the totals given above.

According to the latest report of the United States Department of Commerce, published in 1941, there were 3,653 plants in the United States in 1939 employing from 250 to 500 wage earners, and 1,495 plants employing 500 to 1,000 wage earners, which would average say 2,300 plants about the same size as our plant, which employ approximately 500 wage earners in normal times.

If these plants could use the arc welding process in maintenance and repair work to as good advantage as we have and average annual savings of $9,000, the total savings to national industry, in these small almost "forgotten" plants alone, would amount to $20,700,000 annually, in addition to many other benefits such as have been mentioned throughout this paper.

Chapter XII—Foundry Sand Rammers

By Michael F. Streidl,

Foreman of Maintenance, The Crucible Steel Casting Co., Cleveland, Ohio.

Subject Matter: Paper discusses: 1. Rebuilding No. 4 floor sand rammers which break off and can be welded by arc cheaply for about $1.50 while new rammers cost $50.65. Welded rammers have been in service for a year without failure. 2. Wear resistant end trucks for overload cranes where wear plates are installed on inside of truck channels. Job costs $7 while renewing the end trucks cost $29. 3. Installing ball bearing cartridges in sleeve bearing motors. Several motors equipped with ball bearings at cost of $45 for a 20 horsepower motor. The end bell castings would have cost $50 but still they would have old sleeve bearings lasting only four months.

Michael F. Streidl

Subject: Rebuilding No. 4 Floor Sand Rammers

Prior to 1940 it had been the practice of the tool repair man to discard sand rammers that had the barrels broken at the packing gland. Within the last 17 months these barrels have been renewed by electric arc welding at a saving of $50.

The barrels of most rammers have this failure:

1. Snap off at the packing gland
2. Crack along the keeper keyway
3. Wear out packing gland threads

Repair procedure for No. 1 is as follows: Chuck in lathe and face off broken end of barrel. Turn from end back 3/4 inch to 1 3/4 inch diameter. Make a bushing from 2 1/4 inch O. D. x 1 1/4 inch I. D. (cold rolled) seamless tube of the proper length for a press fit on barrel. Vee the barrel and rammer at welding point and weld solid. Turn O.D. to 2 inch and thread 12 T. P. I. Turn I. D. to 1 1/2 inch for sliding fit for packing retainer. Cut 1/4 inch x 1/8 inch keyway for keeper key.

It has been our experience that the welding does not affect the hardness of the cylinder. The barrels show no excessive wear and have been in service 17 months with no sign of failure.

Repair procedure for No. 2 can be the same as No. 1. Weld up crack on outside and inside of barrel, weld up keyway and weld all around barrel so that new threads and a new keyway can be cut. Bore out inside of pack-gland to 1 1/2 diameter for sliding fit of packing retainers.

Repair procedure for No. 3: Weld up keyway and weld all around the barrel so that new threads and a new keyway can be cut.

The cost of a new No. 4 sand rammer is approximately $50. The cost of labor is $1 an hour for 4 hours. The steel, we have in our scrap. The cost of steel in a length amounts to $.50 per rammer.

This is practically 100 percent as the barrels were scrapped before

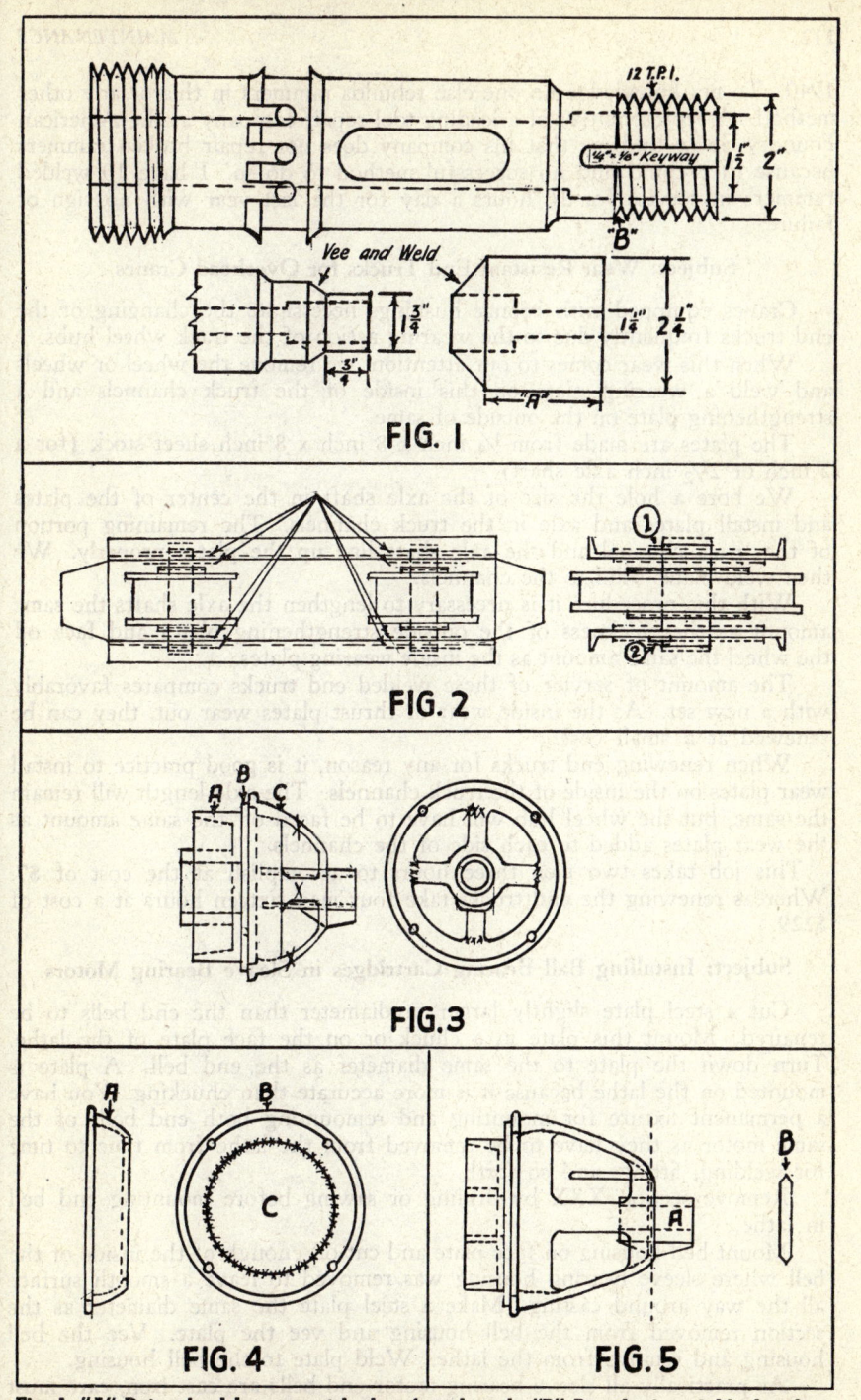

Fig. 1. "A" Determined by amount broken from barrel. "B" Barrels, invariably break at this point. Fig. 2. Dotted lines show plates added to channels, shaft extended, and wheel hub faced off. Fig. 3. "A" Face plate or chuck. "B" Face plate machined for end bell. "C" End bell. Fig. 4. "A" End bell after being machined. "B" End bell with plate welded inside and out. Fig. 5. "A" Face off brush end bell to dotted line. "B" Make plate and weld to end bell at dotted line.

1940. To my knowledge no one else rebuilds rammers in this or any other method. A representative of a leading tool repair company at the American Foundry Show told me that his company does not repair broken rammers because they could find no successful method to do so. I have 10 welded rammers in service for 16 hours a day for the last year with no sign of failure.

Subject: Wear Resistant End Trucks for Overhead Cranes

Cranes equipped with bronze bushings necessitate the changing of the end trucks frequently due to the wearing action of the track wheel hubs.

When this wear comes to our attention, we remove the wheel or wheels and weld a wearing plate on this inside of the truck channels and a strengthening plate on the outside of same.

The plates are made from $\frac{1}{4}$ inch x 8 inch x 8 inch sheet stock (for a 2 inch or $2\frac{1}{2}$ inch axle shaft).

We bore a hole the size of the axle shaft in the center of the plates and install plates and axle in the truck channels. The remaining portion of the truck channel and the axle shaft line up the plates properly. We then weld plates solid to the channels.

With this procedure it is necessary to lengthen the axle shafts the same amount as the thickness of the outside strengthening plates and face off the wheel the same amount as the inside wearing plates.

The amount of service of these welded end trucks compares favorably with a new set. As the inside wear or thrust plates wear out, they can be renewed at a small cost.

When renewing end trucks for any reason, it is good practice to install wear plates on the inside of the truck channels. The axle length will remain the same, but the wheel hub will have to be faced off the same amount as the wear plates added to each side of the channels.

This job takes two men three hours to accomplish at the cost of $7. Whereas renewing the end trucks take four men sixteen hours at a cost of $229.

Subject: Installing Ball Bearing Cartridges in Sleave Bearing Motors

Cut a steel plate slightly larger in diameter than the end bells to be repaired. Mount this plate in a chuck or on the face plate of the lathe. Turn down the plate to the same diameter as the end bell. A plate is mounted on the lathe because it is more accurate than chucking. You have a permanent fixture for mounting and remounting both end bells of the same motor as they have to be removed from the lathe from time to time for welding, fitting, and so forth.

Remove section XXX by drilling or sawing before mounting end bell in lathe.

Mount bell housing on face plate and cut off enough of the inside of the bell where sleeve bearing housing was removed to leave a smooth surface all the way around casting. Make a steel plate the same diameter as the section removed from the bell housing and vee the plate. Vee the bell housing and remove from the lathe. Weld plate to the bell housing.

As practically all sleeve bearing motor end bells are cast iron, care must be taken in welding a steel plate to the cast iron housing.

The thickness of the steel plate depends on the width of the mounting ridge of the motor cartridge (for a 10, 15, 20 h. p. motor, we used $\frac{1}{2}$ inch plate and for a 3 and 5 h. p. motor we used $\frac{3}{8}$ inch plate).

After the plate has been welded in the end bell, mount bell on face plate and face off front of welded plate. Bore a hole in the plate to the diameter of the cartridge to be installed so as to have a drive fit. Remove from lathe and install bearing cartridge in end bell. Locate grease fitting and drain plug in proper place on bell and drill 4 holes through cartridge and bell equally spaced with a tap size drill depending on the bolts to be used.

Remove cartridge from end bell. Enlarge holes in cartridge to bolt size and tap holes in end bell.

For a 3 h. p. motor we used four $5/16$ inch x 1 inch bolts.
For a 5 h. p. motor we used four $3/8$ inch x 1 inch bolts.
For a 10, 15 & 20 h. p. motor we used four $1/2$ inch x $1 1/2$ inch bolts.

Bolt the cartridge to the end bell and install 2 taper pins. This procedure is for both end bells of induction motors and for the front end or opposite the brush end of wound rotor motors such as those used on cranes.

Installing bearing cartridges in the brush end bells of reversible motors, do not remove the whole sleeve bearing housing. The end bell is mounted on the face plate in the same manner as the front end bell and the sleeve bearing housing is faced off flush with the end bell.

A plate is made the diameter of the section faced off and welded solid. Then the same procedure is used as for the front end bells.

We installed ball bearing cartridges in 5 motors. We used Aerisweld welding rod with great success, these motors are in service 24 hours a day. 4 of them are reversible rotor wound crane motors and have shown no sign of failure in the last 16 months.

Time spent on the large motors was about 10 hours for dismantling, machining, welding, and assembling.

The smaller motors took about 7 hours time. For a $2 1/16$ inch bearing cartridge for the 15 and 20 h. p. motors, the cost was $16.50 each or $33 per set.

Actual cost of fitting cartridges in a 20 h. p. motor was
 $33.00 per pair
 10.00 for labor at $1.00 per hour
 2.00 welding rod, plates, etc.

 $45.00 for complete job

To have these end bells cast and machined would entail a cost of $50 each, but we would still have oil lubricated sleeve bearings which would have to be changed every four months.

The babbitted bearings cost approximately the same as the new ball bearings. When installing these M. C. type cartridges in motors, the motor or the rotor shaft does not have to be changed in any way. The cartridges have locking cam-like rings to fasten the bearings securely to the shaft at both sleeve bearing surfaces, reducing the end play to a minimum.

Chapter XIII—Furniture Manufacturing Plant

By WM. H. DIETRICHS,

Maintenance Engineer, The Kroehler Mfg. Co., Cleveland, Ohio.

Subject Matter: Various examples are given in this paper of the general applications of arc welding to plant maintenance (manufacturing upholstered furniture). Some substitutions of arc welded construction for wooden parts and motor mounts are illustrated and described. Also conveyor system, road scraper and miscellaneous plant jobs including a boiler repair job are discussed.

Wm. H. Dietrichs

Our company purchased a 200 ampere dual control unit in April 1941. I was certainly pleased that the management selected this size unit as it has proved satisfactory for all our requirements without question. It may be interesting to note that the maintenance department has for some years been trying to sell the management on the economy and convenience of a welding machine.

In the evolution of this plant (manufacturing upholstered furniture) the demand for its products had grown so extensively that revision of production methods were required and in this modernization arc welding appeared essential and proved indispensible; first in construction of units required, second, in erection, and third, in repairing. (Please note that while the units, namely upholstering bucks, were not made by myself but by another manufacturer, I wish to show by Figs. No. 1 and 2 the advantages obtained when using arc welded construction over the former wooden units made in our plant.) However, in erection of the conveyors and their drive mountings is where our welding unit played a decisive part in economy, durability and rigidity. Other machines throughout the plant from then on also indicated the presence of a welder on the job.

The value of an arc welder right in the plant for use by the maintenance department cannot be stressed enough. In the past I had to farm out all our welding jobs or call in a firm with a portable unit and make repairs. In farming out jobs, many cost items were overlooked, such as:

1. Unit or machine unproductive for indefinite period.
2. Machine or part must be taken down or off.
3. Haul to welding shop, tying up driver and truck, and in many cases I was on hand myself to be sure of getting work done as required.
4. In some cases when welding shop was too busy the job had to be delayed and required a return trip for pickup at convenience of welding shop.

Actual welding charges were not seemingly high and therefore delayed

ARC WELDING

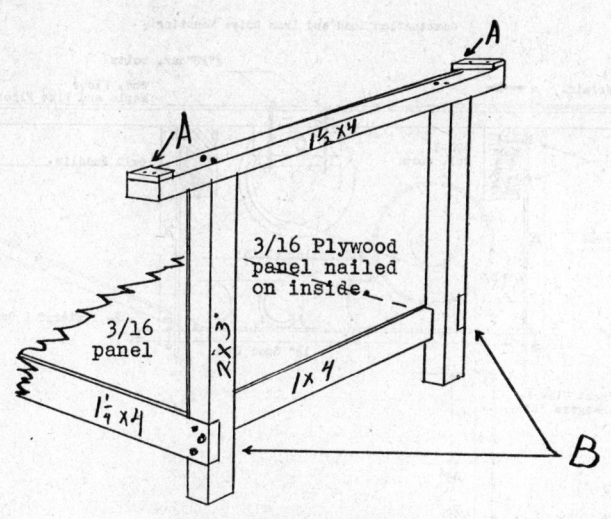

Fig. 1. Wood construction.

purchase of welding machine for some years but I have always felt that these hidden costs often tripled and sometimes quadrupled our welding costs and would therefore justify a welding machine. The satisfaction gained in the past year in availability and economy in time alone has justified my convictions and feel much progress has been made in acquiring the arc welder.

Fig. 1 shows one end only of a wooden buck assembled with glue and screws. Major objections were that the 1 x 1 x 2 inch blocks "A" on ends of top rail often split off leaving sharp screw heads which tore upholstery covers. Panels slivered considerably. It was also bad for workers' hands as all stock used is piled on base panel for each job. Joints at "B" usually loosened in 8 or 9 weeks' time making whole unit wobbly, necessitating frequent repairs.

Fig. 2 shows the rings welded on ends of pipe do not snag upholstery cover. Tack welded panels cannot injure workers' hands when reaching for materials. (The piece to be upholstered is merely laid on the top rails

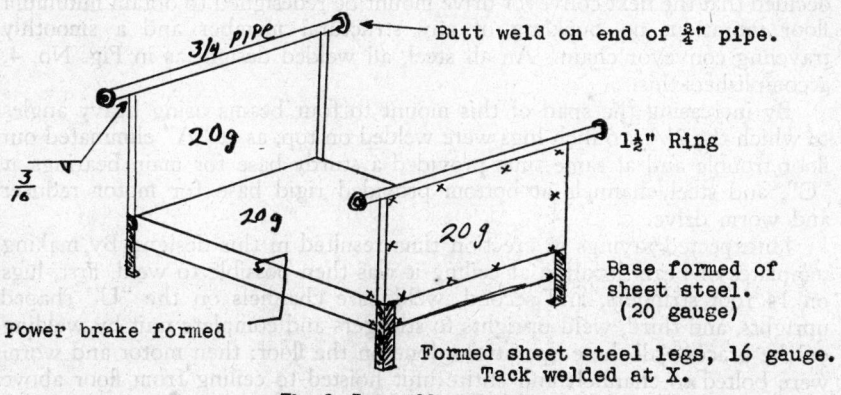

Fig. 2. Arc weld construction.

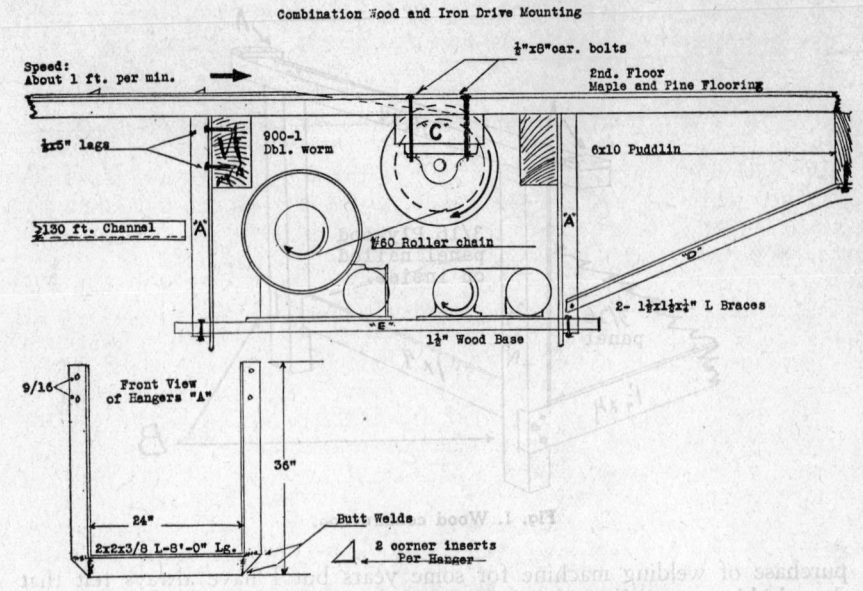

Fig. 3. Combination wood and angle iron motor mount.

and base panel serves as tray for stock.) No steel bucks have become wobbly in 16 months of operation, nor can I see any reason for them to ever do so.

My first application was on conveyors. The problem was to erect formed steel channels 12 gauge, 10 foot end to end for 130 feet, rigidly on ceiling and mount framework for motor drive.

Our first motor mount was simply made of a combination of wood and angle iron. See Fig. 3.

It will be noted from Fig. No. 3 that such a low speed as 1 foot per minute constitutes a continuous starting load. Entire load was carried by four $1/2$ inch x 8 inch bolts through floor and blocks at "C" causing floor puddlins (beams) to "breathe" about $1/4$ inch. Planks "E" also pulled upward $1/4$ inch to $3/8$ inch and braces "D" became bowed. After two days of experimenting, adjusting, checking, track lubrication and shoring, it was decided that the next conveyor drive mount be redesigned to obtain minimum floor vibration, no buckling of any structural member and a smoothly traveling conveyor chain. An all steel, all welded design, as in Fig. No. 4, accomplished this.

By increasing the span of this mount to four beams using heavy angles to which the $2\frac{1}{2}$ x 6 inch lugs were welded on top, as at "A" eliminated our floor trouble and at same time provided a sturdy base for main bearings at "C", and steel channels at bottom provided rigid base for motor reducer and worm drive.

Unexpected savings in erection time resulted in this design. By making templates of beam location at ceiling it was then possible to weld, first, lugs on 14 foot stringers, and second, weld base channels on the "U" shaped uprights, and third, weld uprights to stringers and complete unit by welding on the braces—all these operations done on the floor; then motor and worm were bolted to channels and entire unit hoisted to ceiling from floor above by slinging chain around shaft at "C". This unit was made in 54 man hours as against 92 in the first unit in which the uprights were lag screwed to ceiling and the platform bolted down and each part of drive hoisted separately and aligned while working on ladders.

Of course this whole unit could have been bolted together and, while not having built one of bolted construction for exact comparison, past experience indicates that layout, center punching, drilling and burring and finally assembling would at least triple if not quadruple the time required as compared to layout, clamp, weld and hoist. In this job the operation sequence is five for bolted construction to three for welded construction. Of more importance in this case, too, was the rigidity requirements. In bolting practice, it is customary to drill bolt holes at least $1/16$ inch larger than the bolts for ease in assembling and to prevent marring of threads when entering bolts. This type construction permits some creep of members so joined and, at best, are only tightened bolts resulting in a clamping action; while with arc welding, properly executed, two or more pieces become as one.

Arc welding also proved best for erecting the 10 foot sections of 12 gauge hot rolled, formed channels. These were hung from ceiling on 1 inch x 1 inch x 14 inch angles welded to one side of channels. See Fig. No. 5.

After becoming more adept in the use of the welding machine, we found faster means of erection, as can be seen in Fig. No. 6. These channels when assembled were nothing more than a trough for the slack side of chain to slide in.

First conveyor built as follows. See Fig. No. 3.

> Three 10 foot channels placed on horses end to end. Two butt welds made in downhand position. This 30 foot length was then raised to ceiling and marked on one side to locate hangers. It was then brought down to floor and hangers welded on; then raised and fastened to beams. It was thought that with all welding done on floor and only one overhead butt weld made where two 30 foot sections met, we would make the best time.

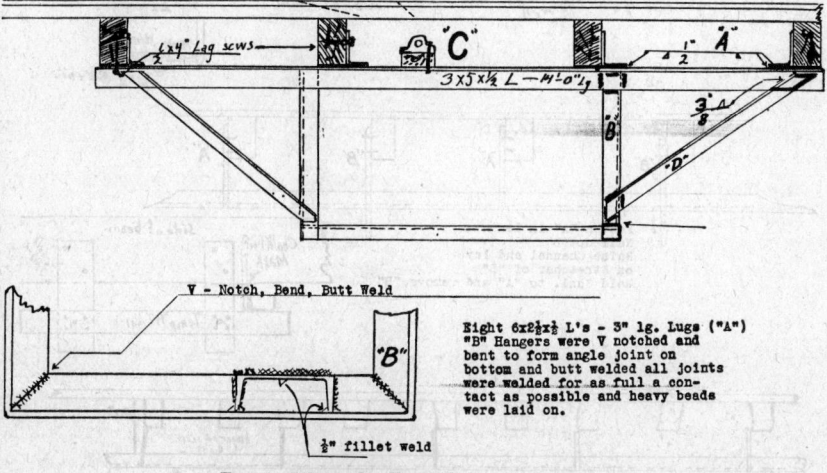

Fig. 4. All steel, all welded motor mount

It can readily be seen that with this type of joint (butt weld on outside of channel only) the interior of completed trough has no seams, rivet heads or bolt heads to catch on or wear off. The arc weld also eliminated the need for formed butt straps, drilling and countersinking and bolting as shown in detail (see Fig. No. 8).

Building and erection time by this method was 226 man hours. Some of this time was consumed in moving finished merchandise as it got the way, then returning it to where we had finished erection. To prevent fires from welding globules we wet down the floor for an entire bay and used a washtub with two inches of water in it set upon a ladder directly below the joint to be welded and posted two fire watchers. Fortunately, these precautions proved ample as only two fires occurred on three conveyor installations, due mainly to not clearing the entire bay under which we were working.

Fig. No. 6 shows an improved method which reduced erection man hours considerably. Starting on a Friday, three men assembled the 30 foot sections and laid in the maple wearing strips and drilled the hangers "A" (18 man hours). The only difference from original procedure being that hangers "A" were not welded to 30 foot sections. While this was being done, three additional men stretched chalk lines leaving chalk marks on beams to locate hangers "A" correctly. Then temporary hangers "B", Fig. No. 7, made of 1 inch x 4 inch pine were assembled and nailed to beams, alternating them so that they would not interfere with mounting hangers "A". View "C" illustrates this clearly. Hangers "A" were then fastened to beams on one side of chalk line. View "D" shows a mounted hanger "A" on beam and hanger "B" nailed on beam directly behind. Enough hangers were mounted to take care of the first two parallel troughs, (12 man hours).

With the plant shut down on Saturday, it was easy to clear the floor below for the entire length of the conveyor, and using four men to raise

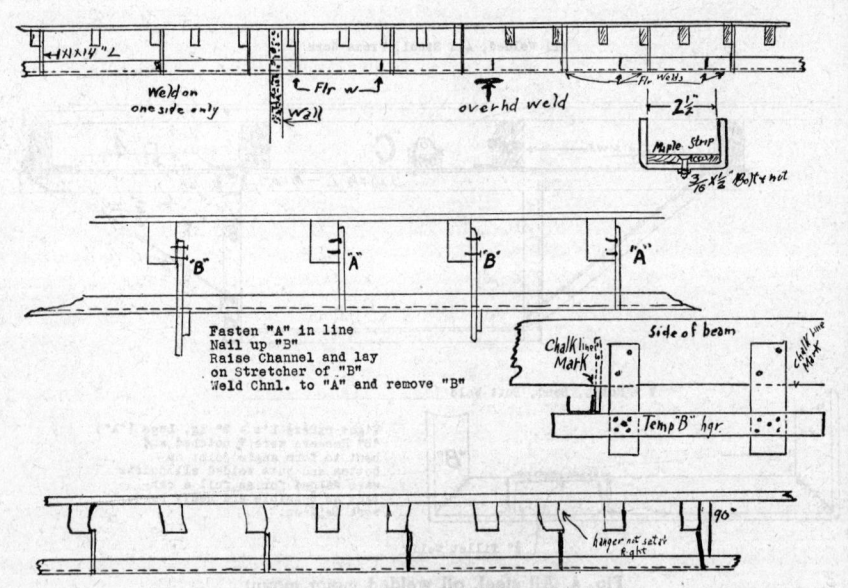

Figs. 5, 6, 7. Overhead channels.

ARC WELDING

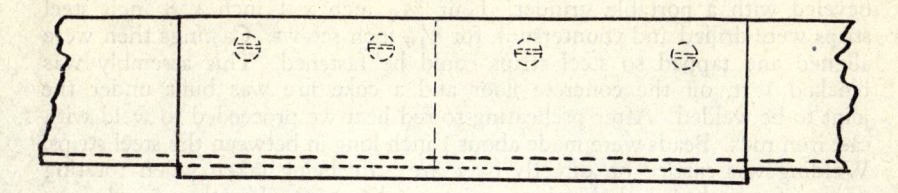

24 pcs. needed for one Conveyor

312 holes to drill in sleeves
Countersinking on inside of
Channel would be very hard to do.
376 holes to drill in channels for
sleeves and hangers.
376 - 3/16x½" bolts and nuts

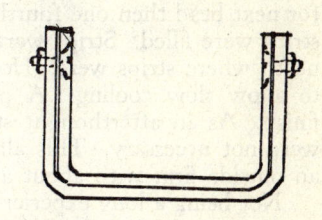

Fig. 8. Arc welding eliminates countersink.

the 30 foot sections and lay them on the temporary hangers and slide them against the fastened iron hangers. One man would then clamp the iron hanger to the channels so that a neat fillet weld could be made in the vertical position. The raising crew meanwhile put up the additional temporary hangers and raised two more 30 foot sections. By the time they finished, the welding for the two sections was completed so that the welding helper could remove the temporary hangers for use on the third section, etc. These operations were carried on simultaneously, and so smoothly that the job was finished on Saturday in seven hours, with six men. Total time: 42 plus 12 plus 18, or 72 hours. Material—6# Shielded Arc, $5/32$ inch electrodes.

Experiences gained from setting up the first conveyor of course helped in reducing erection time, but the largest time saver was the opportunity to assemble by arc welding the steel parts that would have to fit wooden beams that were slightly warped and variably spaced. It was under these circumstances that so much time was lost on the first unit. Fig. No. 7, shows why trouble occurred in fastening hangers previously welded on the floor located by templates or marking channels on ceiling. Fig. No. 7, also for the same reasons, proves conclusively that bolted construction would be impractical considering the extent to which modern welding practice has been developed to date.

For comparison, the following reference (Fig. No. 8) is given whereby the parts are fitted in place at ceiling without the use of arc welding. List of extra parts needed for channel assembling and mounting are also shown in Fig. No. 8.

Another project was a swing stock saw. This machine was shipped in from one of our other plants to be used in expanding our own mill. This unit was of such length as to require a $12\frac{1}{2}$ foot ceiling in order to maintain proper working height. However our basement ceiling is only 10 feet in height, so in order to install this unit we had to cut out a 24 inch section (Fig. No. 9) near the center of the main casting. We merely hacksawed through this casting, which was elliptical in shape, one half inch thick in the large segment and one inch thick at the sides. It was then beveled with a portable grinder. Four $3/16$ inch x 1 inch x 8 inch steel strips were drilled and countersunk for $5/16$ inch screws. Castings then were aligned and tapped so steel strips could be fastened. This assembly was blocked 1 ft. off the concrete floor and a coke fire was built under the joint to be welded. After preheating to red heat we proceeded to weld with cast iron rods. Beads were made about 1 inch long in between the steel strips. Welding was carried on directly over fire, care being taken when rotating casting for each 1 inch bead to maintain alignment. In other words, one 1 inch bead was made on the top side of castings, then turned one half turn for next bead then one fourth turn for next bead, etc., until spaces between strips were filled. Strips were then removed and welding completed underneath where strips were. Hot ashes were piled up where joint was welded to allow slow cooling. A portable grinder was used to give a pleasing finish. As an afterthought steel strips were replaced but more than likely were not necessary. This alteration was quoted at forty dollars ($40) by an outside firm with about a four day delivery, due to a crowded shop.

Not being a long experienced welder on any iron, let alone cast iron, the management hesitated a little before letting me tackle a job needing accuracy of alignment, but I had watched several castiron repair jobs and was eager to start. With the "go ahead" signal we went to work. Costs were broken down as follows:

1. Make two cuts with hand hacksaws. ($1\frac{1}{2}$ manhours.)
2. Saw and grind bevel. ($3/4$ manhours.)
3. Cut four strips of 1-inch iron. Drill and countersink ($3/4$ manhours.)
4. Line up, block castings, drill and tap eight $5/16$-inch screw holes and fasten together. (2 manhours.)
5. Preheat and weld. ($4\frac{1}{2}$ manhours.)
6. Finish grinding and touchup paint. (1 manhour.)

Total: $10\frac{1}{2}$ manhours.

Materials used: 4 lbs. nonmachinable castiron rod $5/32$ inch; $1/2$ dozen shovelsful red hot coals; four $3/16$ inch x 1 inch x 8 inch hot rolled strip; eight $5/16$ inch x $3/4$ inch flat head machine screws.

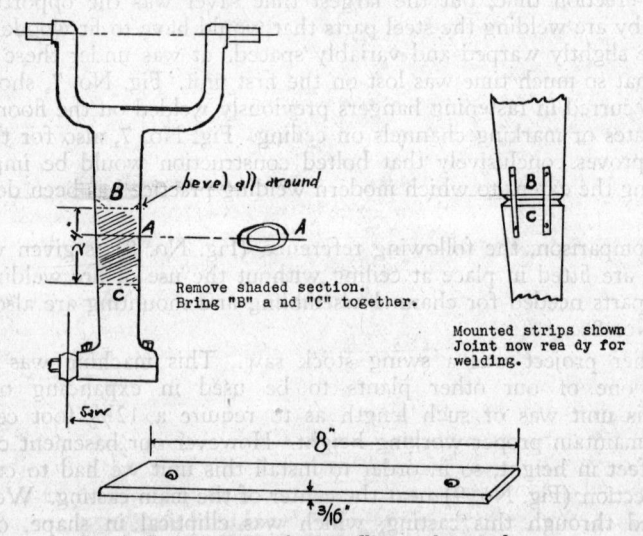

Fig. 9. Cut-out section for installing swing stock saw.

ARC WELDING

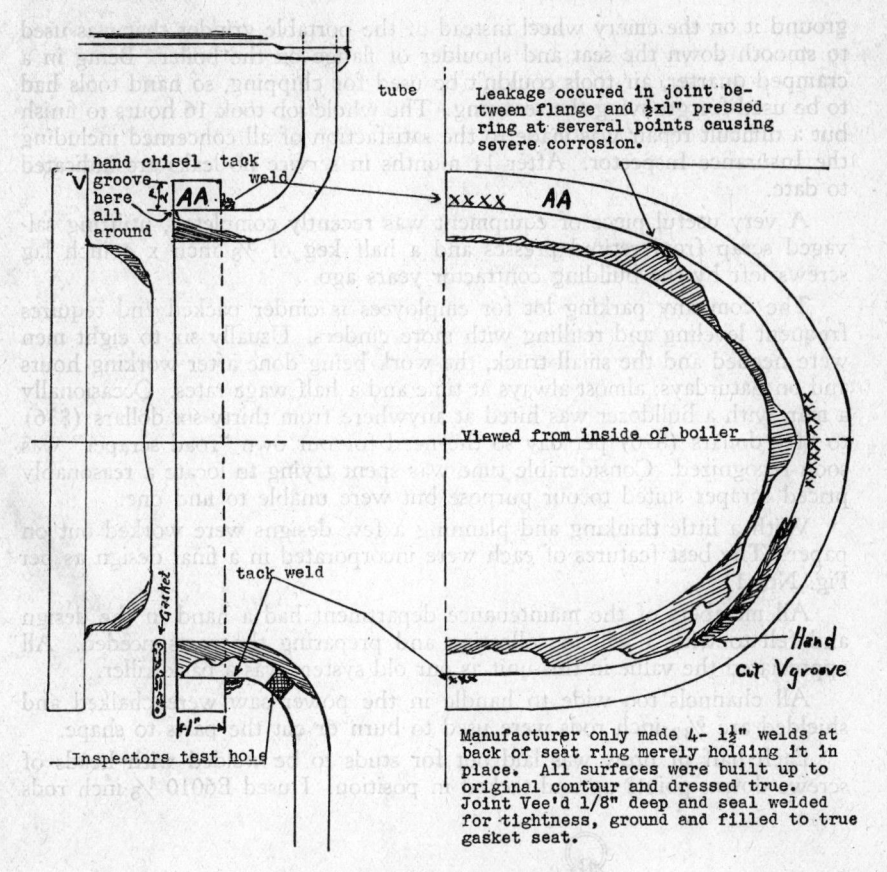

Fig. 10. Welding of heating boiler.

Labels in figure:
- tube
- Leakage occured in joint between flange and ½x1" pressed ring at several points causing severe corrosion.
- hand chisel tack groove here all around — weld — AA
- xxxx AA
- Viewed from inside of boiler
- tack weld
- Inspectors test hole — ⊢1"⊣
- Hand Cut V groove
- Manufacturer only made 4- 1½" welds at back of seat ring merely holding it in place. All surfaces were built up to original contour and dressed true. Joint Vee'd 1/8" deep and seal welded for tightness, ground and filled to true gasket seat.

Summary: This job was altered, setup, wired, and in production two days before we could even get it back to our plant from an outside repair shop. Our total costs were less than fifteen dollars ($15), so our savings amounted to twenty-five ($25), plus any trucking charges that would incur.

Another maintenance repair problem that came up, in which welding seemed to be the only answer, was on a front manhole on our 80-horsepower heating boiler, illustrated in Fig. No. 10.

Faulty shop fabrication resulted in excessive corrosion on the tube sheet at the manhole.

The job was handled over the Fourth of July weekend period while plant was shut down. It has usually been difficult to get a firm to do welding over the holiday periods because many plants are shut down at the same time and welding outfits are rushed. Having our own machine, it was a simple matter to make arrangements for cooling down and draining.

Operations were as follows: Remove manhole cover, wirebrush and chip to bare metal. Weld with general purpose 5/32 inch rods, starting at bottom, running short beads to minimize distortion of flange. (Using the electric arc gives much better control than gas, where warping is concerned.)

The same procedure was followed on the manhole cover, except that I ground it on the emery wheel instead of the portable grinder that was used to smooth down the seat and shoulder of flange on the boiler. Being in a cramped quarter, air tools couldn't be used for chipping, so hand tools had to be used for grooving the seat ring. The whole job took 16 hours to finish but a difficult repair was made to the satisfaction of all concerned including the Insurance Inspector. After 11 months in service no leaks are indicated to date.

A very useful piece of equipment was recently completed, utilizing salvaged scrap from retired presses and a half keg of ⅝ inch x 4 inch lag screws left by the building contractor years ago.

The company parking lot for employees is cinder packed and requires frequent leveling and refilling with more cinders. Usually six to eight men were needed and the small truck, the work being done after working hours and on Saturdays; almost always at time and a half wage rates. Occasionally a man with a bulldozer was hired at anywhere from thirty-six dollars ($36) to fifty dollars ($50) per day so the need for our own "road scraper" was soon recognized. Considerable time was spent trying to locate a reasonably priced scraper suited to our purpose but were unable to find one.

With a little thinking and planning a few designs were worked out on paper. The best features of each were incorporated in a final design as per Fig. No. 11.

All members of the maintenance department had a hand in the design and fell to with a will in collecting and preparing the parts needed. All appreciated the value in this unit as our old system was a back killer.

All channels too wide to handle in the power saw were chalked and shielded arc 5⁄32-inch rods were used to burn or cut the parts to shape.

Each half of prow was laid out for studs to be welded with heads of screws down, points up and tacked in position. I used E6010 ⅛-inch rods

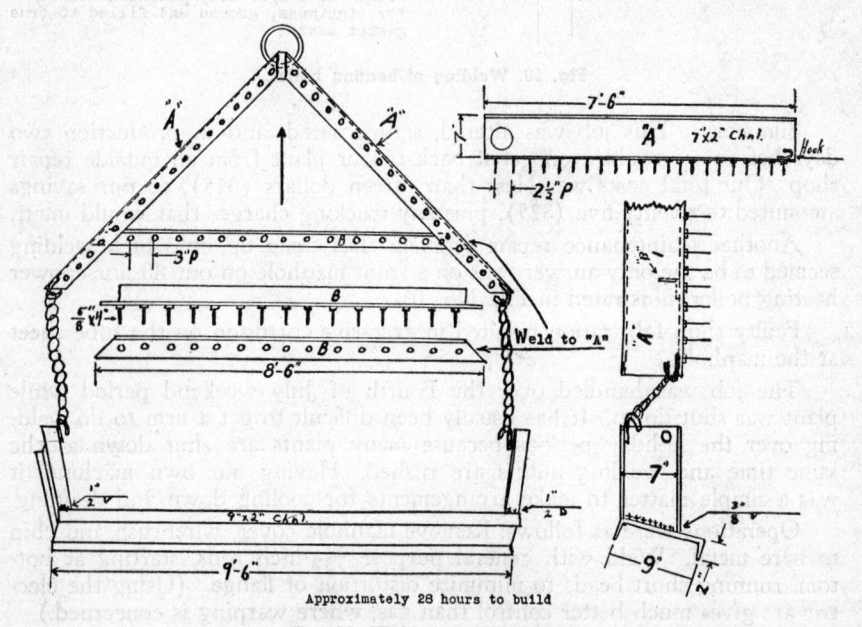

Fig. 11. Welded road scraper.

for tacking then switched to 5/32-inch shielded arc rods and welded completely around the square heads. To prevent warping only one of the four sides of each head was welded at a time, resulting in a straight row of "spikes" sturdy enough to cut down the high spots on the lot. A bullring was made from an old 5/8-inch brace rod, and slipped into nose of prow before welding shut.

Two "U" hooks were welded on the tail of the breaker and leveling scraper made, which could be hooked and chained to breaker.

In using this scraper the results have been most gratifying, doing the job better than was thought possible, using the aforementioned truck and driver and only one additional man to help turn the scraper at the main entrance and gather large lumps of fire brick clinker from the lot, as unit goes back and forth bringing them up. This tool fostered a build up of morale among the workers, no more broken springs on cars, tires are safeguarded, yard appearance greatly improved and upkeep expense tremendously reduced. All this from the scrap pile and a good welding machine. Operating time for this unit approximates 4 manhours maximum against 64 manhours maximum by hand methods. Construction details and time data will be found in Fig. No. 11.

This by no means completes the list of items our welding machine has handled, but, proximity of the deadline precludes further descriptive matter.

Chapter XIV—Gravel Plant

By Henry Barrett,

Foreman Welder & Steel Mechanic, Construction Aggregates Co., Ferrysburg, Mich.

Subject Matter: Miscellaneous apparatus such as maintenance of sand and gravel equipment, tug boats, scows, towing cables, cranes, screens, dragline buckets, pipes, jaw and roll crushers, etc., are discussed quite fully and costs estimated for repair as compared with new parts. Total savings on three cranes estimated at $13,937.24 per year.

Henry Barrett

I take great pride in the contents of this paper, not because it is a great opportunity to enter a great industrial award program, but for the reason I can express my satisfaction and appreciation for the past fifteen years in the study, actual experience and awards I have received in that time, due to my great desire and faith in one of the world's greatest inventions—welding. My paper is based on not what I have heard, not what I have seen, but on my actual experience, sometimes doing the job myself, sometimes with my fellow welders, but always on the job day after day, year after year, welding, welding, in one of the world's largest gravel plants.

I do not think there is anything more severe on the machinery, mechanical equipment, mobile equipment and structures as the aggregation of gravel. I think it would be a fit time to mention that for this past two years our average tonnage dug, screened and shipped in a nine months producing period has been one million tons. The remaining three months—winter months—are spent in overhauling and repairing. There is no better way to express my facts, than to invite you on a visit to our plant; follow me through these lines and I am sure you will be more than just interested.

You cannot miss the plant with its huge storage tanks—nine in all—capable of storing two hundred thousand tons of gravel, from sand up to two inch stone, and the screening plant towering 150 feet in the air. But—"Beg pardon, what did you say?" "Who is that fellow with the funny hat, and what is he doing?" "Oh! he is a welder." Remarkable how all visitors are fascinated with the purr of the motor, the crack and the flash of the arc. Yes, he is one of the most important men in the plant, the burner and welder.

Come with me and I will show you how these fellows play the most important part in our every day schedule of maintenance. Here is our fleet of tugs: No. 1 the Willard; No. 2, Robert Johnson; No. 3, the Kingfisher, and No. 4, the tug Vivian. The Johnson is our star of the fleet. The hull of steel construction, propelled by Diesel power, and designed by us to either tow her scows or push them at will. She was originally steam, so we

ARC WELDING

Fig. 1. (A) The Willard. Fig. 2. (B) The Robert Johnson. Fig. 3. (C) The Kingfisher. Fig. 4. (D) The Vivian. Fig. (E) Loaded scows. Fig. 6. (F) Close-up Scow A-30. Fig. 7. (G) Scows in river.

had to rebuild her. The part of her hull that was to receive her engine bed was reinforced with plates in between the frames and all arc welded, and her engine bed, looks as if it were casted; but no, we designed that, fabricated from channels, angles and gusset plates, and fused into one solid mass by the use of electric welding. And the pilot house and engine room; pretty, isn't it, and so compact using every inch of spare space for fuel tanks, tool lockers, etc. Must have cost a lot of money for the shipbuilders to rebuild that. Oh no, we did the work ourselves and cut the cost of estimates in half. Now, the tug Willard (steam) calls for a boiler, fire cracks, flues, rudder damage and hull damage. Yes, we weld those fire cracks, weld the flues, build up propeller shafts in worn spots and machine same. Those towing cables are very neat, no loose ends tied up with wire. Oh no, we weld those cable ends. Our two smaller tugs, the Kingfisher and Vivian, are gas engine driven and owing to shallow water we are troubled with cracked heads and cylinders caused through dirt, but we weld them right in our repair shop. Miscellaneous parts, such as pipe lines, links and every kind of small breakage are repaired by welding, and in many instances cast iron is definitely out when we can produce in steel.

Next you see our fleet of scows—eight in all—capable of holding a deck load of approximately 800 tons per scow. These scows have to be kept in constant repair, but being constructed of steel, welding again plays the important role. Damage to the hulls and decks caused by bumbicy and abrasion from the buckets are easily repaired by electric welding. There is no let up in the use of the tugs and scows; they are used twenty-four hours per day. There is no greater test of equipment than a twenty-four hour schedule, and welding is required on maintenance of this equipment about 80 percent.

We will now leave the plant and continue up to our gravel pit which is situated about fifteen miles down the river from the plant. The tug arrives at the pit with empty scows and, waiting at the pit are two scows loaded with 1600 tons of pit-run gravel. These scows were loaded with a fifty-ton crane which is sitting on scow with a 100-foot boom and two-yard bucket. This crane operates twenty-four hours per day, six or seven days per week as required, but approximately digs 33,600 tons per week. The maintenance of this crane is very important and a crane without a bucket is still more important. Welding plays a very great part in the maintenance of this equipment. Spare shafts, pins, sheaves, hinge bushings, cutting edges, play an important part, sheaves, pines, shafts are welded and machined at a great savings and are kept ready for replacement at any time. I will give data of savings on these different parts when welded and actual cost of new parts as we go along.

We leave the pit and the tug arrives at the unloading dock at the plant. Another crane of the same class as at the pit, is waiting to unload scows and the gravel is conveyed to the screen house. The pumps are working; the gravel is washed and screening takes place. Thirty-two screens ranging from sand to 2-inch stone are employed in this operation. Thirty-three thousand six hundred tons per week pass through chutes to screens, causing an enormous amount of wear to high carbon, steel lining plates and screens. Here our welders are on constant watch for wear. A hard-facing, impact-abrasion electrode is used exclusively on the vital spots saving an enormous amount of steel that would otherwise have to be replaced. The screens are treated in the same way, hard faced on the wires. Every precaution has to be taken to save waste. So that welding plays its part. Bad spots are removed from the larger sheets and new pieces welded in. Good workmanship is also essential at all times. The welder must be sure of his weld, because if a plate broke adrift, great damage could be caused to the conveyor belts, etc. The oversize stones are crushed with jaw and roller crushers, and here we have great faith and wonderful results with an abrasion-and-impact resistent electrode. From the screen house the different grades of gravel pass over conveyors through hoppers over junctions all designed of steel. Twenty tons of steel are put into this plant in the form of liners every year, but if it were not for arc welding, this same amount would have to be replaced every working month. As I have mentioned before, the vital spots are saved by welding in a pattern of single beads so that the welder forms 1-inch squares.

These patterns can be kept under supervision and more hard face applied directly over worn pattern. I might mention these liner plates were previously bolted in the chutes, but owing to the terrific abrasion, bolts had to be constantly replaced and leaks were very prevalent. Arc welding the plates in position simplified this operation, with results of less cleaning of the floors, and less deterioration of wood floors caused by water. Hundreds of feet of water pipes supply the water to screens, chutes, etc. Pipes ranging from 1 inch to 30 inches in diameter. Welding plays a great part in the installing of new liners, no plumbers are needed, I myself design the patterns and welding does the rest. One hundred per cent no-leak joints. Simple, and a neat looking job. The nine storage tanks are erected over a concrete tunnel, 1000 feet long. In this tunnel are six tunnel cars, built of steel with conveyors built in. These cars are operated with electricity. The hoppers are adjustable so as we can give a percentage of any kind of mixed gravel, according to our customers' specifications. So you see these cars are subject to severe abrasion during the loading process. When loading ships, we average 1500 tons per hour. Liners and welding electrodes play an important part in this operation. The gravel is now conveyed to the rinsing plant for its last rinsing, and passes over eight screens, on to the loading shuttle and to the boats or the railroad cars as the case may be.

I mention these operations not to tell how gravel is made, but to stress the important fact that without the use of welding in all its many forms, this great plant could not possibly run on schedule and produce to a satisfactory advantage. It makes no difference whether we save a nickel or save a thousand dollars, so long as we save; reduce overhead to a minimum; repair fast and efficiently and try and make shutdowns impossible. Welding answers all these factors.

There is also a great many advantages to be gained by the maintenance department. New machines and equipment can be installed but are not always efficient after they are put into service. Breakages occur, sometimes caused through weakness of construction, vibration or many other causes. It is most always the welding engineer or foreman that are called. Then comes the question, "Can it be welded or reinforced with the application of welding?" Through years of experience, we study the particular break and know as soon as we look at it whether we can weld it or not, and very often through the welder and his job comes new design gained through the application of his repair.

The road gravel plant recently added to our equipment is capable of making 150 tons of road gravel per hour. The double deck screens, jaw crusher and 36 inch diameter roller crusher are subject to severe abrasion during the sixteen or twenty-four hour producing period per day. The rolls and crusher plates are kept to size with the use of hard-facing, impact abrasion, resistant electrode, replaced at different intervals; sprockets are built up, welding is applied everywhere, there are no lay-offs in this gravel plant.

We now come to the maintenance of the cranes; four 50-ton cranes and two smaller ones are in constant use. They travel up and down the yard —busy every hour, great amount of wear on the traveling machinery. To replace these worn parts would run into thousands of dollars, so wherever welding can be applied, it is used to a great advantage. I will try and illustrate by the use of various pictures I have procured to demonstrate welding at its best as applied for maintenance. Crane No. 1 used on the dock for unloading from scows to plant, and if necessary around the yard, twenty-four hours per day is the maximum of performance and great care is given these machines,—as shown in Fig. 8. After veeing out with burning torch, was welded by myself complete in six hours, using twenty pounds of 3/16, 85 wire.

Approximate cost of job:
Wire	$ 2.00
12 Gal. Gasoline	1.20
Labor, 6 hrs. @ $1.50	9.00
Total cost	$12.20

New frame would have cost approximately $500.

The sprockets and wheels as shown in Fig. 11 are built up by arc welding, pads welded, stub axles take up axle and caps. This picture represents 558 welding hours in the repair shop, using approximately 1662 pounds 1/4 inch E6012 rods. Following is the actual report of 1942 repair list and cost and also new part list:

4 Sprockets—each:
Welding Wire	Welding Hrs.	Wages	Overhead	Total	New Parts
50 lbs. 1/4	16	$1.00 hr.	32 gal. gas	$24.33	$150.00
				x 4	x 4
				$97.32	$600.00

Actual Saving: $502.68

8 Wheels—each:
Welding Wire	Welding Hrs.	Wages	Overhead	Total	New Parts
25 lbs. 1/4"	8	$8.00	$1.44	$33.19	$100.00
				x 8	x 8
				$255.52	$800.00

Savings: $544.48

8 Stub Axles (1 take up) 10 in all. Each:
Welding Wire	Welding Hrs.	Wages	Overhead	Total	New Parts
36 lbs. 1/4 rod	12	$12.00	$2.16 gas	$28.12	$145.00
			10.00 machine work	x 10	x 10
				$281.20	$1450.00

Savings: $1168.80

100 Pads—each:
Welding Wire	Welding Hrs.	Wages	Overhead	Total	New Parts
9 lbs. 1/4 rod	3	$3.00	$ .72 gas	$4.71	$67.50
				x 100	x 100
				$471.00	$6750.00

Savings: $6279.00

10 Caps (each) 1 layer bronze
Bronze Rod	Welding Hrs.	Wages	Overhead	Total	New Parts
10 lbs.	5	$5.00	$3.00	$9.00	$30.00
			Act. & Ox. machine work	5.00	
				$14.00	$30.00

Savings: $16.00

Total cost of New Parts	$9630.00
Cost of Welded Parts	1121.84
Total Saving	$8508.16

There being three machines of this class undergoing this repair every two years, our approximate savings on these are $13,937.24 every year. Our

Fig. 8. (A) Crane No. 1. Fig. 9. (B) Crawler assembly. Fig. 10. (C) Sprockets, drive gear, shaft, pads.

other machines are of a different class and are not subject to the hard wear caused through traveling, but nevertheless, approximately $5,000 per year is saved by the application of welding.

Crane 73 and crane 75 are both of the same class and as you see in Figs. 12 and 14. Fig. 13 shows crane 75 on blocks with her traveling parts and pads removed to the welding shop for welding. The general crane is used for light work but has her regular share of welding applied to keep her in perfect shape. At this time when our nation requires economy in steel, welding plays a great part in the savings of this precious metal, in fact some parts cannot be supplied by the manufacturers, and it is here we can save that certain part by the application of welding.

Our buckets are the next item for general maintenance; three buckets in the class of bucket No. 19 are of the two-yard class, draglines, and smaller buckets, amounting to ten buckets in all, are kept under constant repair. Cutting edges are built up with E6012 wire and hard faced with hard facing electrodes. Shafts, pins, arms, sheaves are watched carefully for cracks, and as a safety method are repaired as soon as damage or wear is reported. Bucket No. 3 has been in constant use for 10 years, and as you see in picture, has just come from welding room in first class shape.

I would now like to draw your attention to one of several 100-foot conveyors that were designed by us. As you will see they are self supporting and were built with a two foot square, burning torch and welder. They can be removed at a very short notice to any part of the yard where they might be required. Simple in construction, they consist mostly of scrap material; short angles were welded together and the walks consists of old screens. Such jobs as these are a credit to the welding profession.

Although we are a maintenance crew, the management works with us 100 percent. Every welder can express his views on any improvement, his plans are carefully studied and in nearly all cases, he is given permission to go ahead with his ideas. Responsible for the thousands of jobs that are carried out in the course of the season, I think it is only fair we mention the machines that enable us to do this work. We are the proud owners of your welders, and in the picture you will see our latest addition—400 ampere heavy duty generator, portable. See Fig. 22. We also have a 300 ampere portable and a 200 ampere stationary welder. The last mentioned we call "Old Faithful", an old relic but she burns them up every day; we have owned her for twelve years. Who owned her before nobody knows, but for upkeep all she has cost us is new brushes. There are no lay-offs for maintenance men. Everyday there is something, jobs that if they had to be repaired by any other method than welding, would cause many great delays and expense to our plant. Of course, we have delays, but they are cut to a minimum with the application of welding.

Note Fig. 26. Here we have one boat unloading sand, one boat just leaving loaded, and two boats waiting to load. These four boats carried

Fig. 11. (A) Crane No. 67. Fig. 12. (B) Loading with Crane 73. Fig. 13. (C) Crane 75 undergoing repairs. Fig. 14. (D) No. 75 on duty. Fig. 15. (E) All purpose crane. Fig. 16. (F) Crane 67 at loading docks.

Fig. 17. (A) Bucket No. 19 two-yard capacity. Fig. 18. (B) No. 3 bucket, weld repaired and ready for service. Fig. 19. (C) Drag lines. Fig. 20. (D) Road gravel plant. Fig. 21. (E) Heavy Bull-Dozer. Fig. 22. (F) 400-Ampere heavy duty generator.

away no less than 22,000 tons of gravel and sand this day. Also you see at the loading dock, our own ship S. S. Sensibar, named after the "Big Boss" taking on 8000 tons of sand and gravel.

As I have based my paper on different notes from day to day and as the closing time of the contest is drawing nearer, I think it would be to your interest to note the different applications of welding as applied in our plant for a few days. Two expert welders are at present employed, I will give the different jobs for each of them:

Friday, May 15, 1942—Welder No. 1—Vee out and weld crack in bucket arm, two hours; weld swing stop on crane, three hours; weld deck angles on scow, one hour; weld tunnel car ratchet, one hour; weld new plates in buckets for bucket elevator—spare, one hour; eight-hour day.

Welder No. 2—Weld and patch tunnel hopper, one hour; welding on crusher plate wedges, two hours; weld turnbuckles for scows, broken links, one hour; weld screen backs, two hours; hard face doors in rinsing plant, two hours; weld sheaves for bucket, two hours. Ten hours welding time (two hours overtime for repair).

Fig. 23. (A) All welded Bollards. Fig. 24. (B) 100-Foot welded conveyor span. Fig. 25. (C) Another view of 100-foot conveyor. Fig. 26. (D) Four boats carry away 22,000 tons in one day. Fig. 27. (E) The "Sensibar" taking on 8,000 tons of sand and gravel. Fig. 28. (F) The "Sensibar" gets help from a tug.

Sunday, May 17, 1942—Both welders built up rolls on road gravel plant. The rolls are thoroughly cleaned and brushed and beads of hard-facing, impact and abrasion resistant rod are applied. Peened with hand hammer on every layer in eight hours these welders applied 80 pounds of rod in that time. By this method the rolls are kept in perfect condition. Saving new shells that cost $300 per shell. These rolls are 36 inches x 20 inches and both welders working each twenty-four hours can complete one layer of welding around the shells. Here represents a great saving to the company.

New set of shells cost—@ $300	$600.00
Labor installing new set	50.00
Total cost	$650.00

Welding Old Shells:

48 hrs. welding @ $1.00	$ 48.00
240 lbs. Electrode @ .50 lb	120.00
Gasoline and oil	12.00
Total cost	$180.00
Total saving on this item	$470.00

It is essential that these shells be kept in A-1 condition at all times to keep a uniform grade of road gravel; therefore, these rolls would have to be replaced pretty frequently were it not for welding.

Monday, May 18, 1942—Welder No. 1—Welding in sand flumes, one hour; hard facing sand screw blades, three hours; welding bearing in sheaves, one hour; welding screen cloth, one hour; welding pad on crane, two hours; welding liners in road gravel plant hopper, two hours; bronzing handles and fittings for grease guns.

Here I wish to express the great pleasure I have enjoyed through these few months in preparing this paper. Fifteen years ago I came to the employ of my present employer as a shipfitter and welder. Welding was young in those days, but I did my best to push the cause ahead; every place welding could be applied—I applied it. The management began to see its many advantages and gave me cooperation in every way. I enjoyed the many trips I made to the office with different ideas and their willingness to go ahead and try my ideas.

Welding on their ships, tugs and scows and in the plant has given me every opportunity to prove the great savings, durability, and proficient maintenance gained by this method; new machines were added, extra help was hired and today we think we are 100 percent efficient in our methods. Today, I am foreman-welder, steel mechanic, and keep in touch constantly with welding experts who give me many valuable hours discussing several problems of welding. In this way we are able to apply any new product or application that will enable to keep maintenance cost to a minimum and production to the maximum.

Welding is here to stay!

Chapter XV—Machine Tools

By H. W. Rushmer,

Research, Jeffrey Mfg. Co., Columbus, Ohio.

Subject Matter: Description of the welding of various shapes for diverse uses of machine tools such as boring bars, parting tools, centers, farming tools, taps, etc. The welding is done by means of stainless steel electrodes. Preheating and postheating are recommended when welding high speed steel tools.

H. W. Rushmer

Many unsuccessful attempts have been made to weld tool steel (especially the high alloy steels) either coated or uncoated, with low carbon steel electrodes. It has been amply demonstrated that all tool steel can be successfully welded by using the 18-8 stainless steel electrodes.

Due to the course of the war, it has diminished several of our most important strategic materials, which are extremely vital to our full war effort.

Tungsten being a heavy constituent of that noble alloy, 18-4-1 high-speed steel is on the priority list, and it behooves us to conserve that which we already have in our plants. If this can be done it will be a real contribution to our full war effort. As it is imperative to conserve our present supply, we present the arc welding method as a means to this accomplishment. By taking advantage of the process, great savings in dollars and cents, as well as time can be accomplished by using that which formerly found its way to the scrap barrel. Even small pieces can be used economically.

It is well to bear in mind that at the present time this is not altogether a proposition of dollars and cents, but will it contribute to our war program.

In Figs. 1 and 2 is shown a test made by arc welding carbon tool steel to 18-4-1 high-speed steel. The samples were ground to shape on the ends as illustrated in Fig. 3. The size of the stock was ⅝ inch x 1¼ inch. The samples were pre-heated with the acetylene torch, then welded by using 18-8 stainless steel electrodes. It is better to heat the parts to be welded in a furnace, as the heating is done more slowly and uniformly. The sample was heated to the proper forging temperature and forged in the center to ½ inch x 1 inch, leaving the ends the original size. The light shaded section on the end is the high-speed steel; the center, the stainless steel, and the opposite end, carbon tool steel.

Fig. 2 illustrates this same sample bent to a U shape, or an angle of 152°. Previous to this bending test, it was heated to the forging temperature and bent in the weld to an angle of 90°, then straightened out flat

ARC WELDING 135

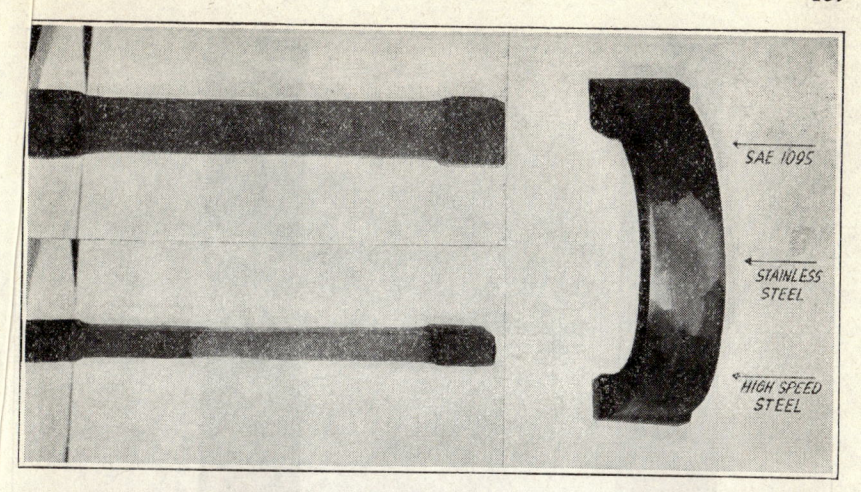

Fig. 1. (left) Front and side views showing typical example in welding carbon tool steel to 18-4-1 high-speed steel. Fig. 2. (right) Same sample as shown in Fig. 1, bent to U shape to test welding.

again, and then by reversing the sides it was bent as shown in the photograph. On the last bending test there were no signs of the weld coming apart.

Fig: 4 shows a weld similar to the above. The stock used was 5/8 inch x 1¼ inch. One piece was carbon tool steel, the other piece was 18-4-1 high-speed steel, welded with 18-8 stainless steel electrode, 3/32 inch in diameter. After the welding operation it was forged to a smaller size, ½ inch x 1 inch, without any signs of failure in the weld.

Fig 5 shows this same specimen after a torsional test. It was twisted 180° without any signs of rupturing the weld. It is well not to spread the weld over too great an area, as a short weld is equal to a long one. Besides, it conserves our limited supply of stainless steel. The reason why the welds cover such a large area as shown in the photograph is due to the stretching of the steel during the forging operation. Fig. 3 shows the specimens ground preparatory to the welding operation. Many tools can be welded without machining the surfaces, either forging or rough grinding is perfectly satisfactory. Of course, a better bond is affected by the scale being removed from the surface to be welded.

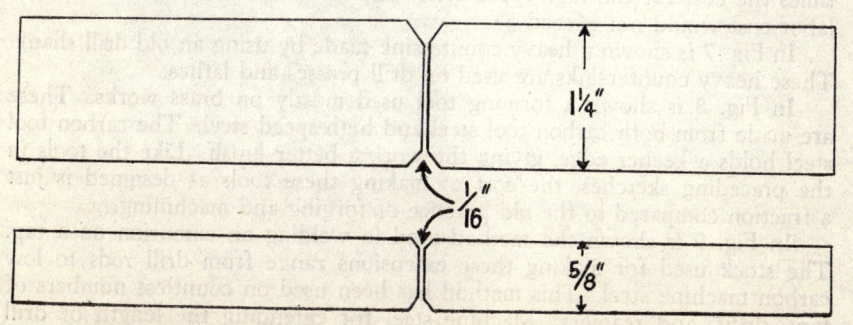

Fig. 3. Method of grinding junction ends and positioning before welding.

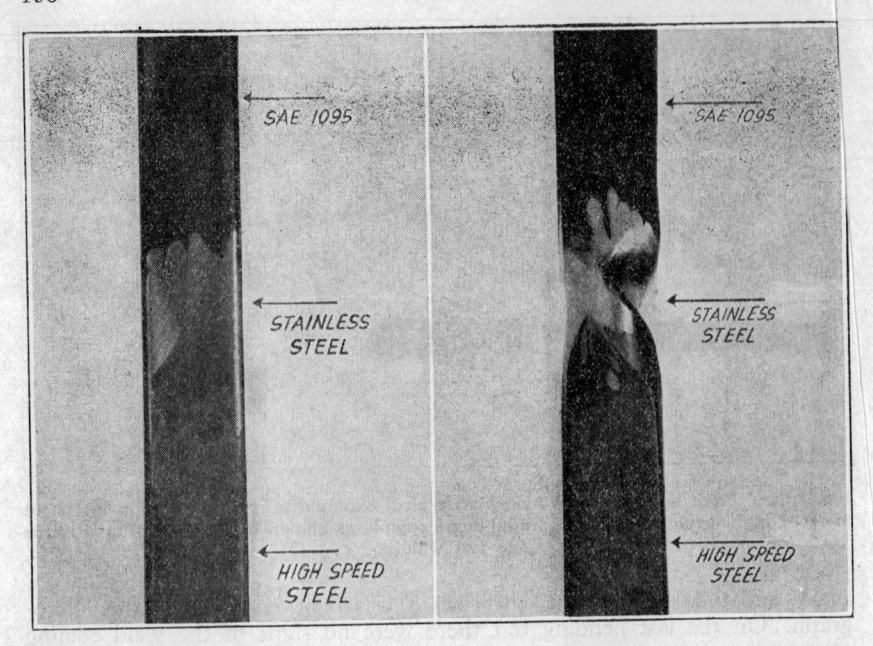

Fig. 4. (left) Close-up of finished weld made in joining SAE-1095 carbon tool steel to 18-4-1 high-speed steel. Fig. 5. (right) Result of torsional test made to determine strength of welded joint previously shown in Fig. 4.

The demand for better lathe production required greater feeds and speeds, thus making the carbon tool steel centers obsolete, consequently, high-speed steel was used as a substitute. The old carbon steel centers can be salvaged by annealing, then machined. It is then welded around the groove as shown in Fig. 6. Even high-speed steel centers that have become too short, can be annealed, and a new center welded on, as illustrated in sketch. After welding has been completed it is important to anneal all welded pieces to relieve the welding stresses. These centers can be annealed, reconditioned and rehardened at pleasure.

The cost of high-speed steel for the blade on a counterbore using the shank of an old drill was less than one dollar. The cost of material, if made from high-speed steel would have been $6. In addition, the forging and machine costs, besides the waste of steel in machining, would be three times the cost for the high-speed steel. Made by this method, material and labor cost would not exceed $3.

In Fig. 7 is shown a heavy countersink made by using an old drill shank. These heavy countersinks are used on drill presses and lathes.

In Fig. 8 is shown a forming tool used mostly on brass works. These are made from both carbon tool steel and high-speed steel. The carbon tool steel holds a keener edge, giving the work a better finish. Like the tools in the preceding sketches, the cost of making these tools as designed is just a fraction compared to the old practice of forging and machining.

In Fig. 9 is shown the method used in welding an extension on a tap. The stock used for making these extensions range from drill rods to low carbon machine steel. This method has been used on countless numbers of taps, drills, and reamers. Machine steel for extending the length of drill usually is satisfactory. Even pipe taps with short shanks are welded and

A.C. WELDING   137

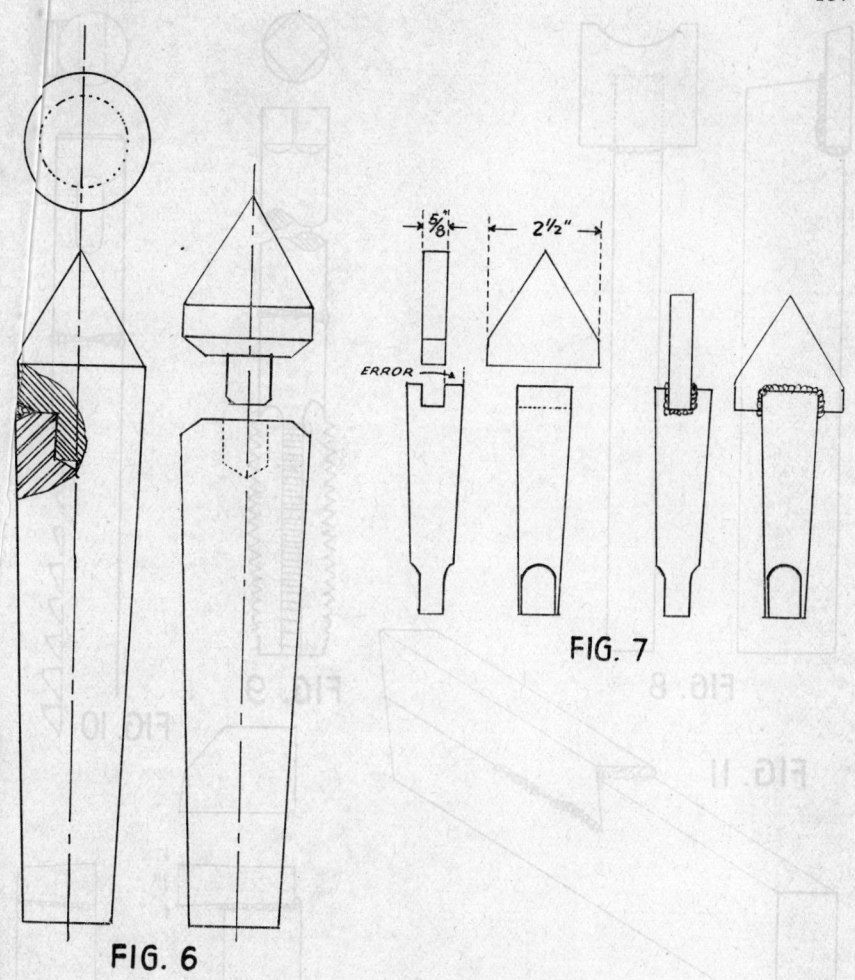

Fig. 6. Details of welded construction on salvaged carbon steel lathe center. Fig. 7. Welded countersink fabricated from old drill shank.

give good performance. In welding taps it is well to cover the threads with asbestos or a thin piece of sheet metal. This precaution is due to the sputtering of the arc which may cause small globules of hot metal to deposit on the threads.

In Fig. 10 is shown a high-speed steel broach broken at the eye. About four inches back of the eyes it was cut off by grinding, the temper was drawn and ground to a point as indicated. A piece of 3/4 inch drill rod was ground to a point and welded to the broach. When the machine work was finished the eye was given a spring temper. It is conceded that carbon tool steel properly tempered will withstand greater pulling stresses than high-speed steel. Hence the broach was stronger in the eye than when new.

The conventional square tool bits are fairly satisfactory for light cutting, but when working against time and heavy cutting they fail, due to the

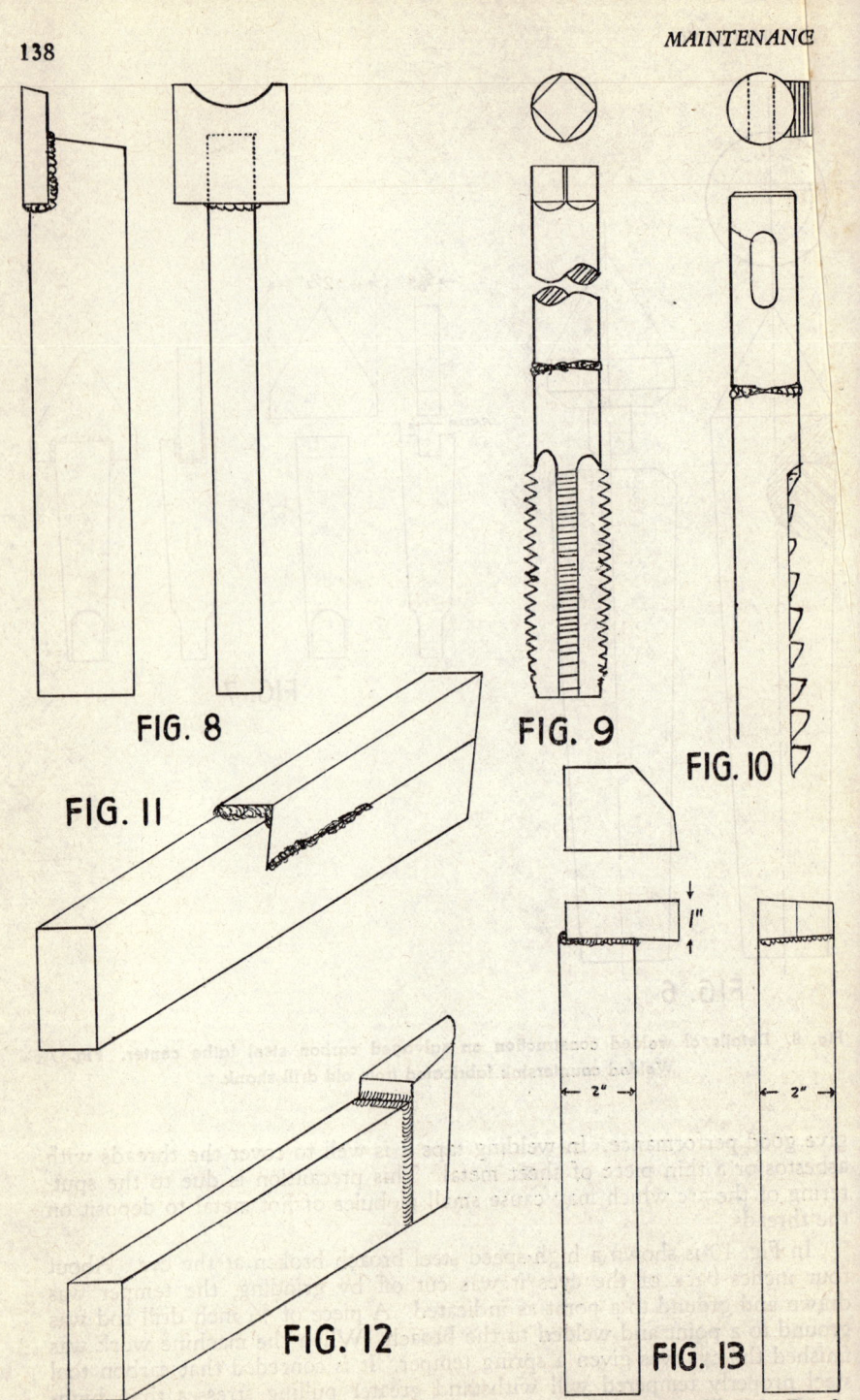

Fig. 8. Welded forming tool made from carbon tool steel and high-speed steel. Fig. 9. Method of welding extension on a tap. Fig. 10. Method for salvaging high-speed steel broach which had been broken at the eye. Fig. 11. Design of weld-built tool for heavy cutting. Fig. 12. Roughing tool of arc welded design. Fig. 13. Heavy side tool for planer.

ARC WELDING   139

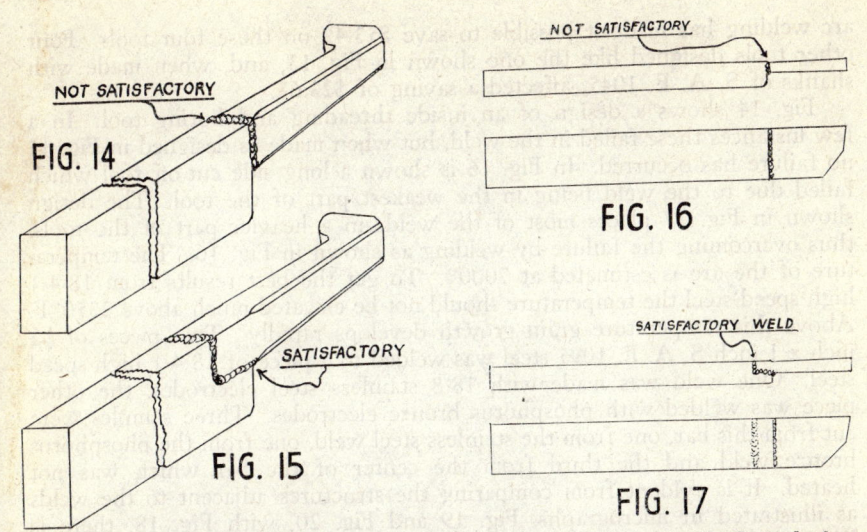

Fig. 14. Inside threading and boring tool of unsatisfactory design. Fig. 15. Same boring with more satisfactory design of welded joint. Fig. 16. Incorrectly welded cut-off tool. Fig. 17. Same cut-off tool with correct type of welded joint.

springing, shattering and the absence of body to the tool to carry away the heat that is so rapidly generated at the cutting edge. Fig. 11 is designed to partly overcome this absence of body to carry away the heat, during heavy, hogging cutting. If the contacting surfaces are perfectly level very little welding will be required. To prevent drawing the hardness, do not leave the arc on too long in one place. Do not use electrodes larger than ³⁄₃₂ inch.

Fig. 12 shows a roughing tool for lathe, shaper, or planer. Several other designs have been used to conserve high-speed steel, but the design shown worked out as being the most practical. These high-speed steel points can be forged in a swage, annealed, then cut to desired length in a hack saw. Old tools that have become too short for further service can be forged to meet the above requirements. After the welding has been completed they are heated and ground to shape while hot. It is considered good practice to give all welded and forged tools a good annealing after these operations. The cost of high-speed steel for a ¾ inch x 1½ inch roughing tool is $3.45. The labor cost of smith and helper is 80¢, totaling $4.25.* The cost of medium carbon steel for the welded tool would be 12¢. The cost of high-speed steel is 16¢. The labor cost of the welder, 25¢, a total of 53¢. A saving of $3.72 per tool of the above size. Furthermore, every time the tool is dressed there is a waste of valuable steel in trimming the tool to the required shape, and in the past many of these short pieces have found their way to the scrap barrel.

Fig. 13 shows a heavy side tool for a planer. These tools were ordered to be made of 2 inch square high-speed steel, which would cost $61.47 for the steel alone. In addition to this, $2.48 must be added for the forging operation, totaling $63.95. The cost of medium carbon steel for the shanks of the welded tools was $1.91. The cost of forging these points to prepare them for welding was $1.25. Labor cost of arc welding the tools was $1.20, the cost of high-speed steel for the points was $6.14, totaling $10.50. The

―――――――――
*The overhead cost has not been estimated in any of these figures given.

arc welding has made it possible to save $53.49 on these four tools. Four other tools designed like the one shown in Fig. 13, and, when made with shanks of S. A. E. 1045, affected a saving of $23.63.

Fig. 14 shows a design of an inside threading and boring tool. In a few instances these failed in the weld, but when made as designed in Fig. 15 no failure has occurred. In Fig. 16 is shown a long side cut-off tool which failed due to the weld being in the weakest part of the tool. The design shown in Fig. 17 places most of the welds in a heavier part of the tools, thus overcoming the failure by welding as shown in Fig. 16. The temperature of the arc is estimated at 7000°. To get the best results from 18-4-1 high-speed steel the temperature should not be elevated much above 2350°F. Above this temperature grain growth develops rapidly. Two pieces of 1/4 inch x 1 inch S. A. E. 1095 steel was welded to a piece of 18-4-1 high-speed steel. One weld was made with 18-8 stainless steel electrodes, the other piece was welded with phosphorus bronze electrodes. Three samples were cut from this bar, one from the stainless steel weld, one from the phosphorus bronze weld and the third from the center of the bar which was not heated. It is evident from comparing the structures adjacent to the welds as illustrated in micrographs, Fig. 19 and Fig. 20, with Fig. 18, there is little or no grain growth as was suspected. It will require further study to determine just what caused the failure and provide a remedy.

The writer has assumed the theory that the high temperature of the arc has caused the formation of new carbides, which may be the cause of the brittleness. It is a difficult operation to attempt to machine these tools after welding, but if the tools are heated to 1500°F. quenched in oil, then followed with the standard practice of annealing high-speed steel, no difficulty will be experienced. Also, it has been noted that the above temperatures and treatments applied to these tools with thin sections result in a gain of strength and less breakage.

Relative to phosphorus bronze electrodes, they can be used to good advantage on some tools. The cost of phosphorus bronze is less than stainless steel. Tools made from high-speed steel must be forged and hardened before welding with phosphorus bronze, but carbon tool steel can be welded before or after the hardening.

In Fig. 21 is shown a lathe side facing tool which can be made by the arc welding method with a considerable saving.

In Figs. 22 and 23 are shown two radii-forming tools for a planer. They

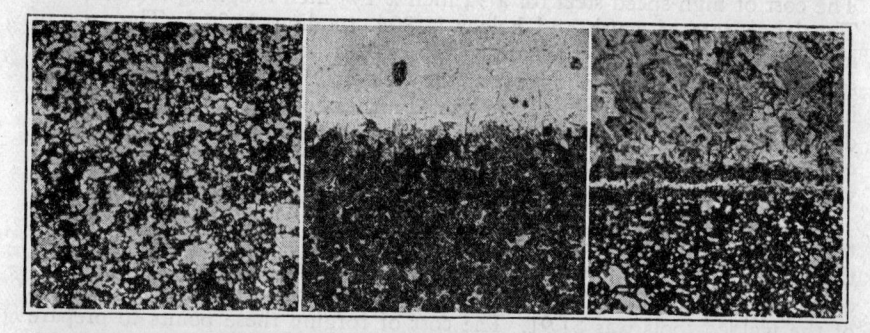

Fig. 18. (left) Microphotograph showing grain structure of welded joint in high-speed steel and bronze **Fig. 19.** (center) Grain structure of welded joint using high-speed steel and stainless steel. **Fig. 20.** (right) Microphotograph of area back of heat effected zone in high-speed steel.

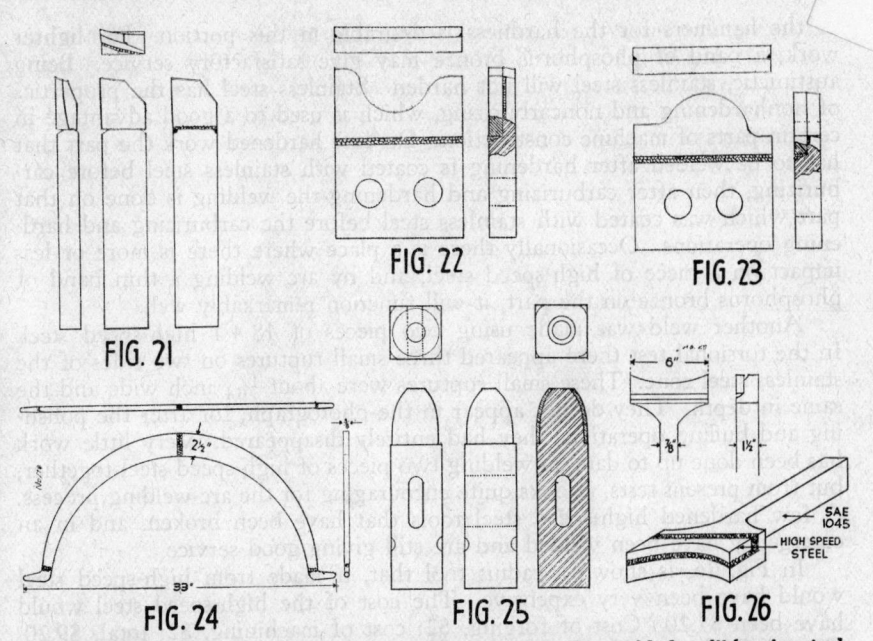

Fig. 21. Lathe side facing tool of welded design. **Fig. 22.** Arc welded radii-forming tool. **Fig. 23.** Radii-forming tool of design similar to that shown in Fig. 22. **Fig. 24.** Snap gauge, are welded in center and at tips. **Fig. 25.** Toolsmith set hammer with bonded head of stainless steel. **Fig. 26.** Welded radius tool.

are clamped in a tool post that is used for scores of finishing tools with various contours and radii. It requires four tools for the set. The cost of high-speed steel for these would have been $15.70. The cost of S. A. E. 1045 steel was 50¢. Cost of high-speed steel, $3.40. Extra labor in machining to prepare for the high-speed steel plates was $3. The cost of welding the plates to the body of the forming tools was $2, totaling $8.40, making a total saving of $7.30. The main factor that prompted the use of the arc welding method was the discovery that no stock was available for the tools. To order the stock from the mill would delay the order three or four weeks. By using the method as stated, the tools were made immediately, and the order was shipped in record time, which is an all important factor during this war emergency.

In Fig. 24 is shown a snap gauge of unusual size. The material specified was carbon tool steel, but being unavailable it was finally made from S. A. E. 1045, with carbon tool steel arc welded on the tip end as illustrated. To simplify and make it easier to forge, it was forged in two pieces and arc welded in the center as indicated. Only the two small points were required to be hardened and ground to precision. There was a saving of $2 in labor and material, but again the main factor was a race against time.

In Fig. 25 is shown a toolsmith set hammer, which illustrates a head banded with stainless steel. When these set hammers are left soft on the head they are soon mushroomed, and if hardened they are liable to chip and injure some one, so arc welding a band of stainless steel was resorted to for longer life and safety. In preparing for the weld, the head of the set hammer is forged down a trifle. After the welding is completed, it is hardened on the head end and drawn to 750°F. Be careful not to weld tip end of the hammers for the hardness is desirable in this portion. For lighter work, a band of phosphorus bronze may give satisfactory service. Being austinictic, stainless steel will not harden. Stainless steel has the properties of nonhardening and noncarburizing, which is used to a good advantage in certain parts of machine construction. On case hardened work the part that has to be welded after hardening is coated with stainless steel before carburizing, then after carburizing and hardening the welding is done on that part which was coated with stainless steel before the carburizing and hardening operations. Occasionally there is a place where there is more or less impact on a piece of high-speed steel, and by arc welding a thin band of phosphorus bronze on the part, it will function remarkably well.

Another weld was made using two pieces of 18-4-1 high-speed steel. In the torsional test there appeared three small ruptures on two sides of the stainless steel zone. These small ruptures were about $\frac{1}{64}$ inch wide and the same in depth. They do not appear in the photograph, for after the polishing and buffing operations they had entirely disappeared. Very little work has been done up to date on welding two pieces of high-speed steel together, but from present tests, it looks quite encouraging for the arc welding process. A few hardened high-speed steel tools that have been broken, and in an emergency have been welded and are still giving good service.

In Fig. 26, is shown a radius tool that, if made from high-speed steel would have been very expensive. The cost of the high-speed steel would have been $5.20. Cost of forging, $2; cost of machining, $2; total, $9.20. Cost of S. A. E. 1045, 25¢; labor cost of burning out, 65¢; labor cost of machining high-speed steel plate preparatory to welding, 90¢. Cost of welding in high-speed plate to the tool, 75¢; total cost, $3.40; saving of $6.80.

It is a difficult task to give the cost data of welding these machine tools due to the fact that there are so many designs and sizes which vary the cost of each tool. But it is perfectly patent, especially to the tool engineer, that a material costing from 3 to 5¢ a pound, used to substitute a material costing fom 65 to 80¢, must represent a large saving. Besides, the cost of welding these tools would be a trifle more or less than the forged tool. Moreover, it is easier, and much more pleasant work than the smithing operation.

In welding these steels it requires clean and careful workmanship. The welder must be careful to avoid slag inclusion if good results are expected. It may impress some that it requires exceptional skill to produce a good weld, but the welding operation shown in Figs. 1 and 2 was the work of one having seven months' experience.

In view of the great savings made possible by arc welding, any concern using many tools and not equipped with a welding outfit, would profit by installing a welding unit which would pay for itself in a few months.

Chapter XVI—Oil Still Tubes

By L. V. HILE,

Welding Foreman, Phillips Petroleum Co., Borger Refinery, Phillips, Texas.

Subject Matter: The author describes a method of welding short ends on 4 and 5-inch 4-6% chromium 0.5% molybdenum tubes for oil stills. Full length tubes are reclaimed by arc welding new ends to replace the eroded and corroded ends. Design of annealing furnace is given including temperature data and comparative costs of new and reclaimed tubes. A saving of approximately $21,000 is claimed for the year 1941 through the use of welding.

L. V. Hile

Introduction—During the spring of 1940 it was decided that something must be done about an accumulation of some two hundred used 4—6 per cent chrome, .5 percent moly, 4 inch x 5 inch furnace tubes, so an experimental test was ordered. With the help of a metallurgist, tests were made and it was decided that these tubes could be reclaimed by arc welding.

Grading of Used Tubes—It was obvious that there would be more than one wall thickness or condition as this accumulation of tubes was from different stills. It was necessary to work out a method of grading. This work of grading the used tube was done by the inspection department. This department decided that the different grades would be identified by No. 2, No. 3, and No. 4; No. 2 and No. 3 to be used in cracking stills at about 800 pounds per square inch, and No. 4 to be used in reboiler furnaces at 300 pounds per square inch. Most of the wear from corrosion and erosion was at each end of the tube. The following method of grading was worked out:

No. 2 Condition—Calipered and marked for cutting and beveling; minimum wall thickness: .48 inch to .59 inch; maximum wall thickness: .62 inch; outside diameter of tube: 5 inches. Length of tube: 26 feet 0 inches, 27 feet 0 inches, 28 feet 0 inches, and 29 feet 0 inches. Chamfer both ends of 26 foot 0 inch and 27 foot 0 inch and weld ⅝ inch wall thickness tip on each end (2 feet 0 inches and 1 foot 6 inches L.G. respectively), cut ends of the 28 foot 0 inch and 29 foot 0 inch tube as per marking below, weld ⅝ inch wall tubing to make 30 foot 0 inch furnace tubes.

No. 3 Condition—Calipered and marked for cutting and beveling; minimum wall thickness: .39 inch to .47 inch; maximum wall thickness: .62 inch; outside diameter of tube: 5 inches. Length of tube: 26 feet 0 inches, 27 feet 0 inches, and 28 feet 0 inches. Chamfer both ends of these tubes and weld ½ inch wall tip on each end to make 30 foot 0 inch furnace tubes.

No. 4 Condition—Calipered and marked for cutting and beveling; minimum wall thickness: .31 inch to .38 inch; maximum wall thickness: .62 inch;

outside diameter of tube: 5 inches. Length of tube: 26 feet 0 inches, 27 feet 0 inches, and 28 feet 0 inches. Chamfer both ends of these tubes and weld ½ inch wall tip to make 30 foot 0 inch furnace tubes.

Marking of Tubes—All tubing will be marked with cold chisel where tubing is to be cut. A plain chisel mark will indicate that tube end is to be chamfered for welding, a plain chisel mark with "#" on short end (to be removed) will indicate that end is to be cut straight and the outside diameter machined to 5 inches to remove mill scale. Figs. 3 and 6 show how to stack tubes according to grades. Tubes are also numbered according to grade. Green paint indicates croloy No. 5 and red paint indicates croloy No. 3.

Description of Tips—All tips shall be cut from new (5 inch outside diameter) croloy No. 5 tubing. Tips for No. 2 grade tubes shall be cut from ⅝ inch wall tubing. No. 3 and No. 4 grade shall be cut from ½ inch wall tubing. The mill scale shall be machined from outside diameter of the ends to be rolled in headers, and chamfered end shall be reamed as per Fig. 1. Length of tips shall be cut 1 foot 0 inches, 1 foot 6 inches, and 2 feet 6 inches.

Fig. 2 shows tips stacked as per different grades.

Fig. 4 shows tip welded to tube with thermocouple in place.

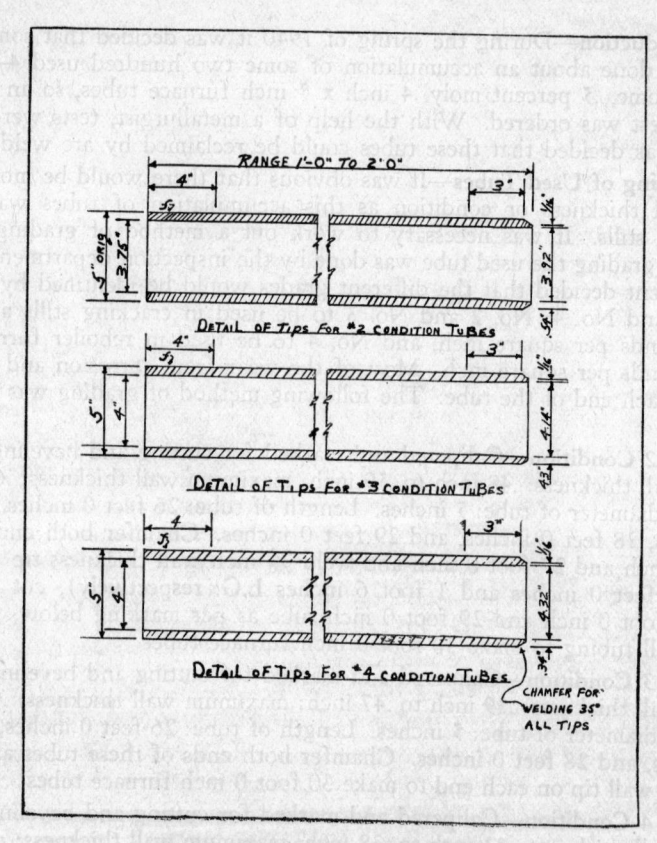

Fig. 1. Chamfered ends for welding.

ARC WELDING

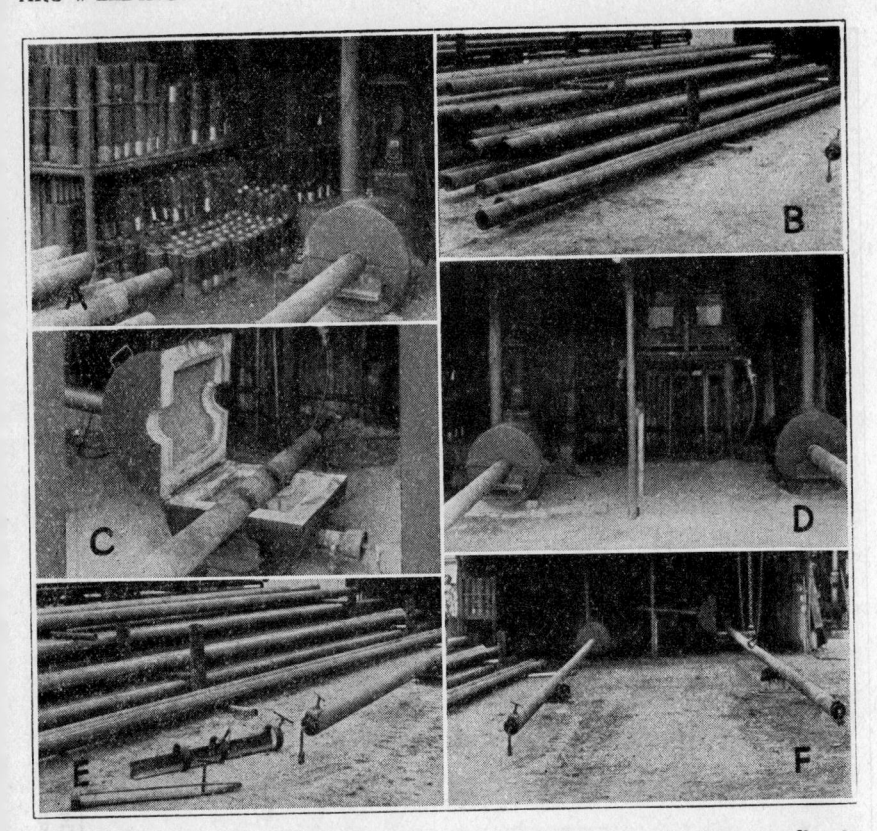

Fig. 2. (A) Tips stacked according to grades. Fig. 3. (B) How to stack tubes according to grades. Fig. 4. (C) Welding tip with thermocouple in place. Fig. 5. (D) Annealing furnaces closed for tip welding. Fig. 6. (E) Another view of stacking of grades. Fig. 7. (F) Method of supporting tubes in annealing oven.

Design of Furnace—The annealing oven was made something like a muffler type furnace as per drawing No. 8. This was made from two halves of a 24 inch pipe cut two feet long (Fig. 4). Angle iron pedestals were welded on bottom section and set in concrete. The top section was hinged to bottom section, openings were made in each end for tubes and a 4 inch pipe stack was installed in top half as per Figs. 5 and 7. A burner was made from a 4 inch x 2 inch swedge as per Fig. 8, and did very good. This was installed in the bottom section of the furnace at exact center of furnace on the lateral. This kept the fire from impinging on the alloy tube. The entire furnace was lined with three inches of "Insulcrete". This proved to be a very efficient annealing furnace and a second one was made to increase our production. Figs. 2, 5, and 7 show furnace with tubes in place.

Description of Jigs—Special jigs are quite necessary for this type of work. Fig. 13 shows details of thermocouple and stand to hold same. Fig. 10 shows details of copper back up ring. This proved to be very successful as it kept the inside of the tube smooth while arc welding first bead. Figure 12 shows

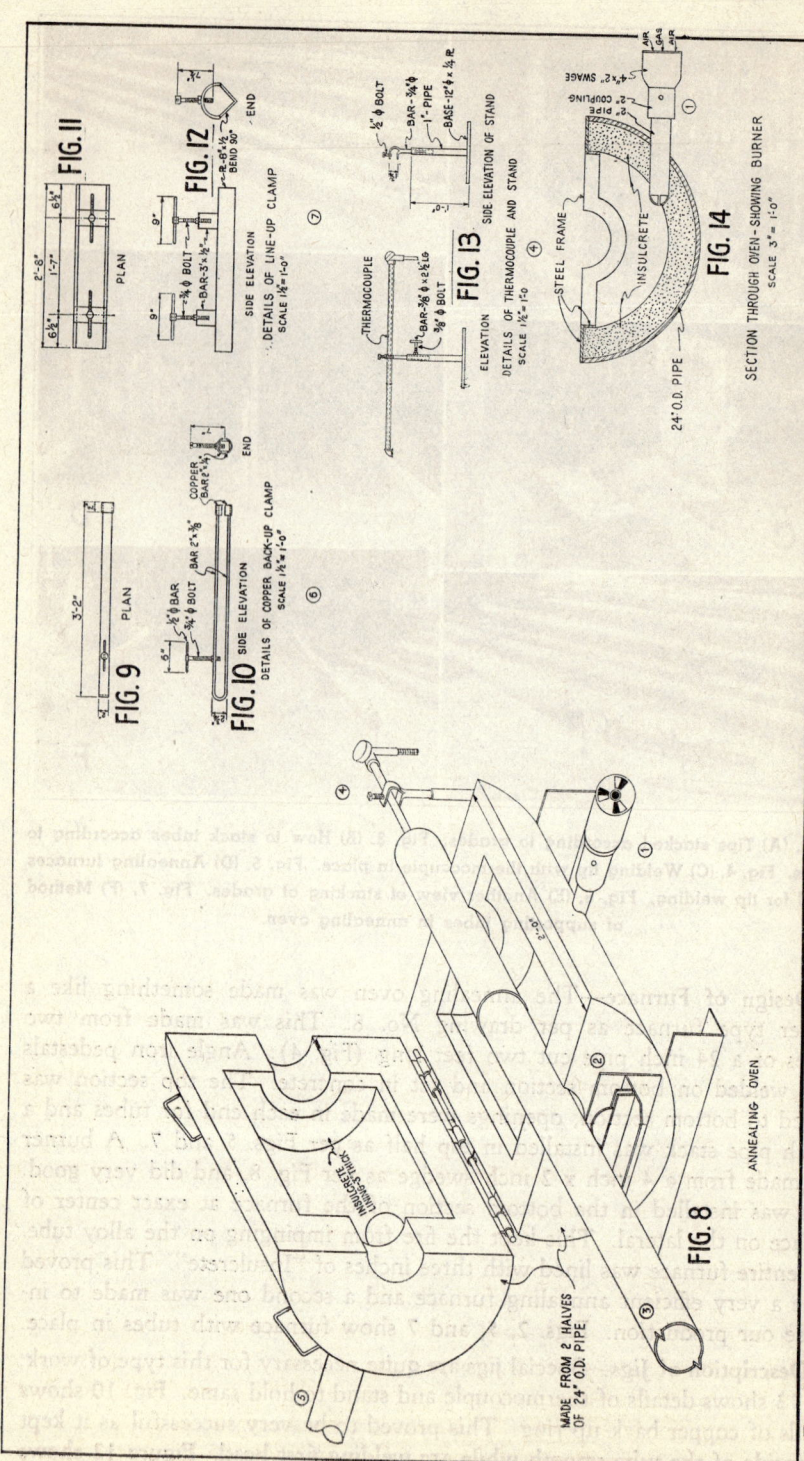

Fig. 8. Annealing oven. Fig. 9. Copper back-up clamp (top). Fig. 10. Details of copper back-up clamp. Fig. 11. Top view of line-up clamp. Fig. 12. Line-up clamp detail. Fig. 13. Elevation and stand of thermocouple. Fig. 14. Section through oven showing burner.

line up clamp, which is very necessary to obtain perfect alignment and proper 1/8 inch spacing of tube and tip. In Fig. 12 there is also shown a ground clamp in end of tube. This clamps to end of tube and used bearing assembly is installed so that ground wire will hang in one position while tube is being turned for welding. Bearings are kept well oiled to prevent balls from arcing, also it prevents ground from arcing tube.

Welding Procedure—The following welding procedure was worked out with the aid of our metallurgist (Figs. 4 and 5):
Preheat time: 600°F.—650°F., 15 minutes.
Weld time: No. 2 condition tubes, 30 minutes.

With tube in furnace line up clamps are installed with 1/8 inch opening between tube and tube tip. The thermocouple is removed and copper back up ring installed. Tack welds are made at three equal spaces, tacks cleaned, and line up clamp removed; first bead is then welded with 1/8 inch 4—6 per cent chrome welding rod. Copper back up ring is then removed, thermocouple reinstalled, and the first bead thoroughly cleaned with light air scaling hammer before continuing with the welding operation. On No. 2 condition tube it will take four more beads with 5/32 inch rod to complete weld. Temperature will drop about 100°F. while welding first bead and then move up to 700°F.—750°F. when weld is completed. Fire must be cracked under tube while welding. Welder will be protected with asbestos paper across fire in front of him.

Heat is now brought up to 1370° F.
(We use 1370° F. to stay on safe side of 1425° F., which is critical temperature)—30 minutes
Heat is held on 1370° F. on a straight line on recording instrument—30 minutes
Heat is reduced to 900° F.—Slow—30 minutes
    Entire time requires 2 hours and 14 minutes

All temperatures are recorded on a strip chart potentiometer (Figs. 4 and 5). When weld is cool enough it is stenciled with welder's stencil, also a heat number. These are marked on recording instrument chart and filed for reference. The engineering department also takes a Brinell test on one out of approximately twenty-five tubes as a check on keeping this work on proper procedure. The Brinell is kept around 170 to 180 and feel safe up to 200 Brinell.

The Cost of Welding Per Tip—The cost would seem somewhat high, however the extra time used to insure carrying out this work in accordance with the exact procedure set up is well justified. A new tube would cost $137.28 and the welded tube takes the place of a new one. The savings made justifies the extra time put on this work to get it right.

Cost of Welding Based on One Foot—0-inch Tip

Labor—
    2 1/4 Hours Welder's Time..........................$ 2.68
    2 1/4 Hours Helper's Time........................... 1.98
    Inspector's Time .... .50
    Pipe Machine Operator's Time.................... .50
    Cut, Bevel, and Ream Tip (Lathe
        Operator).. 2.25 $ 7.91

Material—
    1'—0", 5" x 4" Tip........................$ 4.58
    1#—4—6% Chrome Welding Rod............. .35
    Electricity .... .02 $ 4.95 $ 12.86

No. 2 Condition Tubes Retipped (1 Tip)

Cost of New Tube		$137.28
Less: Depreciation of Reclaimed Tube....$37.28		
Retipping Cost................ 12.86		
Junk Value 7.50	57.64	
Net Saving per Tube................	79.64	
78 Tubes Reclaimed at $79.64............		$6,211.92

No. 3 and No. 4 Condition Tubes Retipped (2 Tips)

Cost of New Tube...............		$137.28
Less: Depreciation of Reclaimed Tube....$41.18		
Retipping Cost................ 25.72		
Junk Value 7.50	74.40	
Net Savings per Tube................	62.88	
234 Tubes Reclaimed at $62.88............		$14,713.92
Total Net Savings		$20,925.84

With two gas fired furnaces (Fig. 5), time is gained by having tip and tube lined up, when welded tube is on last fifteen minutes of reducing temperature, the new tube is started on preheat time.

In 1941, 312 alloy retipped tubes were installed on our stills; as these retipped tubes took the place of new 4—6 percent chrome tubes, a saving from this work was estimated at close to $20,925.84. This saving was made possible by following a very definite procedure and was one of the outstanding savings in our plant.

Increased service life and social advantages from the use of arc welding 4—6 percent, 4 inch x 5 inch x 30 feet 0 inch chrome tubes are many. One very important advantage is that it releases a very valuable alloy to be used in war work and still permits carrying on the never ending battle against corrosion and erosion caused by West Texas Crude.

Acknowledgement

In closing this paper I want to thank the following men for their help and encouragement as their strong belief in arc welding was a very valuable tool in carrying out this work.

Mr. C. C. Tate, Chief Engineer, for his zeal and encouragement that this work could be done.

Mr. M. E. Holmberg, of the Engineering Department, in working out the metallurgical procedure.

Mr. L. M. Coburn, my immediate superior, for the help he gave the welding department in bringing this work to a successful conclusion.

Mr. A. Sweeney, Chief Inspector, for the help he gave on grading of the tubes.

Chapter XVII—Power Generating Station

By R. C. Fitzgerald,

Welding Engineer, Consolidated Gas Electric Light & Power Co. of Baltimore, Md.

Subject Matter: The place and importance of arc welding in power plant maintenance is stressed in this paper and proper control such as supervision and procedures are emphasized. Several instances of repairs effected by welding are given which include repairing a leak in an economizer tube, manifold, resurfacing induced draft fans and reinforcing a badly corroded smoke stack by welding rings of angles longitudinally inside. No comparative cost data are furnished of stack repairs but for the other three jobs a saving of $31,459.90 is claimed as a result of welding over alternative methods.

R. C. Fitzgerald

If there is any field where the welding art has been obliged to prove its worth thoroughly, it is the field of power generation. The reason for this is that dependability and useful life of equipment used in power generation must be predictable within very close limits and any design or construction method that is not proved either by good hard engineering tests or by experience cannot be used. The costs of unforeseen outages are not only large in dollars and cents but also costly from the standpoint of company customer relationship. So it is that power plant operating engineers and those responsible for maintenance are among the world's most particular people as regards to the workmanship and materials in equipment that is used in their power houses.

For some years welding of any kind was decidedly unpopular in power generation circles owing to its general unreliability and the so-called "human element" involved. However, when welding was able to demonstrate its worth and reliability, it was at once adopted by power companies. Welding has been and is being used very extensively not only in the construction of turbines, boilers, piping and auxiliaries, but also in the maintenance of that equipment after installation.

Although quality is a prime requisite in power plant welding, very often on maintenance jobs time is also of the essence. The time necessary to weld a given job has to be vey carefully estimated, and the estimate lived up to on the job. This is particularly true of shutdown jobs when the work must be done and the equipment back in operation in a specified time.

Another aspect of welding in power house maintenance is the variety of materials and shapes to be welded. Metals that are repaired and not infrequently welded range from copper and its alloys to special steels of the stainless and heat resisting types. This variety of materials necessitates a very flexible welding procedure or perhaps a greater variety of welding procedures than a welding program involving fewer metals. For this type of work, it is necessary to "know a little about a lot." With the advent of higher steam pressures and temperatures in our power plants, the use of special steels has increased manifold, and the necessity for welding these steels has correspondingly increased.

In welding for power plant maintenance work, as elsewhere, one of the first requirements for the most efficient use of welding is a well-organized and trained personnel. This means not only skilled welding operators and good equipment but adequate supervision. The trend in many industries to regard welding only as a supplemental tool has a tendency to lessen its effectiveness. This is true because foremen of various work groups within an organization who have welders working in their groups often know little or nothing about the work the welder does. This, in effect, leaves the entire responsibility for the welding he does up to the individual welder with the result that his limited knowledge and experience often get him in difficulties that could have been eliminated by adequate supervision. There are aspects of the welding art which makes it every bit as much a separate trade or art as are pipe fitting or carpentering, yet very often the welding in a work group is delegated to the "handy man" with no supervision beyond his immediate foreman. The answer to this situation is to make all welders responsible to a welding foreman as regard to the quality of their work and the welding procedures employed. In this way, the entire maintenance program will receive the benefit of uniform procedures and direct responsibility.

Procedure in Welding for Maintenance—Maintenance work in power houses can be roughly divided into two classes:

1. Repair of unforeseen failures which may or may not cause a shutdown of operating equipment.
2. Repair of failures or worn parts found during routine inspection of equipment which has been shut down for the purpose of general overhaul.

By far the greater part of maintenance work is in the second classification.

However the work originates, it is the job of the plant engineer and his maintenance organization to get the work done right and in as short a time as possible so that the equipment can go "back on the line" on the hour it is required. If welding is indicated, the plant engineer calls the welding foreman in on the job to decide, first, if the job is weldable; second, how it should be welded.

In deciding weldability and welding procedure, the welding foreman considers the following:

1. **Weldability of materials**

   The question of weldability of materials is of especial importance in power house maintenance work. Very often the analysis of materials that must be welded is unknown and material which looks like one thing can very easily be something else. Here the welding foreman is called upon to exercise his judgment in deciding weldability. Where it is possible, the nature of the materials is decided by some quick test such as: sparking with an emery wheel, acid attack, magnetic properties, or chipping the metal and observing the nature of the chip. Very often the behavior of the metal under the arc or torch is a very good indicator of the analysis. Any one or a combination of these quick tests enable the foreman to predict weldability with a fair degree of certainty.

2. **Availability of the weld**—Almost as important as weldability of the materials to be welded is the availability of the welding job. By availability is meant the ease with which a weld can be seen, reached, and welded. Equipment in power houses is very often inaccessible in the extreme. Before any weld can be made, the welder must have room to see his weld and room to perform the maneuvers necessary to make the weld. Very often welds must be made under the most adverse circumstances, and it is the foreman's function to decide the possibilities of obtaining an adequate weld. Considerable ingenuity must often be used in "tight places."

Usually in maintenance work it is not possible to choose the position of welds that must be made, but where it is possible, the welding foreman is always consulted on where the welds can be made to the best advantage.

3. **Welder personnel**—After deciding the weldability and availability of the weld to be made, the only other variable to be settled is the selection of the welding operator who does the job. Here the choice is a matter of the conditions under which the weld is to be made and the characteristics of the men available to do the welding. Some welders seem to perform better when the job is hard, and conversely some welders "can't cut it" when welding conditions are not entirely to their liking. Some men can crawl into a tight place and make a good weld while other men who could perform as well under ordinary circumstances, or perhaps even better, will in the same place turn out an unsatisfactory job. Also, some men get the knack of making one type of weld better than others can. These characteristics are important in choosing the man to do a particular job, and it behooves the foreman to know his men and their work under all conditions.

4. **Welding Process**—Having settled the three questions discussed above, the matter of welding process follows more or less automatically. The process selected, of course, is that which will give the best weld in the shortest period of time. Whether the process is gas or arc depends on the materials to be welded, their size and shape, location, and analysis. Other variables of the welding process such as weld preparation, welding rod or electrode are settled in the choice of the process.

SUMMARY OF ARC WELDED MAINTENANCE JOBS FOR THE PERIOD 1940-1941

Many people are aware of the great advances in boiler design and construction that are attributable in a large part to the strides made in the welding art. However, few people realize how much the use of welding has stream-lined maintenance, as well as construction.

The welding jobs that are described herein are only a few of the jobs done during a two-year period of operating and maintaining steam generating equipment of approximately 276,000 kw capacity.

Along with the description of the welding job, a cost comparison will be made with the alternative method of making the repair. Cost data on the alternative method are estimated on the basis of experience with similar jobs in the past.

Labor costs are calculated on a basis of the average mechanic's wage for the two-year period, 1940 to 1941, plus 15 percent for supervision, insurance, etc.

Material costs are based on known costs of materials used or on estimated quantities that would have been used if welding had not been possible.

The costs of idle equipment are much more serious to a power company than are the costs of maintaining the equipment. The value or cost of outage for generating equipment varies throughout the year with each piece of equipment and is accurately known for any period of time. Factors influencing these costs for a given period are:

1. Peak load or kw demand
2. Average kwh load
3. Availability and cost of power from "tied in" electrical systems

These factors are weighed in with depreciation and retirement charges, and the value of the equipment at any time is so determined.

1. **Emergency Repair to Economizer Tube**—A faulty tube in an economizer element of a high pressure boiler had developed a leak and the boiler had to be shut down. The leak occurred at the end of the economizer unit where it was easily available for repair. Repair was made by chipping out the crack and welding with a mild steel electrode. See Fig. 2.

The total time for making this repair did not exceed one hour, and the cost in man hours was about $2.30.

As an alternative to welding the leak, it would have been necessary to cut the economizer unit off at both the injection and the exit headers and weld blanks into the stub ends. This remedy would have eliminated the leak, but it would also have reduced the margin of extra capacity in the economizer in addition to destroying an economizer unit. To cut and repair weld the stub ends at the headers would have required an additional day shutdown on the boiler.

Cost of welded repair

Labor cost .... $ 2.30
Shutdown cost on boiler for 38 hrs........ 828.00

Total cost $830.30

Estimated cost of alternative method

Labor cost .... $ 18.40
Shutdown cost on boiler for 60 hours.. 1,386.00
Replacement value economizer unit—
$295.00 .... 295.00

$1,699.40

II. **Repair to Steam Manifold**

A forge-welded steam manifold that had been in service for some years had developed a number of leaks. This manifold was used as a distributing header for the main generating units, and steam driven auxiliaries. With the header out of service, the whole generating station had to be shut down.

Upon examination of the equipment, it was decided to replace it with a modern fusion welded manifold, but in the meantime it was necessary to keep the station in operation. To this end a further examination was made to determine the nature of the cracks and find means of repair that would insure the header until it could be replaced.

Fig. 1. (left) Repair of economizer element. Defective tube chipped out ready for welding.
Fig. 2. (center) Repair to steam manifold. Fig. 3. (right) Repair to induced draft fans.

The extent of the cracks was determined by magnetic examination. Then the cracks were chipped out and welded. (See Fig. 1). In addition to welding the chipped cracks, pads of welded metal were added transverse of the crack location to act as reinforcing straps.

After repairing, the manifold was placed in service and gave no further trouble until it was replaced some weeks later.

This repair served to maintain the service of approximately 70,000 kw of generating capacity.

Since there was no alternative to arc welding the manifold, there is no comparison to be made with any other method of repair. However, the savings effected by this temporary repair are important, and are approximated in the following:

The shortest estimated time for replacing this manifold was from 20 to 30 days. The header was designed for 600 lbs., 700° F. steam and was 25 inches outside diameter, about 14 feet long with five sixteen-inch Van Stone necks.

Use value of the generating station for a 20-day period............................$14,320.00

Cost of outage for repair plus cost of repair 368.00

Although 20 days was the minimum estimate used to determine the outage cost of this job, it is probable that the time would have run much more. It was necessary to design and fabricate the manifold under the rules of the Boiler Code, and this entails heavy reinforcement of the necks and stress-relief of the entire vessel, all of which adds to the time of fabrication.

III. **Repairs to Induced Draft Fans**—This repair is not strictly an arc welded repair, but it is felt that arc welding played such an important role in making the repair possible and later in repairing "the repair job" that its description here is warranted.

In one generating station the steam capacity of two boilers was increased about 16 percent by improving boiler circulation and slagging conditions in the furnace.

This increase in boiler capacity meant that the present boiler auxiliaries had to carry more load.

Under the old boiler ratings, the induced draft fans which carry the products of combustion from the boilers to the stacks lasted about one year as they were then constructed. Each time the boilers were shut down for general overhaul, the rotor blades were replaced or repaired in place.

It was found in operating the induced draft fans at the new boiler ratings that the blades were dangerously eroded after an operating period of three months. The increased volume of the products of combustion, and the increased speed of the fans had so accelerated the rate of erosion on the mild steel rotor blades that the fans were considered unsafe to operate beyond the three-month period. (See Fig. 3).

To change a fan rotor involves a shutdown of at least eight days, and this would have meant that each of the two boilers would be shutdown for fan changes at least three times during the year, the fourth change coming during the general overhaul period.

In order to increase the life of the fans it was decided to weld on to the blades wearing plates of abrasion-resisting material. It was found that a thin layer of hard surfacing material could be applied to an appropriately shaped thin plate, and this in turn welded to a rebuilt fan rotor.

Hard surfacing material was applied to the thin steel plates in such a manner as to reduce distortion and dilution of the hard material to minimum. The wearing plates were then heated to 1,700° F. in a gas-fired furnace and straightened. After straightening, the plates were cooled slowly and then welded on to the fan rotor.

Due to the necessity of keeping the thin plates as flat as possible during welding, it was not feasible to use arc welding for the deposition of the hard surfacing material. However, other characteristics of the arc welded deposit were superior to the method used and longitudinal cracks in the deposits were repair welded with the arc both in the new installations and in the fans, after service wear had shown bad spots. Arc welding is the only possible means of repair welding the hard surface deposit with the wearing plates installed in the fan rotors.

In welding the wearing plates to the fan blades it was necessary to produce joining welds of proper shape to give the best lines of flow for the gases during operation of the fan. This was done by the selection of the proper type of welding electrode, and by the proper positioning of the rotor during welding.

Although it was necessary to repair weld some of the hard facing on the first installation that had been applied incorrectly, (except for the few hours necessary to make this repair), this first installation has been in service for seven months and still has many more months of wear in it. It is anticipated that the hard surfaced wearing plates will increase the useful life of these induced draft fans about four times. In other words, the rotors need be changed only once a year instead of four times as indicated by the wear after three months' operation.

Although the repair in itself is an expensive one, the saving in operating time for the two boilers more than justifies the additional cost.

Cost of hard surfacing fan blades (One boiler)

Labor charges for hard surfacing and installing wearing plates ....$ 552.60

Cost welding materials................................ 328.50

Total cost $881.10

For two boilers the cost of this job is....$1,762.20

Cost of replacement of fan rotors for three periods—aside from annual shutdown for general overhead (One boiler)

<table>
<tr><td>Labor costs for three jobs of reblading and installing rotors</td><td>$2,226.40</td></tr>
<tr><td>Cost of replaced fan blades</td><td>85.68</td></tr>
<tr><td>Cost of four days' shutdown on boiler (working two shifts to replace rotors) 3 x 4 x $574.00</td><td>$6,888.00</td></tr>
<tr><td>Total cost</td><td>$9,200.08</td></tr>
</table>

For two boilers the cost of this job is..$18,400.16

IV. Repair to Smoke Stacks

The two stacks at one of the company's generating stations are fabricated of steel and are not lined.

During some years of operation, considerable corrosion had taken place throughout the inside of the stacks and especially at the lapped section joints. Inspection of the plate thickness indicated that the stacks should either be replaced or reinforced.

Fig. 4. Stack repair.

From an operating standpoint it would have been better to have replaced the stacks at this time, but due to the high system load it was not economical to shut the station down for the length of time necessary to wreck the stacks and build new ones. In addition, it would have been necessary to make changes in the boilers and flues, that would have kept the station out of service for an even longer time.

The stacks were reinforced by placing three-inch angles longitudinally around the inside periphery at appropriate intervals. The lapped section joints were reinforced where necessary by placing annular channel sections above the joints as indicated in Fig. 6.

In considering means for joining these reinforcement members to the stack, welding was obviously the only practical method. If riveting had been considered, it would have been necessary to supply cover plates for the internal angle bracing. This would have added considerably to the weight of steel used, also riveting would have necessitated more time and expense for field layout and drilling of rivet holes.

This stack repair was accomplished within the time allotted for another repair job on the boilers and did not add to the shutdown time.

Cost data on reinforcing the two stacks are not available, and since the repair was made during an outage for other reasons, there are no outage costs chargeable against this job. However, this repair is estimated to have increased the useful life of the stacks by two or three years and that fact is important at a time when power is as vital as it is today.

Conclusion

Totaling the costs for the three maintenance repairs where cost analyses were made, the following represents the net saving attributable to arc welding:

Costs of alternative methods of repair.. $34,419.56
Costs of welded repairs................................ 2,959.60
$31,459.90

The maintenance jobs represented in the figures above are only a few of the maintenance repairs that have involved welding and have saved considerable time and money. Almost every day jobs are welded, which, if analyzed from a cost standpoint, would show savings as remarkable as those discussed above. The repairs chosen for description were chosen because they showed the unique way that arc welding has solved so many of the problems of power house maintenance.

Arc welding in maintenance repair used to be a resort and usually the last resort. Today arc welding is the first thing to be considered, and it generally provides the answer.

Chapter XVIII—Railway Bridge

By A. M. KNOWLES,

Assistant Engineer of Structures, Erie Railroad Co., Cleveland, Ohio.

Subject Matter: Repairing and strengthening steel bridges by welding vs. riveting. Salt brine dripping from refrigerator cars aids materially in the corrosion of structural steel members of bridges, thereby weakening these structures and lowering their factor of safety. Paper describes welding repairs to floor beams, deck girders, trusses, loose eye bars, etc. Estimated that company saves about from $12,000 to $15,000 annually by arc welding rather than riveting in new sections. Welding has added advantage of having less corrosion from the salt brine than they had formerly with the highly stressed rivet beads.

A. M. Knowles

Preface

Salt brine which drips from refrigerated cars loaded with fruit, packing products and other perishable commodities handled in large numbers by railroads is a very destructive agent to steel. It is spouted out of the cars in such a way that it does not contact the steel underframe and running gear of cars very much and is dropped about one foot outside of the track rails. To some extent it is blown and spattered on the rails and their fastenings causing some deterioration but it also, to a greater extent, drops onto the steel work of open floor railroad bridges and causes corrosion and deterioration in their main and secondary members below the track level. (Fig. 1)

Although extensive research and experimentation with many types of paint and other protective coatings have been made, nothing has been found effective for a reasonable time against the destructiveness of the brine. Therefore the loss in section of all or parts of bridge members, such as stringers, floor beams, deck girders and trusses and even the lateral bracing becomes so great in time as to materially reduce their strength resulting in excessive and unsafe unit stresses under the locomotive and train loading which they carry.

Any repairs made to these corroded and deteriorated bridge members must be carried out with as little interruption to railroad traffic and train schedules as possible. The heavier the traffic the more difficult and expensive is the application of repairs.

In some cases, old bridges are so highly stressed under modern traffic, not considering any loss of section of their members, that it is necessary to either replace them with modern bridges or reinforce them to provide the required strength. In many such cases, and especially when many members in the bridge became reduced in section, it was the custom fifteen years or more ago not to consider strengthening them but to renew complete bridges.

If repairs were made, deteriorated parts of or whole members of a bridge

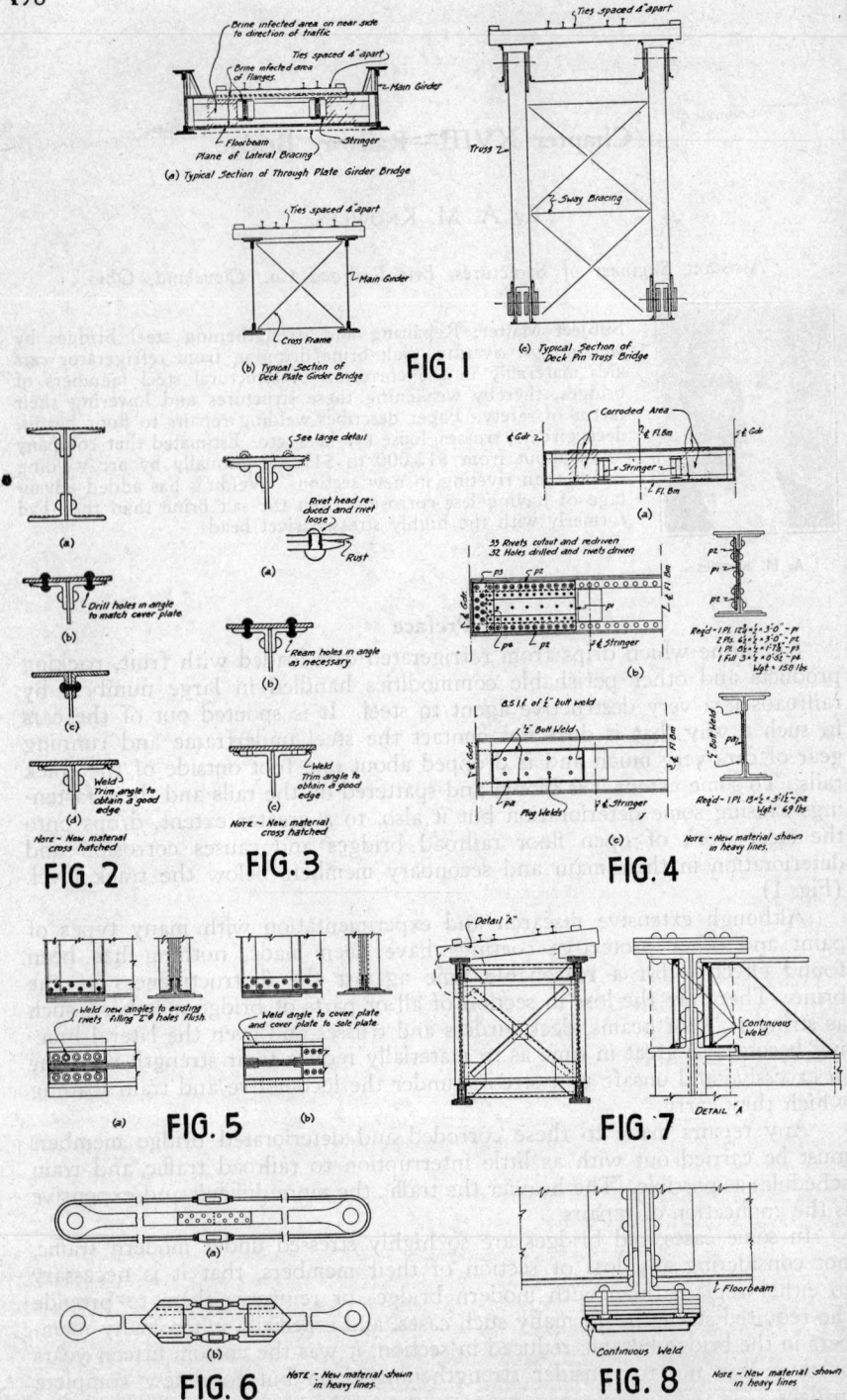

Fig. 1. Top flanges, deck girders and trusses. Fig. 2. Riveting method and weld of girders. Fig. 3. Comparisons of rivet and weld. Fig. 4. Welding methods for floor beams. Fig. 5. Girder bearing. Fig. 6. Shortening loose eye bars. Fig. 7. Deck girder strengthening. Fig. 8. Cover plates over old plates.

were renewed. This sometimes required the use of extensive falsework and in all cases there were many rivets to be cut out, deteriorated parts removed, new parts installed and reriveted. When complete reliable records of shop details of steel work were available the new members or parts of members could be prefabricated and a fairly good fit would result. Sometimes, however, unreliable or no records were available and the repair steel was either brought to the job unpunched and placed on the old parts retained as a template and drilled to match the holes in these old parts; or, if field measurements of rivet spacing was made to permit prefabricated new parts, the latter method frequently resulted in much mismatching of holes.

In early bridge construction the location of punched holes in structural iron and steel on exact gauge lines and spacing was less accurate than is the practice in more recent years. Rivet heads also were not always driven concentric with their shanks and, if they are unevenly reduced very much from corrosion, it is extremely difficult to determine accurately the spacing of rivet holes before rivets are cut out. These methods were slow but when electric arc welding came into accepted use the repairing and strengthening of old bridges was simplified and expedited in many respects.

Comparison of Riveting and Welding Methods

I. **Stringer Repairs**—Stringers are usually made up of I-beams or a web plate and two flange angles, top and bottom, with or without cover plates. The effect of brine extends over the upper surfaces and is most severe on the outer edges of the top flanges and, when no cover plates exist, the width of flanges is materially reduced and the edges become wedge shaped and scalloped. (Fig. 2a) Where cover plates exist the deterioration affects both the plates and the outer edges of the angles and frequently excessive thickness of rust is built up between the cover plates and angles and extends to the rivets connecting them. In such cases the rivet holes are frequently enlarged and the heads and shanks of rivets are reduced and become ineffective. (Fig. 3a)

Riveting Method—There are two common ways of making repairs using the riveting method when there are no cover plates: First, drill rivet holes in the horizontal legs of the old angles to match prepunched plates and rivet the plates to the angles. (Fig. 2b). This can be only done if the reduction in the angles both on upper surfaces and edges is not too great. Tight rivets cannot be driven when angle surface in contact with the plates is pitted very irregularly and the width of remaining flange angles must be sufficient to provide adequate edge distance for rivets. Usually the track rails are over the lines of rivets or nearly so which makes it necessary to move the rails to obtain good holes and rivets. (Fig. 1a) The second method is to renew the top flange angles cutting out and redriving rivets connecting them to web plates. (Fig. 2c) This also required the removing and replacing of angles connecting stringers to floor beams when they extend over the vertical legs of the flange angles unless there is enough space above the ends of the stringers under the top flanges of floor beams to permit removing and installing flange angles without fouling the floor beam flanges.

When there are cover plates and only their connecting rivets are badly reduced, the rivets may be redriven, but when plates are also badly reduced they should be renewed with prepunched plates and reriveted. (Fig. 2b)

In order to do the work above described, about half the ties are temporarily removed to provide room to do the work. The remaining ties are shifted back and forth as necessary to expose all the rivets. This requires temporary speed reductions of trains between, as well as during, working hours and slows up traffic considerably.

Welding Method—In the case of stringers without cover plates the wedged and scalloped edges of flange angles may be cut back with a burning torch to where there is thickness enough to take a good edge weld. Plain plates may then be placed on the flanges and continuous fillet welds run along the cut edges of the angles attaching the plates and at the same time sealing any space between the angles and plates due to unevenness of the top surface of old flange angles. (Fig. 2d)

In the case of stringers with cover plates, if the plates are suitable to retain, the feather edges of the angles and plates may be trimmed back as necessary and continuous fillet welds run along the edges of the angles as above described. If the plates require renewal they should be removed and flange angles cut back and new plain plates applied and welded as described above. (Fig. 3c) This repair leaves no rivets above the plates to corrode and require redriving later. In order to do this work it is not necessary to remove any ties or shift them sideways. All that is necessary is to raise the complete track and deck intact with track jacks between the passage of trains to insert cover plates on the stringers and then let the track and deck down in normal position. The flame cutting and welding is done from below. In this way, there is very little if any interruption of railroad traffic for repair work. Similar treatment is applicable if stringers are composed of I-beams.

Deck Girders and Trusses—The section of girders and trusses are much greater than that of stringers, and a loss of the same thickness of metal as that in the small section of the stringers does not weaken them as much, requiring much less attention for repairs from corrosion except the rivets.

It is frequently necessary to cut out and redrive the rivets connecting cover plates to the top flange angles of girders and upper angles in top chords of trusses on account of the loss of heads from corrosion. If, however, these rivet heads are not allowed to become reduced in size too much or become loose, they may be built up with weld metal at much less cost than to redrive them. The heads built up with weld metal will outlast many years the original or redriven rivets.

II. Floor Beam Repairs—Floor beam sections are usually made up of a web plate, two flange angles and one or more cover plates. The brine drip attacks the upper surfaces of the top flanges most severely and the web plates next and the bottom flanges lastly. (Fig. 4a)

Riveting Method—The usual repair by riveting is to remove the only or outer plate on the top flange and replace it with new material. (See Fig. 4b) A patch plate is usually attached to the web plate covering the full depth between top and bottom flange angles and with a length sufficient to extend beyond the deteriorated area and splice onto good old material. This extends sometimes from the floor beam connection to the stringer connection. That the patch plates may function properly, splice plates are connected over their edges and the vertical legs of the flange angles, and when necessary, similar splice plates are applied over the end connections of the floor beams, stringers and patch plates. This involves drilling new holes for rivets in the old web plate and providing matching splice and patch plates and cutting out and redriving rivets in flange and connection angles.

Repairs to the bottom flange when needed may be made by either applying a patch plate on the upper side of horizontal legs by removing and redriving rivets or, when vertical leg of flange angles is too poor, apply another angle over them or remove all or sections of old angles and set in new ones with splices as required.

Welding Method—To repair floor beams by welding, apply a new plate over the upper plate in the top flange a little wider or narrower than old plates to take fillet weld. (See Fig. 4c) The new plate to have large enough holes to match and fit over old rivet heads. Weld rivet heads to plates filling holes to provide smooth surface to exclude brine and water and if desired to seal spaces between uneven surfaces of old plate and edges of new plate, run fillet seal weld along edges.

Another method is to remove a section of the old cover plate to just beyond the limits of its corroded and reduced area and insert a plain new plate, butt welding its ends to the ends of the old plate left in place and fillet weld new plate to old flange angles. If desired, the new plates may be attached to old flange angles by riveting, in which case the new plates should preferably be prepunched.

Repairs to the webs may be made by cutting a patch plate with beveled edges to fit in between top and bottom flange angles and connection angles of floor beams and stringers with the required clearance and butt weld all four sides to flange and connection angles. This leaves a smooth surface and no additional rivet heads to corrode.

Repairs to the bottom flanges may be made by placing a patch plate prepunched with large holes to fit over rivet heads in horizontal legs of flange angles and weld old rivet heads to new plate filling holes in plates full to exclude brine and water.

III. Special Details of Repairs—Girder Bearing—Occasionally the bottom flange angles of girders of deck and through bridges at points of bearings on bridge seats become broken in the roots of the angles from insufficient uniformity of surface of bridge seat concrete, due to it crumbling away under pounding of trains or to excessive loss of steel from the upper surfaces of the horizontal legs of angles from corrosion. In such cases the bottom of the girders are only a few inches above the bridge seats and are supported on bearing plates only about an inch thick. Consequently, there is not enough room without lifting the girder to redrive any vertical rivets connecting the flange angles to the cover and sole plates even if bearing plates are removed; for this reason, a wholly riveted job is not practicable.

In such cases, fair repairs can be made by applying a new angle the length of the bearing over each flange angle and connecting them by rivets through the vertical legs punched to match rivet holes in old flange angles. The horizontal legs of the patch angles are prepunched with large holes to go over old rivet heads. Weld old rivet heads to the new patch angles filling holes flush to exclude brine and water. It is also usually advisable to add stiffeners over the patch angles. These may be heavy plates welded directly to the web and flange angles of girders. (Fig. 5a)

A more substantial repair at these bearing points is to cut out the defective ends of the flange angles and splice in new angles. These may be connected to web plate and splice angles beyond the bridge seat by rivets, but the horizontal legs of the new angles may be easily connected to bottom cover plate, and cover plate to sole plate by fillet welds. (Fig. 5b)

Shortening Loose Eye Bars—Eye bars in pin connected truss bridges, and the pins to which they connect, often become badly worn at bearing points and consequently the bars become slack. All the bars in a group are in some cases so affected and in other cases only one or more are so affected.

To repair this by riveting, it is usually necessary to provide a riveted splice on the slack bar after cutting out a section of the bar to shorten it. The rivet holes in the bar which must be drilled in the field, reduce the section of the bar making it necessary to apply reinforcement to make up this loss. This is usually done by installing a looped bar over the heads of the shortened eye bar or directly on the pins if there is room for the new bar between the old eye bar. The looped bar has two turnbuckles to permit proper adjustment. (Fig. 6a)

This is a crude method of shortening bars. It is quite difficult to secure a proper shortening of the slack bars in this manner. It is not possible to predetermine the correct shortening necessary and is difficult to draw together the cut ends of the bars and hold them in position while the splice is being made. Furthermore, when splice is made it precludes any readjustments without complete change in splice.

A much simpler and satisfactory method of shortening slack eye bars is to weld two sets of plates across the two sides of the bar and about two or three feet apart, depending on the size of bar to be repaired. The plates should project enough beyond the edges of the bar to permit connecting two threaded turnbuckle stubs by welding, thus providing clearance for turning turnbuckles outside the bar. With the turnbuckles installed take a light strain on the newly installed device and cut a short section out of the eye bar and adjust the turnbuckles to secure the desired shortening of the bar. (Fig. 6b) This detail provides means for not only adjusting the length of the eye bars in the first instance but also at any later time.

Effect of Use of Welding on Costs of Bridge Repairs—A riveting gang usually consists of four men—a riveter, bucker up, heater and rivet sticker. The equipment required for riveting includes a compressor with gas engine drive, pipe and hose air line, riveting hammers, dollies, forge, drift pins, reamers, fitting up bolts, washers, cutting off chisels and rivet busters.

A welding gang usually consists of two men—a welder and helper. The equipment required for welding includes a 300 or 400 ampere gas engine driven welding unit, rubber covered copper cable, electrode holders, clamps and a burning outfit to clean the steel for welding.

Beside the riveting and welding gangs, about four more men are required for riveting gangs and two more for welding gangs to assemble and adjust any material to be applied and remove any old material to be discarded, etc. Temporary scaffolds are required for both classes of work but generally that for work done by riveting must be sturdier than for work done by welding. Steel frames or brackets to support scaffold planks are commonly used. They are temporarily welded to the bridges. This is found to be a very satisfactory, convenient and economical fastening.

While it is necessary to have riveting equipment to repair and strengthen riveted bridges, the work is expedited and the costs of repairs are reduced materially, if, with the riveting gangs a good welder and welding equipment are included, so that riveting or welding may be utilized to the best advantage. The welder should be able to rivet or do other work in the riveting gang when no welding work is required. Occasionally a whole repair job can be done by a welding gang without the assistance of riveting gang. The cost of such jobs is cut about half when done by welding.

The usual run of bridge repair work is of such a varied nature that the proportion of such work which can be done by either process cannot be estimated without considering each job separately. However a conservative estimate of the average saving, by use of the welding method for the past fifteen years, in the cost of such work done on the Erie Railroad with which the author is familiar, has increased gradually each year and within the last year amounts to about $15,000 on a $100,000 repair program. This averages about $7 per mile of railroad. If this average could be applied to all the principal railroads in the United States it would amount to an annual saving of about $1,500,000.

Strengthening Bridges to Carry Heavier Loads Than Existing Construction Permits—Floor systems of bridges are strengthened by the application of additional material about as described hereinbefore for repairing bridges, except that more material is applied and both flanges of stringers and floor beams are reinforced. The main girders of through or deck plate girder bridges can generally best be strengthened by addition of cover plates to their flanges. This can be done to good advantage in some cases by cutting out the rivets, adding new plates (sometimes in between the old plates) and reriveting. In other cases, welding on new material works out to a great advantage. A job illustrated by Fig. 7 is a typical case.

Deck Girder Strengthening—This is a 100-ft. double track deck girder span carrying two tracks on a curved alignment over several tracks of another railroad. Western Union telegraph lines and a canal. No space was available on the lower track level to place falsework to support the girders while being cut apart, reinforced and reriveted unless the tracks at the lower level were rearranged and consolidated. The reinforcement, instead of being added in cover plates on top and bottom of the two flanges of each girder, were added on the sides of the flanges between the upper and lower pair of flange angles in each flange of the girders. This made falsework unnecessary and, by preheating the new plates before welding them, they took initial dead load stress as soon as their ends were secured by weld. Thirty-six inches of new steel was added to each flange of one of the track spans and twenty-three inches to the other track span and the loading capacity was increased from Coopers E40 and E50, loading respectively, to E70 loading.

This bridge is located in a very busy section of the Erie Railroad and no interruption to railroad traffic here was important. As the tracks are on a 4 degree curve and superelevated 6 inches, the timber deck construction is heavy and cumbersome to move which would have been necessary if the strengthening had been done by riveting. The strengthening work, as carried out, was all below the track deck and did not interfere in the least with railroad traffic. The welding of the reinforcing plates was synchronized with train movements to insure the best welds possible. The cost of this job was $11,800 and to have done it by riveting, including the falsework if it could have been installed, would have cost $20,000. It probably would have been necessary, however, to replace the old spans with new ones with the required strength, which would have cost still more.

Through Girder Strengthening—Another illustration of the adaptation of welding where the riveting method could not be used is the strengthening of center girders carrying load from two tracks. The bridge spans a busy city street. The bridge floor consists of I-beams spaced 13 inch centers and rivet-connected to the web of the girders. A continuous floor plate carrying waterproofing, track ballast and tracks extends over the beams. This made access to bottom flanges of girders difficult. The bottom flanges of the beams are directly over the rivets in the horizontal legs of the bottom flange angles. For this reason these rivets could not be redriven if removed to apply cover plates by the riveting method.

The method adopted was that shown in Fig. 8 and consisted of attaching cover plates over the old plates. This required no falsework and did not interrupt railroad traffic. The working platforms hung under and from the bridge and only reduced the clear height over the street temporarily. A considerable saving in cost was made by the use of welding.

Viaduct Strengthening—Another example of the advantages of welding is the case of two viaducts. One 732-ft. long and 70-ft. high and the other 488-ft. long, 45-ft. high. They were built in 1876 of wrought iron throughout, and were limited in loading capacity to engines weighing 180,000 pounds and cars with gross weight of 120,000 pounds.

The plates and angles making up the major parts of the viaducts were one-quarter inch thick. Consideration had been given several times to reinforcing them to permit using heavier locomotives and cars but, on account of the frailness of the wrought iron members and the tendency for the laminations of the iron to separate, it was decided that to reinforce them by removing old rivets and riveting new material to the light wrought iron would damage the old material and an unsatisfactory job would result.

It was estimated to cost $167,000 to renew the viaducts which was a greater expenditure than could be justified. It was finally decided to reinforce them by welding new material onto the legs of the viaduct towers and renewing the stringers which were of such poor detail that they could not be reinforced. This was successfully done at a cost of $75,000 and permitted the use of locomotives weighing 344,600 pounds and cars weighing 200,000 pounds.

The structures have shown no sign of distress under this loading. Incidentally, a considerable annual saving was effected in operating costs by reason of the use of the heavier equipment.

Other examples of the advantages of welding could be cited but those mentioned here should suffice. There have been eleven bridges and viaducts on the Erie Railroad which have been reinforced by attaching new material by welding, costing $160,000. It is estimated that this is $100,000 less than it would have cost to have provided the required strength by riveting or rebuilding the structures as the cases might require.

Cost Savings—It is not possible to say with any degree of accuracy what the average yearly saving might be on the Erie Railroad or all the principal railroads in the United States to strengthen by the application of reinforcing material by welding to all light bridges to permit operation of heavier equipment, as the conditions and requirements are so different on various roads. It is not unreasonable to estimate that it would run into many millions of dollars if the examples cited are considered typical. The Erie Railroad Company has expended an average of $130,000 per year for the years 1927 to 1934 inclusive, and is spending $90,000 this year for this purpose. A conservative estimate of the savings in cost of the work by the use of the welding method so far as applicable is $12,000 to $15,000 per year. This year's saving will be near the latter figure.

Repairs and strengthening of railroad bridges by the attaching of new material by welding eliminates to a large extent one element of riveted work, i.e., rivet heads, which are more seriously attacked by brine than the main section of the bridge members. This is a great advantage and thus is a factor in prolonging the usefulness of the bridge.

Furthermore, many bridges repaired today by welding would have been rebuilt had not the art of welding been developed to the point where competent engineers have enough faith in its reliability to use it.

Chapter XIX—Corrosion Control in Refinery Pressure Vessels

By W. W. McClow,

Assistant General Maintenance Foreman, The Pure Oil Co., Toledo Refinery, Toledo, Ohio

Subject Matter: Corrosion control in refinery pressure vessels by means of arc welded stainless steel lining. Paper shows the economic advantages of extending the life of fractionating towers in gasoline refining by arc welding into these shells No. 12 BWG 12–14% chromium steel of 0.08% carbon. Steel strips are 4 inches wide, pickled and purchased on reels. Average cost per square foot per year of stainless steel liner is $0.33 as compared with carbon steel lining at $2.48 or a granite lining at $2.16.

W. W. McClow

The most common reason for installing stainless steel linings in refinery pressure vessels is to combat high temperature corrosion which is probably the most dreaded and the most destructive of all agencies tending to destroy or reduce the useful life of such equipment. Any vessel such as a fractionating tower, evaporator, accumulator, etc. which is subjected to such corrosion will ultimately be reduced to its minimum safe wall thickness for the pressures and temperatures involved. Unless some definite protection against corrosion is provided before this point is reached, the final result may be explosion and fire, accompanied by possible loss of life, extensive damage to other equipment, and a prolonged shutdown of the entire process unit.

The industry has tried various methods other than stainless steel linings for controlling corrosion. Among these are brick linings, cast concrete linings, various types of sprayed ganister and cement coatings (ordinarily known as gunite), various kinds of protective paints, sprayed molten metal coatings, chromium plating, and welded carbon steel linings. Experience with several of these methods and investigation of the remaining ones have revealed that from standpoints of economy, durability, and prolonged corrosion resistance, they are not to be compared with the much superior arc welded stainless steel linings now used so extensively throughout the industry.

Stainless linings are often installed in new vessels at the time of fabrication. Obviously this is the most economical procedure, not only because the surface is clean but also because all welding can be performed downhand and the welders can work unhampered by such obstructions as trays, baffles, and other accessories with which such equipment is often fitted. While this method is preferable where it can be applied, it has no application in the extensive use of field welded linings in existing vessels which are approaching their minimum safe wall thickness. The installation of a lining in such a vessel often provides the choice between completely renewing the vessel at an enormous capital investment or prolonging the life of the old one for an unlimited period of time.

Fig. 1. Plan view of bottom head.

The present standard adopted in our plant for vessel linings is a No. 12 BWG (0.109-inch thick) 12-14 percent chromium, 0.08 percent maximum carbon, stainless steel. However, it is understood that some in the industry have employed various thicknesses ranging from $\frac{1}{16}$-inch to $\frac{1}{8}$-inch, also a number of compositions containing varying percentages of chromium, nickel, molybdenum, carbon, columbium, and titanium. While the thinner material is cheaper and more easily formed to the irregularities of a vessel shell, it is extremely difficult to apply because of its tendency to burn away under the arc. A welder must have considerable experience in its application to obtain a satisfactory job. For these reasons, it is ordinarily advisable to specify the heavier sheet in spite of the disadvantages mentioned.

The carbon content should always be the lowest possible to reduce embrittlement, which often occurs in the sheet next to the fusion line of the weld. Such embrittlement is caused during the welding operation by the formation of chromium carbide between the grain boundaries of the steel. Until recently 0.08 percent was the lowest carbon content ordinarily obtainable commercially; however, it is understood that 0.06 percent is now available.

The two most commonly used methods for field applications of stainless linings are known as "plug welding" and "strip welding." For plug welding the sheets are perforated with holes on relatively close centers. The sheets are fastened to the shell by welding through these holes as well as along the edges. The holes generally range in size from $\frac{1}{2}$- to 1-inch depending upon the preference of the designer and the technique and experience of the welders to be used. Spacing of the holes may vary from about $2\frac{1}{2}$- to 6-inches depending upon the service conditions of the vessel. Generally the higher the temperature, the closer the spacing. For strip welding the sheet is furnished in narrow strips generally from 3- to $4\frac{1}{2}$-inches wide which are attached to the tower only at the edges. In this case also, the higher the temperature, generally the narrower the strips.

In our experience with the two types of linings, the strip type has been found preferable for the reason that it is more readily formed to the irregularities of the vessel shell without the excessive warping and twisting which is often experienced with the wider sheets employed in the plug weld method. The strip method also allows the strips to be butted while the plug weld method generally necessitates that the sheets be lapped to compensate for the distortion described above. Lapping represents a waste of material and is another reason for adopting the strip method.

This presentation will deal with the field application of an arc welded stainless lining of the strip type to an existing pressure vessel, described as a cracking still bubble tower with an inside diameter of 8-feet, 6-inches, a height of approximately 104-feet, and an original wall thickness of $1\frac{9}{16}$-inches. This vessel is typical of several in our plant to which stainless steel linings have recently been applied by arc welding. It should be borne in mind that while the discussion deals with a field application, all of the procedures and layouts described are equally applicable to new vessels under shop fabrication. It should also be noted that these methods are not necessarily confined to either the use of stainless steel or to the application of linings to refinery vessels. In fact they may be applied to the installation of any sort of weldable sheet metal lining to practically any type of vessel, regardless of the industry in which it might be found.

General

Materials

Tower Shell—ASTM No. A-70-36 flanging grade firebox steel, originally $1\frac{9}{16}$-inch thick, but reduced through corrosion to approximately $1\frac{3}{16}$-inches.

Lining Material—No. 12 BWG 12-14 percent chromium, 0.08 percent maximum carbon hot finished stainless steel strip, 4-inches wide, pickled, and furnished in reel form.

Welding Rod—$\frac{1}{8}$-inch and $\frac{5}{32}$-inch welding rods stabilized with columbium.

Welding Machines—300-amperes direct current welding machines.

Blasting Sand—No. 11 Silica Blast Sand from Ottawa, Illinois.

Preparation for Welding—All tower surfaces which were to be lined were thoroughly cleaned and sandblasted before proceeding with the welding operation.

Application of Lining to Bottom Head

General Description—The tower head under discussion is described as a semi-ellipsoidal surface generated by a semi-ellipse rotating about its minor axis and having a ratio between its major and minor axes of 2 to 1. Such a surface is known generally as an ellipsoid of revolution or specifically as an oblate spheroid.

Although this discussion deals with a head having the shape of an oblate spheroid, it should be noted that the same line of reasoning and layout methods would be equally applicable to prolate spheroids as well as the sphere itself, although there is no evidence available to indicate that the former is used to any extent for refinery vessels. A prolate spheroid is distinguished from an oblate spheroid by the fact that it is generated by an ellipse rotating about its major axis instead of its minor axis. The sphere is a special case of the spheroid in which the major and minor axes are equal in length.

Basis for Selection of Design—After having reviewed past experiences with tower head linings, it was decided that an effort should be made to reduce costs of liner application and if possible to produce a more satisfactory installation in general. Accordingly, preliminary layouts and templates were made in the office to determine the limitations of various conceivable designs.

Referring to Fig. 1, which is a photograph showing the design finally adopted, it was found that at least one ring of radial strips would be needed to produce conformity to the sharp change of curvature occurring at the outer extremities of the semi-ellipsoid. It was evident that the most economical design would result from only one such ring, this to surround a circular patch in the center and consist of alternate rectangular and wedge-shaped strips. The inside diameter of the ring was calculated and laid out on the generating ellipse to determine the feasibility of the arrangement. The bottom portion of the ellipsoid proved to be sufficiently flat to permit the installation of a central patch of the calculated diameter and on the basis of this determination it was decided to adopt the design.

Calculations

Number of Radial Strips Required in Ring—In order to determine the proper number of radial strips required to build up the outer ring shown in Fig. 1, it was necessary to first decide upon the desired width of spacing between adjacent strips. Former experience had shown that by proper fitting and welding technique this spacing could be maintained at approximately ¼-inch. With this assumption calculations were carried out as follows:

Inside diameter of tower — 8-ft. 6-in. or 102-in.
Width of lining strips — 4-in.
Width of spacing between strips — ¼-in.
Let N = Total number of radial strips
Then $4.25 N = 102\pi$
Solving, $N = 75.4$

Since it was desirable to have a whole number of strips for layout purposes and since it was also necessary to decide upon an even number of strips in order to carry out the alternating relationship between rectangular and wedge-shaped strips, the choice was limited to either 74 or 76 strips. It was decided more economical to adopt 76 strips and if necessary trim the wedge shaped strips slightly narrower than originally planned rather than to fill in by welding the extra spacing which would be created by using only 74 strips. Accordingly, the design was set up on the basis of 76 strips.

Inside Diameter of Ring—It was obvious that the wedge-shaped strips in the outer ring should not be brought to a point at the narrow end for the reason that the welds on opposite sides of the strip would fuse into each other as they approached the point and in effect be equivalent to nothing more than an excessively wide single weld. A width of approximately ⅜-

ARC WELDING

inch was considered satisfactory for the narrow end and on the basis of this assumption, calculations were carried out as follows:

$$I.D. = \frac{(38 \times 4\tfrac{3}{8}) + (76 \times \tfrac{1}{4})}{\pi}$$

Solving, I. D. = 59-in. or 4-ft. 11-in.

Preliminary Layout

Purpose—It is obvious that after the lining design had been adopted, templates could have been developed on the job as installation progressed. However, preliminary layout work and template development was considered advisable in order to check the feasibility of the design before installation and to determine the most economical layout from the standpoints of scrap loss and labor requirements for cutting liner material into the desired shapes.

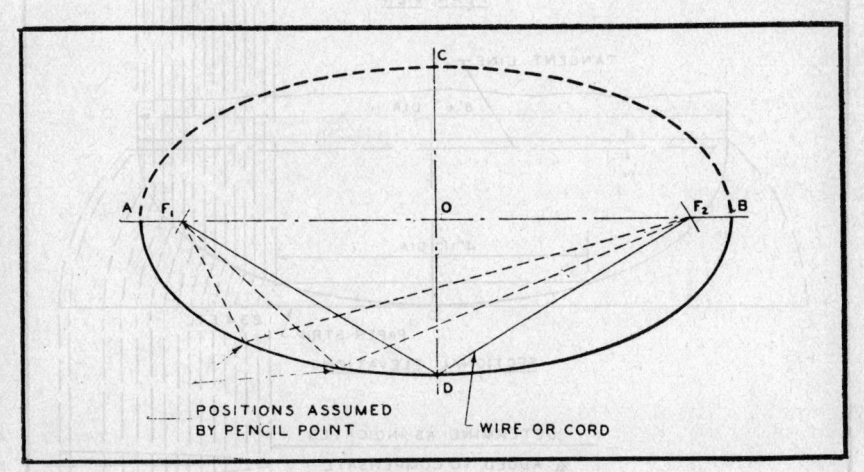

Fig. 2. Development of ellipse.

Development of the Ellipse—The following development was carried out for the purpose of reproducing the semi-ellipse used in generating the ellipsoidal head under consideration.

By definition an ellipse is the locus or path of a point which moves so that the sum of its distances from two fixed points remains constant. The fixed points are known as the foci and the sum is equal to the length of the transverse or major axis.

Referring to Fig. 2, AB is the major axis and CD the minor axis. For the particular tower under consideration AB was drawn equal to the tower diameter of 8-feet, 6-inches. Since the ratio between the major and minor axes was 2 to 1, the length of the minor axis was 4-feet, 3-inches. The lengths of the two axes were the only known quantities and therefore were necessarily the basis for further development.

Foci F_1 and F_2 were located by cutting the major axis AB with an arc having its center at C or D and a radius equal to AO or OB. Nails were driven at points F_1, F_2, and D and a flexible wire was drawn tightly around D with the ends tied at F_1 and F_2 as indicated. The ellipse was described by removing nail D and moving a pencil point in the loop in such a manner as to keep the wire taut at all times.

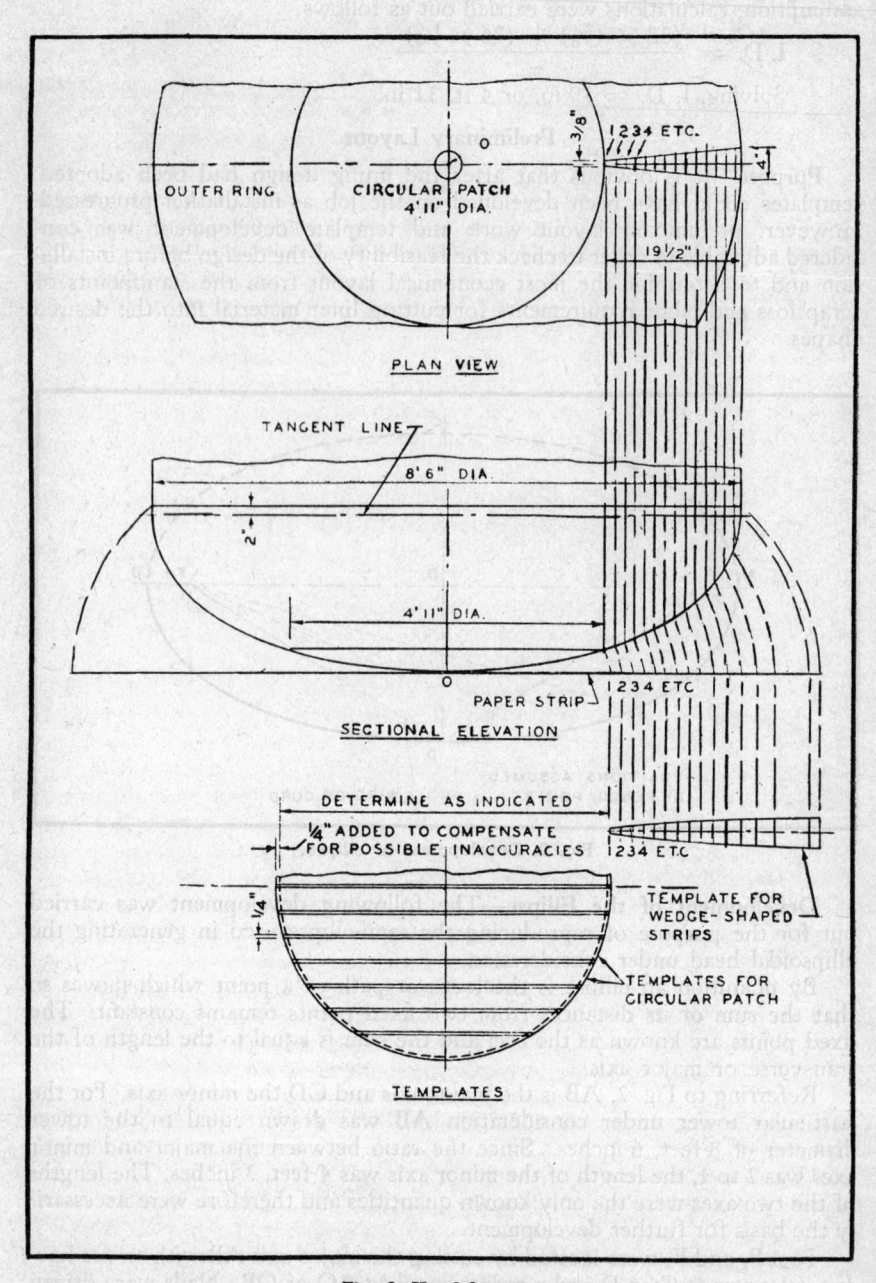

Fig. 3. Head layout.

Although there are several other methods of drawing ellipses, some of which are accurate and some approximate, the method described is probably the best suited to developing a true, full-size ellipse of the dimensions specified.

Development of Circular Patch—The following development is approximate and was carried out primarily for the purpose of providing templates for cutting strip lining into shapes which could be fitted into the desired circular patch with a minimum of final trimming.

Template development for the circular patch was carried out as outlined in Fig. 3. Referring to the sectional elevation, the length of the elliptical curve lying between points 0 and 1 was determined by bending a paper strip to conform to the ellipse, marking at the above points, and measuring the distance between the marks after the strip had been straightened out again. It was considered advisable to add approximately ¼-inch to this distance to compensate for inaccuracies which might exist in the tower head. A circle with its radius equal to this sum was drawn and then divided as indicated into 4-inch strips with approximately ¼-inch existing between adjacent strips. The 4-inch strips thus formed represented the finished templates.

Development of Outer Ring—As previously stated, the outer ring in the particular case being described was composed of a total of 76 alternating rectangular and wedge-shaped strips. A wedge-shaped strip was laid out in horizontal projection as shown in the plan view of Fig. 3. The center line of the wedge was divided into equal segments of convenient lengths, 1-inch being used for the case described. The end points of the segments were marked 1, 2, 3, etc., and lines perpendicular to the center line were drawn through these points to cut the sides of the wedge. Points 1, 2, 3, etc. were then projected vertically downward to the ellipse as shown in the elevation. Distances along the curve between successive points were laid out by bending a flexible strip to the contour of the ellipse, marking it at the points described and again straightening it out. The marks thus produced were projected to a new center line and a series of vertical lines were drawn through the projected points perpendicular to the center line and equal in length to corresponding lines in the plan view. The template was completed by joining the terminal points of the vertical lines as shown.

The foregoing development was essential to an intelligent analysis of the job. However, lining material was not cut according to the wedge-shaped template until all rectangular strips had been completely welded in place and an opportunity given for checking the template against the actual installation. In the particular case under consideration a perfect fit was obtained by using the original template; however, had there been any appreciable inaccuracies in fabricating the tower head or in carrying out preliminary layouts and calculations, it is obvious that alteration of the template would have been necessary.

All rectangular pieces in the outer ring were straight 4-inch strips equal in length to the wedge-shaped strips discussed in the paragraph above.

Layout of Tower Head and Application of Lining

General—In order to derive full value from the preliminary layouts, calculations, template developments, etc. already discussed, a highly accurate layout of the actual tower head was made preparatory to the lining application. Details of the layout used are outlined in Fig. 4.

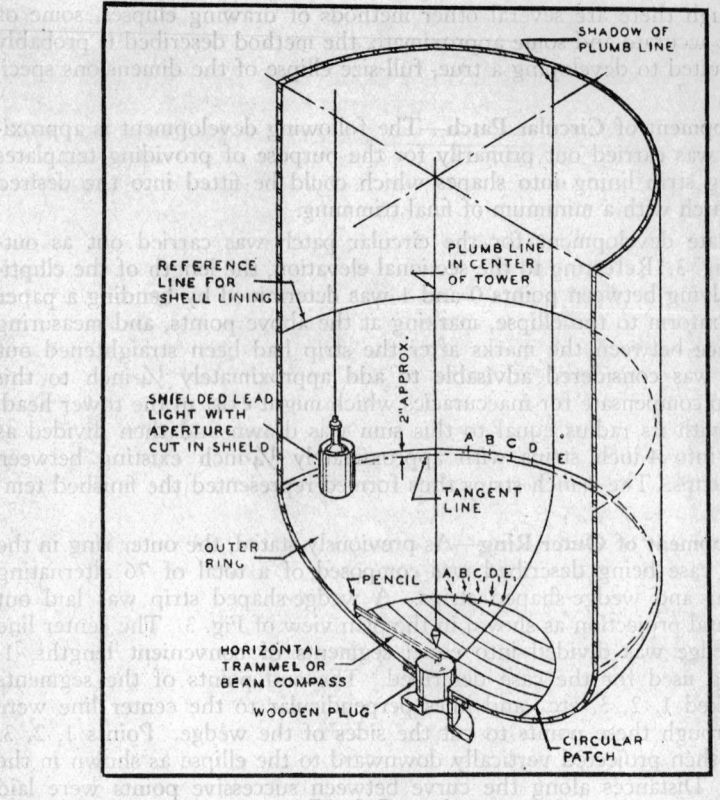

Fig. 4. Tower layout.

Layout Installation of Circular Patch—As shown in Fig. 4, a round wooden plug was fitted snugly into the bottom tower nozzle with the top at approximately the same elevation as the position designed for the edge of the circular patch. A wooden trammel was then fitted with a pencil at one end and a nail at the other, spaced so that the distance between them was equal to the radius of the patch in its horizontal projection. The trammel was placed in a horizontal position with the nail driven into the center of the plug and the pencil at the opposite end free to bear upon the tower head. A beam compass could have been used instead of the trammel had it been desired.

Installation of Circular Patch—After cutting strips according to templates previously developed, the installation was started at the center of the tower and carried outward simultaneously in both directions by installing the strips in pairs as indicated by the letters A, B, C, etc. in Fig. 5. Each strip was bent to the contour of the head, laid in place, and marked at the ends with the trammel. With the strip still in this position its inner edge was checked and marked to indicate the removal of any material necessary to produce conformity to the edge weld of the adjacent strip. Trimming of the edge was required only by those strips which had to be twisted slightly to conform to the tower head. As shown in Fig. 5 the material removed was in the form of narrow slivers and in every case was cut from the edge near the ends of the strip. The amount of wasted material represented was negligible inasmuch as the pieces removed never exceeded approximately 12-inches in length and 3/16-inch in width at the wide end.

After trimming, the strip was again laid in position and its edges welded, the inner with tack welds only and the outer with a continuous edge weld. Fig. 5 shows the approximate sequence adopted for weld application. As indicated, a continuous weld was applied first to one edge only and the sheet then allowed to cool thoroughly before completing the opposite edge with a similar weld. This procedure, accompanied by proper welding technique, was responsible for eliminating possible cracks resultant from contraction of the sheet. The extreme importance of welding with as low a current as possible consistent with proper fusion was recognized and, all welds were made accordingly. Each weld was completed in two passes. The first took the form of an edge weld as previously stated and was run to slightly overlap the edge of the sheet in order to produce proper penetration. The second was run to slightly overlap the edge of the adjacent sheet and completely cover the first weld. This method proved to be very satisfactory and more economical than any other tried previous to its adoption.

Layout for Installation of Radial Strips—The method used for laying out the tower head preparatory to the application of alternate rectangular and wedge-shaped strips in the outer ring is shown in Fig. 4.

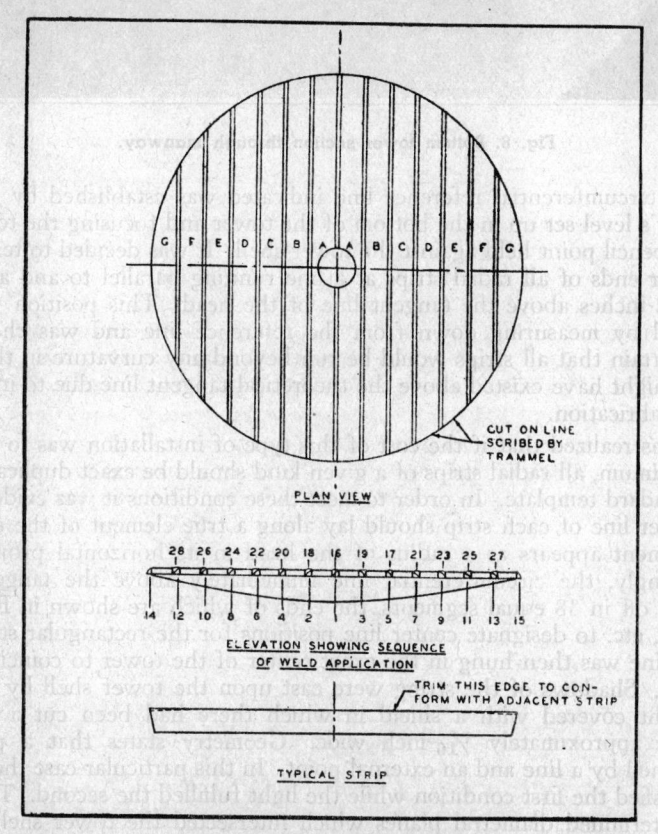

Fig. 5. Installation of circular patch.

Fig. 6. Bottom tower section through manway.

The circumferential reference line indicated was established by using a surveyor's level set up in the bottom of the tower and focusing the telescope upon a pencil point held against the tower shell. It was decided to terminate the outer ends of all radial strips at a line running parallel to and approximately 2-inches above the tangent line of the head. This position was determined by measuring down from the reference line and was chosen to make certain that all strips would be run beyond any curvature in the head which might have existed above the theoretical tangent line due to inaccuracies in fabrication.

It was realized that if the cost of this type of installation was to be kept at a minimum, all radial strips of a given kind should be exact duplicates, cut to a standard template. In order to meet these conditions it was evident that the center line of each strip should lay along a true element of the ellipsoid (an element appears as a radius of the head in its horizontal projection). Accordingly, the circumferential line immediately above the tangent line was laid off in 38 equal segments, the ends of which are shown in Fig. 4 as A, B, C, etc. to designate center line positions for the rectangular strips. A plumb line was then hung in the exact center of the tower to coincide with the axis. Shadows of the string were cast upon the tower shell by using a lead light covered with a shield in which there had been cut a vertical aperture approximately $\frac{1}{16}$-inch wide. Geometry states that a plane is determined by a line and an external point. In this particular case the plumb line satisfied the first condition while the light fulfilled the second. Together they determined diametral planes which intersected the tower shell in the form of shadows. It is obvious that since all planes thus formed passed

ARC WELDING

through the axis of revolution of the ellipsoidal head, all shadows falling on the head lay along true elements of the ellipsoid.

The light was moved so the shadow of the plumb line passed progressively through points A, B, C, etc. For each of these positions the intersection of the shadow with the edge of the circular patch was marked. These points, indicated by A_1, B_1, C_1, etc. in Fig. 4, were prick-punched for permanency.

Installation of Radial Strips—The first rectangular strip was installed with one end at A and the other at A_1 such that its center line passed through the points. One edge was welded with a continuous edge weld while the other was tack welded. After all 38 strips had been installed in this manner the tacked edges were completed with continuous welds applied in the same sequence used for installation of the strips.

The template previously cut for the wedge-shaped strips was checked against the spaces existing between the rectangular strips, and excellent conformity was found. Strips were cut according to the template and installed in a manner similar to that described for the rectangular strips. Tack welds were applied to one edge while a continuous weld was run along the other to slightly overlap the edge and cover completely the weld previously applied to the adjacent rectangular strip. After all wedge-shaped strips had been installed, the tacked edges were completed in a manner similar to that just described.

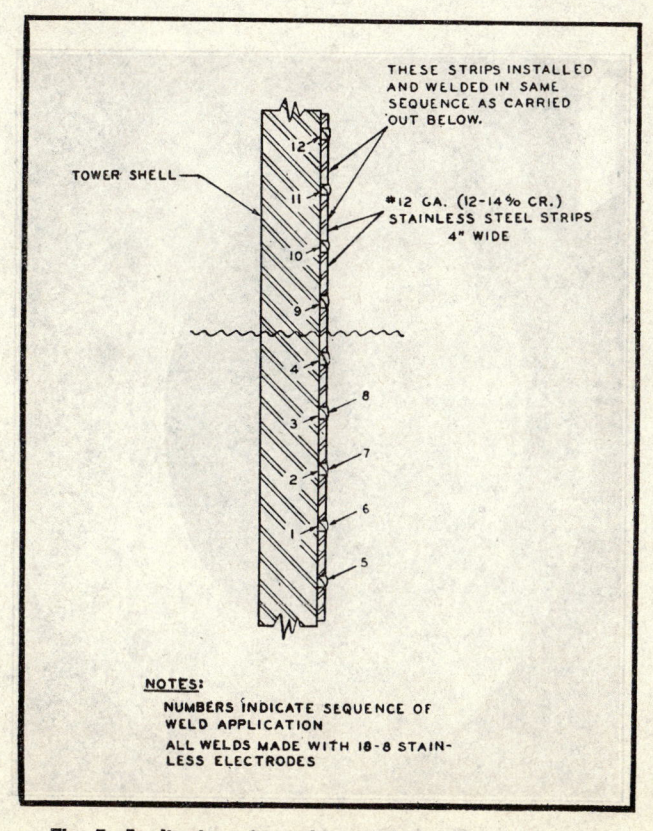

Fig. 7. Application of stainless steel lining to tower shell.

Application of Lining to Shell

General Description—A 12-gauge stainless steel lining in the form of 4-inch strips was applied to the tower shell as shown in Fig. 6.

Layout of Tower Shell—In order to facilitate accurate fitting of the lining strips, circumferential reference lines were drawn in true sections of the tower. As discussed under head layout, the first of these, indicated in Fig. 4, was established by using a surveyor's level. As the installation progressed upward, successive lines were laid off as required by measuring back to the preceding line. One of these lines can be faintly seen on the shell immediately above the lined section shown in Fig. 6, which is a photograph of the actual installation. Accurate fitting of the strips was made possible by keeping their edges parallel to the reference lines described, thereby preventing the twisting of sheets and a resultant lack of uniformity in spacing.

Fitting and Welding—All strips were fitted and welded as shown in Figs. 6 and 7. As indicated in Fig. 7, all work proceeded from the bottom to the top of the section being lined. Each successive strip was installed by moving it down until its bottom edge came into contact with the edge weld of the strip below. The bottom edge was then tacked in place and a continuous edge weld run along the top edge. Four or five complete rings were thus installed before dropping back to weld the bottom edges, which were

Fig. 8. View of manway lining.

completed in the same order. By this method, time was allowed for dissipating the heat produced by welding the top edges. As a result, cracking of the sheet was reduced to a minimum. All bottom edge welds were applied as shown, by producing a sufficiently wide bead to slightly overlap the edge and cover the weld previously laid along the top edge of the sheet below. All welds were thus completed in two passes, every effort being made to reduce deposition of weld metal to a minimum consistent with good practice.

Application of Lining to Manways—Fig. 8 is a photograph showing the application of 4-inch strip lining to a tower manway. The same procedure was used in this installation as already described for the application of lining to the tower shell.

Costs and Economics
Labor Rates

(For reference in connection with following cost analyses).

Welder	$1.50/hr.
Sandblaster	1.00 "
Helper	.80 "
Laborer	.75 "

Labor and Material Costs
Application of Lining to Bottom Tower Head (83-Sq. Ft.)

Labor	Wldr.	Blstr.	Hlpr.	Lbr.	Costs
Sandblasting		3.5		3.5	$6.13
Fitting & Welding	67.5		26.0		122.05
*Payment for time not actually worked	17.2	0.5	2.0	0.5	28.27
Total Labor	84.7	4.0	28.0	4.0	$156.45

Material
369# St. Steel @ $23.35/cwt.	$86.16
24# " " Scrap @ $23.35/cwt.	5.60
70# 1/8" Electrode @ $0.90/lb.	63.00
Total Material	$154.76

Overhead & Miscellaneous
Contact man (for hiring men, etc.)	$7.70
Time keeping and clerical work	4.18
Compensation, insurance, taxes, etc.	16.40
Trucking	1.19
Miscellaneous (contractor's fee, etc.)	14.90
Total Overhead & Misc.	$44.37

Grand Total	$355.58

*Note—Payment for time not actually worked consisted of payments in excess of the regular wage for overtime work, etc.

Cost excluding payment for time not actually worked $355.58–28.27 $327.31

Summary

Total Cost per sq. ft.	= 355.58/83	= $4.28	
Cost per sq. ft. excluding payment for time not actually worked	= 327.31/83	= $3.94	
Actual labor per sq. ft.	= 100.5/83	= 1.21	Man hours
Actual fitting & welding time per sq. ft.	= 93.5/83	= 1.125	" "
Actual welding time per sq. ft.	= 67.5/83	= 0.814	" "
Welding wire per sq. ft.	= 70/83	= 0.843#	

Labor and Material Costs
Application of Lining to Shell Section Adjacent to Bottom Head
(80.1-Sq. ft.)

Labor	Man Hours				Costs
	Wldr.	Blstr.	Hlpr.	Lbr.	
Sandblasting		3.5		3.5	$6.13
Fitting & Welding	62.0	....	25.0	....	113.00
Payment for time not actually worked	24.4	0.5	10.5	0.5	45.87
Total Labor	86.4	4.0	35.5	4.0	$165.00

Material

356# St. Steel @ $23.35/cwt.	$83.13
22# 5/32" Electrode @ 0.75/lb	16.50
30# 1/8" Electrode @ 0.90/lb	27.00
Total Material	$126.63

Overhead & Miscellaneous

Contact Man (for hiring men, etc.)	$8.15
Time keeping & clerical work	4.40
Compensation, insurance, taxes, etc.	17.30
Trucking	1.25
Miscellaneous (contractor's fee, etc.)	15.70
Total Overhead & Miscellaneous	$46.80
Grand Total	$338.43

Cost excluding payment for time not actually worked $338.43–45.87 $292.56

Summary

Total Cost per sq. ft.	= 338.43/80.1	= $4.23	
Cost per sq. ft. excluding payment for time not actually worked	= 292.56/80.1	= $3.66	
Actual labor per sq. ft.	= 94.0/80.1	= 1.17	Man hours
Actual fitting & welding time per sq. ft.	= 87.0/80.1	= 1.085	" "
Actual welding time per sq. ft.	= 62.0/80.1	= 0.774	" "
Welding wire per sq. ft.	= 52/80.1	= .65#	

Labor and Material Costs
Application of Lining to Shell in Tray Section of Tower (191.4 sq. ft.)

Labor	Man Hours				Costs	
	Wldr.	Carp.	Blstr.	Hlpr.		
Scaffolding	1.0	4.0	....	4.0	$7.94	
Sandblasting	....	....	3.0	......	3.00	
Fitting & Welding	186.0	....	....	92.5	353.00	
Payment for time not actually worked	159.4	....	1.0	81.5	305.30	
Total Labor	346.4	4.0	4.0	178.0		$669.24

Material
852# St. Steel ....@$23.35/cwt.....................$198.94
 78# $5/32"$ Electrode   @ 0.75/lb. 58.50
100# $1/8"$ Electrode   @ 0.90/lb. 90.00

Total Material $347.44

Overhead & Miscellaneous
Contact man (for hiring men, etc.) $32.65
Time keeping & clerical work 17.64
Compensation, insurance, taxes, etc. 69.50
Trucking 5.02
Miscellaneous (Contractor's fee, etc.) 62.90

Total Overhead & Miscellaneous $187.71

Grand Total $1204.39

Cost excluding payment for time not actually worked 1204.39–305.30 $899.09

Summary
Total cost per sq. ft. .... = 1204.39/191.4 = $6.29
Cost per sq. ft. excluding payment for
   time not actually worked .... = 899.09/191.4 = 4.69
Actual labor per sq. ft. .... = 290.5/191.4 = 1.52 Man hrs.
Actual fitting & welding time per sq. ft.= 278.5/191.4 = 1.455 "   "
Actual welding time per sq. ft. .... = 186/191.4 = 0.972 "   "
Welding wire per sq. ft. .... = 178/191.4 = 0.93#

Comparison with Previous Stainless Lining Applications—Soon after starting our stainless steel lining program it became apparent that the costs of installation were running too high and would have to be materially reduced to bring them within satisfactory limits. Immediate steps were taken to improve layouts and procedures with the result that each succeeding job showed improvements in costs. This program finally culminated in the layouts and procedures described in this report and adopted as standard in March, 1940. The rate of progress in reducing costs is shown by the following figures. In analyzing these it should be remembered that all work was performed by welders picked up from outside sources. Had the plant welders been available for the various jobs, somewhat lower costs undoubtedly would have been experienced throughout.

Shell Lining

(Comparisons made on square foot basis. Do not include payment for time not actually worked.) Strip method used except as noted.

	April, 1938 D-3 Tower No. 1 Unit (Tray Section) Plug Weld Method	May, 1939 D-3 Tower No. 1 Unit (Unobstructed Section)	May, 1939 D-2 Tower No. 1 Unit (Unobstructed Section)	Sept., 1939 D-3 Tower No. 1 Unit (Unobstructed Section)	Subject Job Adopted as Standard March, 1940 D-3 Tower No. 2 Unit (Tray Section)	Subject Job Adopted as Standard March, 1940 D-3 Tower No. 2 Unit (Unobstructed Section)
Cost. Total Labor	$10.28		$8.82	$4.56	$4.69	$3.66
Fitting and Welding	3.25 Man hrs. 2.78 Man hrs.		2.6 Man hrs.	1.70 Man hrs.	1.52 Man hrs.	1.17 Man hrs.
Welders' Time	2.88 Man hrs. 2.27 Man hrs.		2.0 Man hrs.	1.39 Man hrs.	1.455 Man hrs.	1.085 Man hrs.
	1.44 Man hrs.			1.09 Man hrs.	0.972 Man hrs.	0.774 Man hrs.
Welding Rod	1.55 lbs.	2.285 lbs.	2.28 lbs.	1.04 lbs.	0.93 lbs.	0.65 lbs.

The above figures indicate that it costs more to line a tray section than it does an unobstructed section. This is explained by the fact that the trays are spaced relatively close together and are a distinct handicap to accurate fitting as well as freedom of movement on the part of the welders. Extra time is also required to seal the lining to the tray supporting angles.

Head Lining

(Comparisons made on square foot basis. Do not include payment for time not actually worked.)

	May, 1939		Subject Job Adopted as Standard March, 1940 D-3 Tower No. 2 Unit
	D-3 Tower No. 1 Unit	D-2 Tower No. 1 Unit	
Cost	$10.28	$8.82	$3.94
Total Labor	2.78 Man hrs.	2.6 Man hrs.	1.21 Man hrs.
Fitting and Welding	2.27 Man hrs.	2.0 Man hrs.	1.125 Man hrs.
Welders' Time			0.814 Man hrs.
Welding Rod	2.285 lbs.	2.28 lbs.	0.843 lbs.

Comparison with Other Methods of Corrosion Protection—In making comparisons between various methods of corrosion protection it is necessary to consider the life of the linings or coatings involved. As already stated the life of a stainless steel lining of the specifications given in this report can be considered almost unlimited for the services ordinarily encountered. However in order to arrive at some definite basis for comparison, a conservative figure of 15-years is assumed.

Arc Welded Carbon Steel Lining (¾" Head Lining, ½" Shell Lining)

Cost per sq. ft. (approximate) $12.62
Life—4½-years
Cost per sq. ft. per year $2.81

Note: The high cost of this lining can be partially attributed to a scarcity of highly skilled welders at the time and partially to having to repair some of the completed welds after they had broken loose because of stresses set up during the cooling period. The latter condition is considered to be one of the inherent disadvantages of a heavy lining of this type.

Gunite Lining

Cost per sq. ft. (approximate) $3.11
Life—1-year, 3-months
Cost per sq. ft. per year $2.49

Note: While the ganister lining being reported was not removed until 15-months had elapsed, it was giving little protection at the time of removal. Therefore, to be correct its useful life should be taken as something less than the 1-year and 3-months indicated. However, since the figures shown are in favor of the gunite lining they will be allowed to stand.

Sprayed Metal Coating—Several experiments were conducted to determine the practicability of corrosion control by means of molten metal spraying. Corroded sections of a tower shell were thoroughly sandblasted and coated with aluminum sprayed from a metal spray gun. While these tests were neither extensive nor conclusive, results obtained indicated the method inferior to stainless linings, largely because of the tendency of the coating to peel off after being subjected to operating conditions. No cost data was kept in connection with these experiments.

Arc Welded Stainless Steel Lining (Subject Job)

Total cost per sq. ft. (Head lining) $4.28
Total cost per sq. ft. (Tray section of shell) 6.29
Total cost per sq. ft. (Unobstructed section of shell) 4.23
Average total cost per sq. ft. 4.93
Life—15-years
Average cost per sq. ft. per year .... .33

Savings

On basis of carbon steel lining   — $2.48 per sq. ft. per year or 88.3%
On basis of Gunite lining   — $2.16 per sq. ft. per year or 86.7%

Conclusions—From the foregoing discussions and figures it has been concluded that the arc welded stainless steel lining is not only by far the most economical of the various methods tried in connection with corrosion control; but it is also the most dependable and the most durable. These statements assume added importance when it is realized that investments as high as $75,000 or even more for a single fractionating tower must often be guarded by some effective protection against corrosion. Unless this protection is afforded the life of certain sections of such equipment may be limited to only two- to 3-years or less, depending upon the rate of corrosion and the corrosion allowance incorporated in the original thickness specifications.

Chapter XX—Saw Mill

By Robert Schliewe,

Assistant Mechanical Supt., Weyerhaeuser Timber Co., Longview, Washington.

Subject Matter: The author points out the outstanding contribution arc welding is able to make in the maintenance of a saw mill plant. The major problems are caused by wear of log handling equipment and welding or building up these parts has proved both efficient and economical. Over 17 items in which welding has been used are described in detail. Comparative cost data are carefully analyzed and furnished. It is claimed that in this plant a saving of over $25,000 annually results from their use of welding.

Robert Schliewe

This paper covers some of the maintenance problems and how they are being solved, with special reference to arc welding, with which I have come in contact in the maintenance department of our lumber division. This maintenance department is responsible for the proper maintenance of all steam, air, sewer, mechanical and electrical equipment needed to manufacture and ship approximately 400,000,000 feet board measure of fir, cedar and hemlock lumber per year. Also, this department is responsible for the proper maintenance of some five hundred fifty-foot logging cars.

In this plant we have four electric welders, three of these machines being electrically driven and one gas driven. The gas machine is used in places where electricity is not available. All of these machines are equipped with rubber tires and a trailer hitch. Three of these machines are located at the machine shop and are of the shielded arc type and the fourth is devoted almost exclusively to log car repair and is of stable arc type. The welding machines and the welders are under the direct supervision of the shop foreman. If a welding machine is needed at any part of the plant, a written order is given to the shop foreman and he, in turn, dispatches a welder, a helper and a machine to the point needed. All labor and material used on any job is charged directly to the order covering that job. Thus a fairly accurate cost analysis can be made of each job if it is desired. It might be said here that the machines are moved out of the shop with a half ton truck. Also, with each welder a helper is furnished whose duties are to assist the welder, to watch for fires and eventually to learn the welding trade.

One must remember that in maintenance work the problems coming up are many and varied and, therefore, the scope of the maintenance work covered may be touched upon by analyzing in detail each of the items listed below. These items were selected because of the part arc welding has played in their repair during the past two years.

1. Welding broken side link in 9118 rivetless chain.
2. Building up log chairs.

3. Building up sprockets for 998 chain to take care of worn sprockets and stretched chain.
4. Welding a broken piece of shafting to keep the mill going.
5. Welding plate in broken and worn out conveyors.
6. Building up and repairing hogs.
7. Splitting roller chain sprockets and welding the same around a shaft.
8. Building up round link chain, varying in size as follows: 1¼-inch x 7-inch, 1¾-inch x 9-inch, 2-inch x 9-inch.
9. Building up the blades of forced draft boiler fan with soft wire.
10. Welding bands in the grooves of cast iron cable sheaves to increase the life of sheave.
11. Repairing refuse conveyor flights.
12. Welding extensions on gang foundation bolts when bolts were buried in concrete.
13. Melting cast iron with the aid of the arc.
14. Fabricating a friction drum.
15. Fabricating a worm spider.
16. Die wheel repair on press-to-logs machines.
17. Repairing lumber grapple arms for bridge cranes.

Now let us consider some of the various welding jobs performed during the past year.

Welding broken side links in 9118 rivetless chain. The chain in question is used to carry logs from the log pond to the sawmill. The 9118 rivetless chain in this case is approximately 550 feet long. We have found the weakest part of the chain to be in the side links near the rivets as shown by the arrow "A" in Fig. 1.

It had been the practice in the past to replace the broken side links with new ones from the manufacturer. Due to our present national emergency, spare side links on order did not come through on schedule and thus we ran out of side links for repairs. To overcome this emergency, a number of broken side links were sent to the shop cut at point "B" in Fig. 1, and the two good halves were welded together with oxy-acetylene. These side links were heat treated and used to replace broken links in the chain. The biggest saving in this particular repair was to prevent the shutdown of the mill.

The approximate cost to make one good side link out of two broken ones was:

Labor	$2.00	
Material	.35	Hy-carbon Rod
		(Oxy-Acetylene Weld)
Total	$2.35	

A new side link costs approximately $1.12.

By using the arc, the above cost of this repair could be reduced still further to a figure comparable to the cost of a new link which cost would be as follows:

Labor	$1.00
Material	.10
Total	$1.10

This will constitute a saving over oxy-acetylene welding of 50 percent. The main saving in this particular case was not a saving of material but continuity of operating time.

ARC WELDING

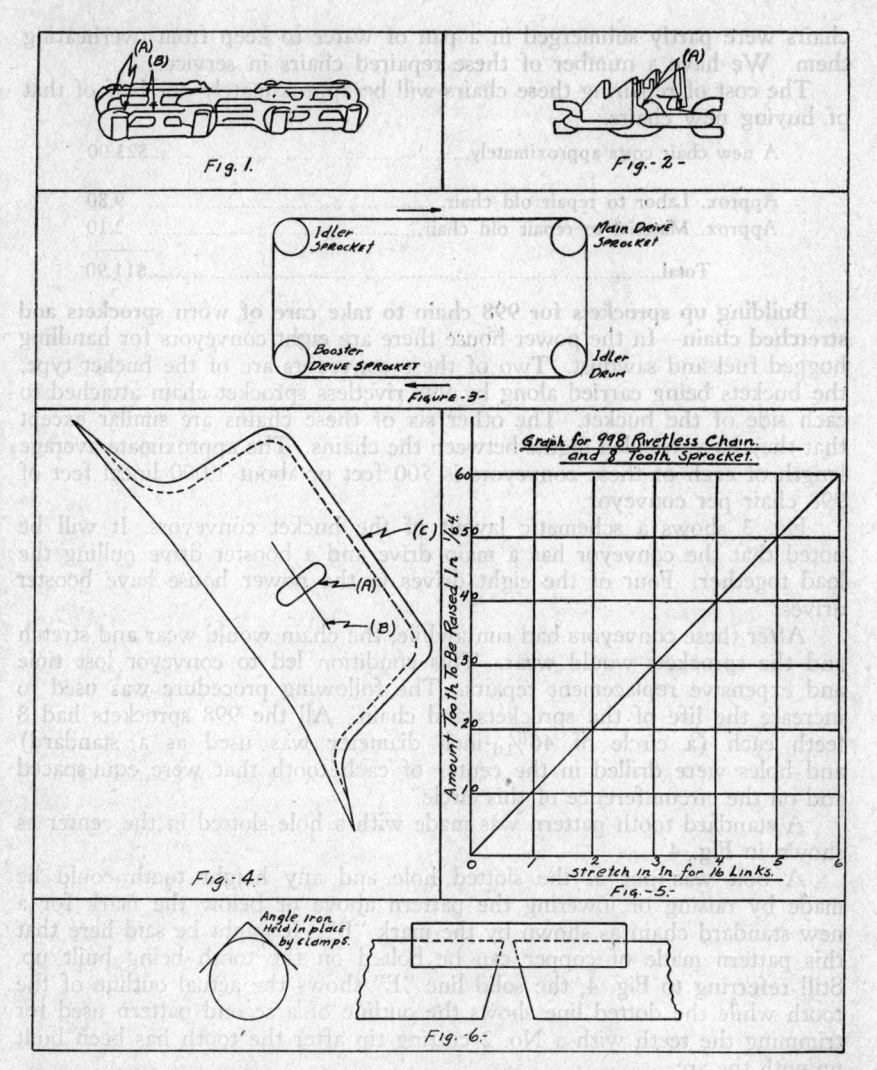

Fig. 1. Weak part of chain. Fig. 2. Log Chair. Fig. 3. Schematic layout of bucket conveyors. Fig. 4. Standard tooth pattern. Fig. 5. Riveltless chain graph. Fig. 6. Line-up of shafts with bolted angle iron.

Building up log chairs—A log chair is a chain attachment used on log haul chains to engage the logs when they are being taken out of the log pond and put into the mill. See Fig. 2.

These log chairs are made of manganese. The wearing strips in the main slip and in the return are made of chilled cast iron. There are approximately 350 of these chairs in this plant. These chairs are wearing out at the points marked "A". As a result, these chairs tend to wear down to a chisel point and thus greatly reduce the strength of the chair as well as make a likely spot where the chair can hang up on the log slip causing chain breakage and mill lost time. These chairs were built up in the shop with manganese rod. As much as twenty-five pounds were put on some chairs. These chairs were partly submerged in a pan of water to keep from overheating them. We have a number of these repaired chairs in service.

The cost of repairing these chairs will be approximately one-half of that of buying new chairs.

A new chair costs approximately	$23.00
Approx. Labor to repair old chair	9.80
Approx. Material to repair old chair	2.10
Total	$11.90

Building up sprockets for 998 chain to take care of worn sprockets and stretched chain—In the power house there are eight conveyors for handling hogged fuel and sawdust. Two of these conveyors are of the bucket type, the buckets being carried along by 998 rivetless sprocket chain attached to each side of the bucket. The other six of these chains are similar except that they have wooden flights between the chains. The approximate average length of each of these conveyors is 500 feet or about 1,000 lineal feet of 998 chair per conveyor.

Fig. 3 shows a schematic layout of the bucket conveyors. It will be noted that the conveyor has a main drive and a booster drive pulling the load together. Four of the eight drives in the power house have booster drives.

After these conveyors had run awhile, the chain would wear and stretch and the sprockets would wear. This condition led to conveyor lost time and expensive replacement repairs. The following procedure was used to increase the life of the sprockets and chain. All the 998 sprockets had 8 teeth each (a circle of $46\frac{5}{16}$-inch diameter was used as a standard) and holes were drilled in the center of each tooth that were equi-spaced and on the circumference of this circle.

A standard tooth pattern was made with a hole slotted in the center as shown in Fig. 4.

A bolt was put in the slotted hole and any height tooth could be made by raising or lowering the pattern above or below the mark for a new standard chain as shown by the mark "B". It might be said here that this pattern made of copper can be bolted on the tooth being built up. Still referring to Fig. 4, the solid line "E" shows the actual outline of the tooth while the dotted line shows the outline of a second pattern used for trimming the teeth with a No. 2 cutting tip after the tooth has been built up with the arc.

Next, the chain was taped. I have found some of these chains stretched from 1-inch to $4\frac{1}{2}$-inches in 16 links or 12-feet. A typical set of readings showing the stretch in inches in 16 links is as follows: $3\frac{1}{2}$-inches - $3\frac{3}{4}$-inches - $3\frac{1}{2}$-inches - $3\frac{3}{4}$-inches - $3\frac{1}{2}$-inches - 4-inches - $3\frac{3}{4}$-inches - $3\frac{3}{4}$-inches - 4-inches - 4-inches - 4-inches - 4-inches - 4-inches - 4-inches - $3\frac{1}{2}$-inches. With this set of readings the pitch circumference of the sprockets was built up to conform with the pitch of the worn chain. In this case the teeth were raised $\frac{9}{16}$-inch with a high carbon rod.

The figuring or calculating of the amount that each sprocket should be raised was greatly simplified with the aid of the following special graph (Fig. 5) worked out for this purpose.

Also, in building up these sprockets the teeth will mushroom in service if they get too hot. It is a good idea to have the welder work on three or four teeth at the same time to prevent overheating.

The advantages gained by building up sprockets in this manner are several; namely,

(a) The life of the chain is increased about 60 percent.
(b) The life of the sprocket is increased indefinitely.
(c) The lost time of the conveyors due to breakdowns is greatly reduced.

A dollar and cents comparison results in the following figures:

Approx. average cost of labor to build up sprocket 20 hrs.	$ 25.00
Approx. average cost of material per sprocket—rod 35 lbs.	3.50
	$ 28.50
Approx. cost of new sprocket	$125.00
Approx. cost of new 998 chain, per foot	$ 2.48
Approx. saving per foot of chain	$ 1.49

Welding a broken piece of shafting to keep the mill going—From time to time a piece of shaft on a rollcase, transfer chain, etc., may break. Many times these pieces of shafting may be so located that from eight to sixteen hours would be needed to replace them. This situation would mean a mill shut down and this is a serious loss of production. Several times during the past two years production was held up for only a short period of time while the broken shaft was welded together. We have had very good results with E6012 electrodes on this particular type of welding job.

It might also be added that the shafts were lined up by bolting a piece of angle iron as shown in Fig. 6.

Shafts in this condition are then run until the mill is down long enough to replace them with new ones.

Here is a situation in which the material saved is of minor importance while the saving of lost production is a very large item. The lost time may be from $2 to $5 a minute, depending upon the amount of machinery it is necessary to shut down. I have seen welded shafts in service as long as six months before they were replaced.

To weld a $2\frac{3}{16}$-inch shaft it is estimated that it would take about one hour for a welder and about one to two pounds of rod. We have been having good success with E6012 rod with this type of job.

Welding plate in broken and worn out conveyors—Here is an item where it is impossible to give any accurate cost figures that would be comparable to anything definite as each and every job is just a little different. All that I am going to do is to point out some of the ways welding is used in repairing worn and broken conveyors. Bottom and sides are lined with steel plate.

The method of repairing a conveyor depends upon the existing situation. In cases where the conveyor chain has worn a hole through the bottom of the full length of the conveyor, it may be satisfactory to weld more plate on the bottom, either covering the whole bottom or just the worn out part. In cases where there is a hole in the bottom or the side of the conveyor, it might only be necessary to trim the hole and weld in a patch.

A very good case where the arc shows definite savings is on the conveyors in our power house. The majority of these conveyors have steel bottoms that are held in place by sleigh bolts. As the steel bottoms wear, the heads of the bolts wear too, thus allowing the plate to come loose and roll up in the conveyor. Mild steel welding rod is being used to repair these conveyors. The life of this job is increased about 50 percent by building up the head of each bolt and welding it to the bottom with the arc thus insuring that the bottom will be held firmly in place.

To show the amount of material involved, a typical conveyor in our power house will have 360 lineal feet of ⅜-inch x 36-inch steel plate. This amount of steel at four cents a pound would be valued at approximately $660 and a welder with eight to sixteen hours of welding time would increase its life about 50 percent.

Building up and repairing hogs—In this plant there are six large and two smaller hogs. The work of these hogs is to grind up into hogged fuel the refuse and waste from a log resulting from the manufacture of lumber. Due to the large volume of fuel that passes through these hogs, there are several parts that wear away rather rapidly. It might be stated here that each of these hogs is cutting about fifteen units of hogged fuel per hour.

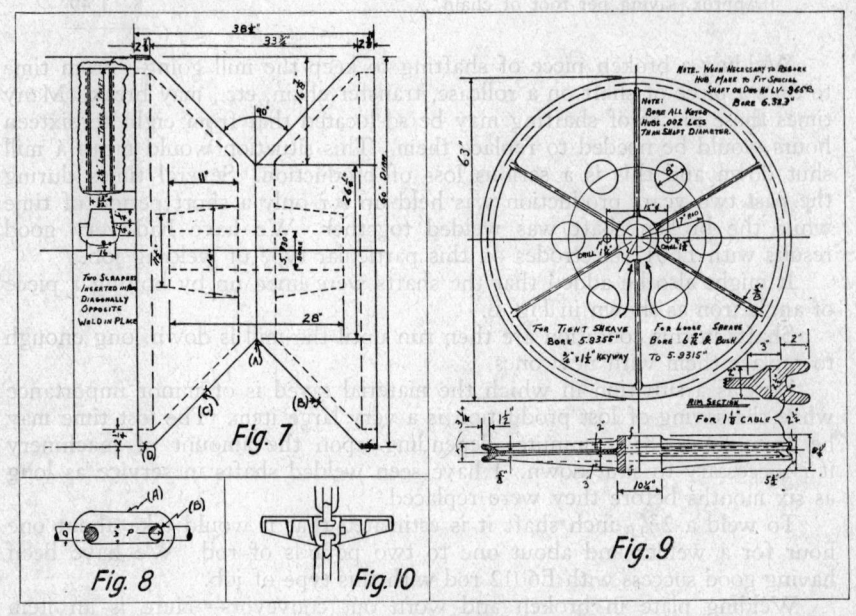

Fig. 7. Design for welded hog. Fig. 8. Joints of greatest wear. Fig. 9. Cable sheave design. Fig. 10. Conveyor flight.

Specifically referring to Fig. 7, points "A" (the V or crotch of a hog), rotor points "B" and "C" (the opening cut into the disc to hold the knives), "D" (the rim of the hog) and "E" (the anvil knife door which is not shown in Fig. 7). Points "A", "B" and "C" were built up with a low carbon rod. In some cases, a part of a pocket would break out and it would be necessary to deposit considerable metal to put it back into its original shape. At point "E" (the anvil knife door), it is necessary to build this point back up as it is one of the points of greatest wear in the hog. Two pieces of copper ¼-inch x 4-inches x 24-inches are bolted together in the form of a V to form as a straight edge. With this straight edge it is possible to build up the anvil accurately as the welding rod will not stick to the copper very easily. A high carbon rod is used here. Under our present operating conditions, with normal wear and tear a new hog will run about twelve months before it is necessary to build up the anvil and rotor. Conservatively speaking, with the aid of a welder the life of these hogs is probably increased four-fold.

A new 65 hog costs about	$3,400.00
A new hog rotor costs about	925.00
Approximate welding hours and cost per year per hog, 72 hours	$ 90.00
Approximate welding material per year per hog, 216 lbs. rod	21.60
Total	$ 111.60

Splitting roller chain sprockets and welding the same around a shaft—There are in this plant numerous transfer chain line shafts in which the shafts and sprockets are hard to reach because of other equipment built around them. At times, it has become necessary to replace a sprocket so installed in a very limited time. This has been done in the following manner. The old sprocket was cut off with a cutting torch and the new steel sprocket was split in two and the pieces were held in place around the shaft with clamps. The sprocket was then welded together again. Here is a case of the application of arc welding in which no material was saved but the labor and time of replacing the worn sprocket was reduced, thus reducing the threat of lost production because of failure to make repairs on time.

To give an example of the amount of saving that is possible through the foregoing explanation, I will show how a job was handled during the past year. It was necessary to replace a 22 tooth #6 roller chain sprocket on a transfer shaft buried in a floor and covered with sheet iron and chain races bolted to the floor. With six mechanics to make the replacement, the job alone would have taken from 12 to 16 hours. A welder and a helper actually completed the job in 7 hours—a saving in man hours alone of approximately 70 hours. This saving does not include any estimate of loss of mill operating time which would be approximately $3.00 a minute.

Building up round link chain varying in size as follows: 1¼ inch x 7 inch, 1¾ inch x 9 inch, 2 inch x 9 inch. In this plant we have several thousand feet of 1¼ inch x 7 inch, about 1,600 lineal feet of 1¾ inch x 9 inch and about 500 lineal feet of 2 inch x 9 inch of round link chain. The 1¼ inch x 7 inch chain is used in refuse conveyors while the other two sizes are used on log hauls.

The greater part of this chain is either running on steel conveyor bottoms or cast iron chain races. The points of greatest wear are at "A" and "B" as shown in Fig. 8.

In repairing the 1¼ inch x 7 inch chain, the wear was mostly at "A" shown in Fig. 8. This chain was repaired with the aid of the arc by welding pieces of bar steel from ¼ inch x 1 inch x 5 inch to ½ inch x 1 inch x 5 inch on the worn surfaces. This is a very economical repair for the chain can be repaired in place. The estimated increased life with this repair is about 50 percent. A welder can repair from 6 to 7 links per hour or, putting the cost comparison in a tabulated form, it would be:

Welder, 1 hour	$1.25
Material, 2 lbs. rod	.22
Total cost	$1.47
Six new links will cost about	$7.50

In repairing the 1¾ inch x 9 inch and 2 inch x 9 inch chain, the worn spots are built up with layers of high carbon rod. In order to get a smooth job at point "B" (Fig. 8), a carbon rod is used to smooth this up. After the chain has been built up, it is put in a fire and heated to relieve the stresses. To repair one link of 1¾ inch x 9 inch chain, the cost is approximately:

Welder, ½ hour	$ .625
Material, 1 lb.	.110
Total	$ .735
New 1¾" x 9" chain costs approx.	$3.00 per ft.
New 2" x 9" chain costs approx.	$3.25 per ft.

Building up blades of a forced draft boiler fan with soft wire.—In one boiler in the power house there is a four foot induced draft fan that has been in service for about 11 years. It has been the practice in the past to use a high carbon rod to build up the fan blades. This had to be done about once a month. As a trial, soft wire was tried with the aid of the arc instead of high carbon rod and the time between repair jobs was increased from about one to three months. At the present time, the blades of the fan are replaced about every eight months, their life being increased about 100 percent with the aid of the arc. On this particular fan the cost to repair the blades and hub on one shut is approximately as follows:

Welder, 24 hours	$30.00
Material, scrap wire	
Total	$30.00
A new set of blades costs about	$50.00

Welding bands in the grooves of cast iron cable sheaves to increase the life of the sheave and save wear on the cable.—In our plant there are twenty-four 1⅛ inch cable sheaves as shown in Fig. 9.

Many of these sheaves have been taken out of service because the groove has been worn too deep and were discarded. With the aid of the arc welder, they have been salvaged in the following manner. First, the groove was trued up on a boring mill. Then a 1½ inch x 2½ inch mild steel band was made and welded together in the groove. It was necessary to heat the band with a torch while its ends were being arc welded. This caused the band to shrink on the sheave upon cooling. As an added safety, six one-half inch rivets equi-spaced were put through the sheave and band to hold the band on in case it came loose. As nearly as can be determined, there is no appreciable difference in cable wear between salvaged sheaves and new ones.

Comparative costs between salvaged and new sheaves are as follows:

Welding Bands, 2 hrs.	$ 2.50
Welding Rods, 2 lbs.	.22
Drill Press, 1 hr.	1.00
Blacksmith, 6 hrs.	7.50
Machinist, 7 hrs.	8.75
15' 1½" x 2½" Mild Steel	7.64
Total	$27.61
A new sheave casting costs	$79.00
Machining new casting	10.00
Total	$89.00
Saving per sheave	$61.39

ARC WELDING

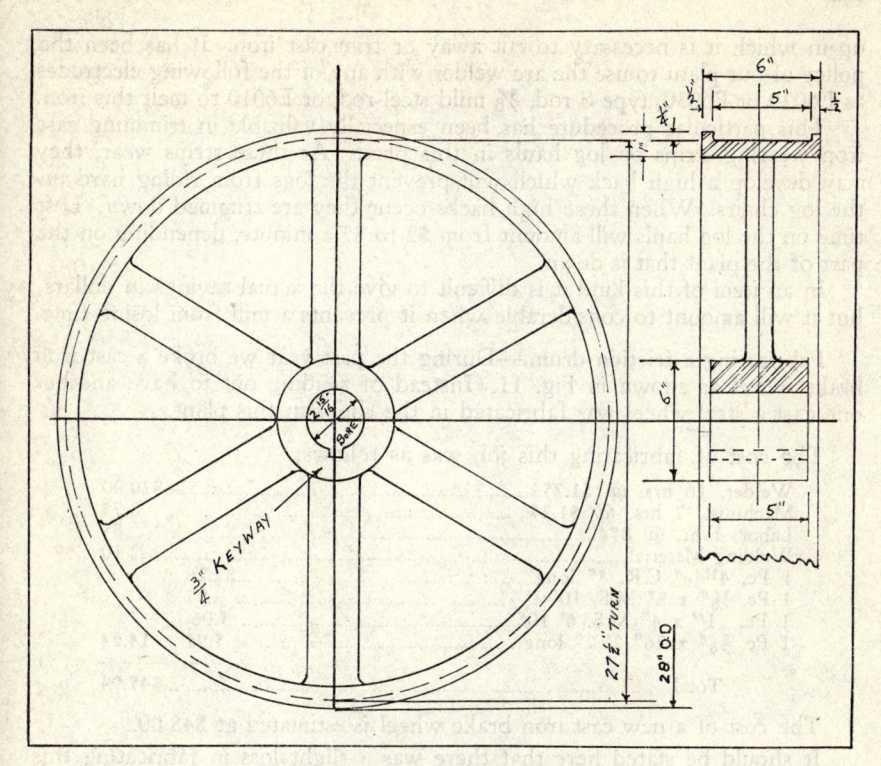

Fig. 11. Cast iron brake wheel.

Repairing conveyor flights—There are several hundred conveyor flights of different widths in this plant. (See Fig. 10.) These flights wear out from being dragged over steel conveyor bottoms, and are usually repaired by welding a piece of angle iron across the face of the flight. The cost of reconditioning the average 30 inch flight is as follows:

Welding and straightling, 2 hrs.	$2.50
Welding rod, 2 lbs.	.22
Material	.20
Total	$2.92
A new flight costs	$8.12

With a 60 per cent increase in life of the flight the saving per flight is approximately $3.75.

Welding extensions on gang foundation bolts when the bolts were buried in concrete. During the past year the foundation under one of the gangs in this plant had settled so much as to cause the machine to produce bad lumber. The gang foundation hold down bolts (4 inches in diameter) were buried in concrete, and it was necessary to weld extensions on these bolts so that the gang could be raised, leveled, grouted, and bolted down. A substantial saving was made on this job with the aid of the arc, although it is impossible to give an accurate estimate of the actual amount.

Cutting off the sides of cast iron log haul wearing strips in order to increase the useful life of the strips.—From time to time a repair job comes up in which it is necessary to cut away or trim cast iron. It has been the policy of our plant to use the arc welder with any of the following electrodes as E6020 or E6030, type S rod, ⅜ mild steel rod, or E6010 to melt this iron.

This particular procedure has been especially valuable in trimming cast iron wearing strips on log hauls in this plant. As these strips wear, they may develop a high back which will prevent the logs from riding hard on the log chairs. When these high backs occur they are trimmed down. Lost time on the log hauls will amount from $2 to $5 a minute, depending on the part of the plant that is down.

In an item of this kind it is difficult to give the actual savings in dollars, but it will amount to considerable when it prevents a mill from losing time.

Fabricating a friction drum.—During the past year we broke a cast iron brake wheel as shown in Fig. 11. Instead of sending out to have another one cast a steel wheel was fabricated in the shops in this plant.

The cost of fabricating this job was as follows:

Welder, 16 hrs. @ $1.25		$20.00
Machinist, 7 hrs. @ $1.25		8.75
Labor, 1 hr. @ 85¢		.85
Welding Material		2.10
1 Pc. 4¹⁵⁄₁₆″ C.R. 5″ long	$2.26	
1 Pc. ⅜″ x 2″ M.S. 10′ 4½″	.97	
1 Pc. 1″ x 4″ M.S. 6′ 10″	5.06	
1 Pc. ⅝″ x 26″ 2′ 2″ long	5.95	14.24
Total		$45.94

The cost of a new cast iron brake wheel is estimated at $48.00.

It should be stated here that there was a slight loss in fabricating this job but the security of being able to keep the mill going was a major item. A mill break down due to the failure of this drum would cost about five dollars a minute.

Fabricating a worm spider.—There are in this plant four lumber stacking hoists which are raised and lowered on an even keel with chains on each side. These hoists are kept level at all times with the aid of two screws keyed to the same power shaft. Each screw drives a worm gear which is on the end of each shaft, used to lower and raise the hoist. Each of these hoists is capable of handling 15MBF of rough green lumber.

On one of the stackers, due to the excessive weight, the cast iron spiders on these gears broke; thus causing the bronze worm ring gear to part in two. No spares were on hand and if new spiders were to be cast and machined, the machine would have been down at least two weeks. It was decided to fabricate these spiders in the plant's shops out of steel. The records show that each spider cost as follows:

Welder, 3 hrs.	$ 3.75
Machinist, 23 hrs.	28.75
Welding material (rod, gas, etc.)	4.05
1 Pc. 1½″ M.S. plate, 354 lbs.	10.80
1 Pc. 1″ M.S. plate, 118 lbs.	6.40
1 Pc. 7¹⁵⁄₁₆″ C.R., 85 lbs.	7.22
Total	$60.97

A rough estimated cost of a cast steel spider is about $50.00. Here is a case in which a small loss was taken in actual repair but a major saving was

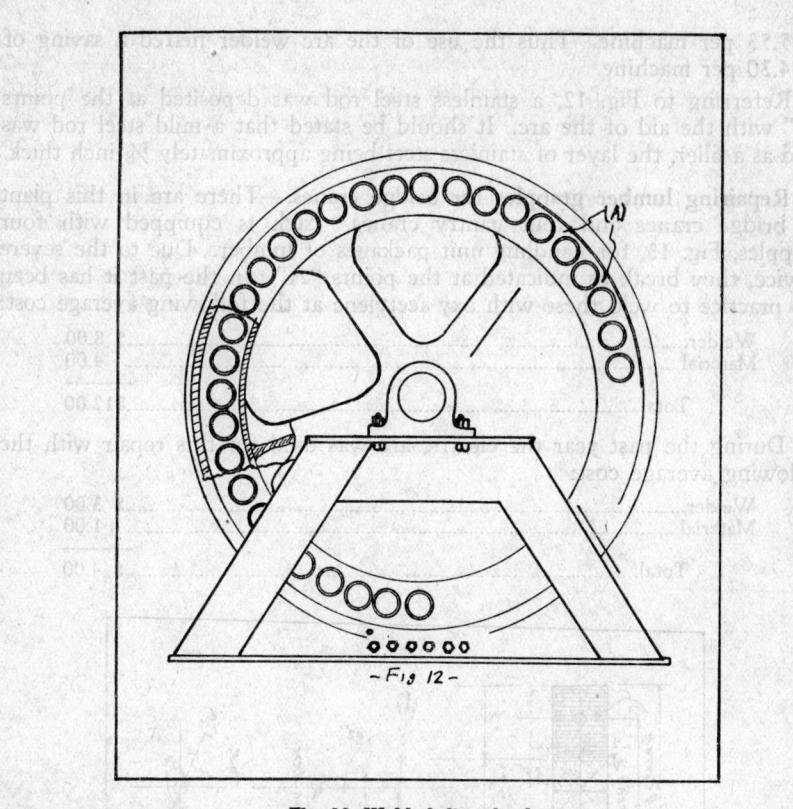

Fig. 12. Welded die wheel.

made in reducing lost time by using the arc welder. The possible lost machine time was reduced by 240 operating hours. This machine runs 22 hours out of each 24. The lost time on this machine may be estimated at $3.00 per hour.

Die wheel repair on Press-To-Log Machines.—Fig. 12 shows a simple sketch of a Press-To-Log Machine. These machines are used to press ground wood into logs weighing about 8 pounds, each log being 4 inches in diameter and 12¾ inches long.

With the aid of a screw arrangement the ground fuel is pressed into dies. As one log is formed, another is pressed out. This die wheel is indexed the space of one die as each log is made. A water jacket surrounds the dies in order to cool the logs. Approximately 15,000 pounds per square inch is necessary to press the ground sawdust into Press-To-Logs.

On the side of the die wheel where the fuel is pressed into the machine, considerable wear occurs. To correct this situation these die wheels were sent to an outside shop, new dies installed, and a machined alloy face welded in place. Four of these die wheels cost $5,960.11 to dismantle, transport, repair, and install; or $1,490.03 each. It became necessary to repair two more of these machines and this time it was decided to build up the worn surfaces in place and to grind the face of the wheel true by improvising a method to turn the die wheel. This was done and the total machine repair cost was

$655.53 per machine. Thus the use of the arc welder netted a saving of $834.30 per machine.

Referring to Fig. 12, a stainless steel rod was deposited at the points "A" with the aid of the arc. It should be stated that a mild steel rod was used as a filler, the layer of stainless steel being approximately ⅛ inch thick.

Repairing lumber grapples for bridge cranes.—There are in this plant 32 bridge cranes and four gantry cranes. Each is equipped with four grapples, Fig. 13, for handling unit packages of lumber. Due to the severe service, they break as indicated at the points "A". In the past it has been the practice to weld these with oxy-acetylene at the following average cost:

Welder	$ 8.00
Material	4.00
Total	$12.00

During the past year the electric arc was used for this repair with the following average cost:

Welder	$ 3.00
Material	1.00
Total	$ 4.00

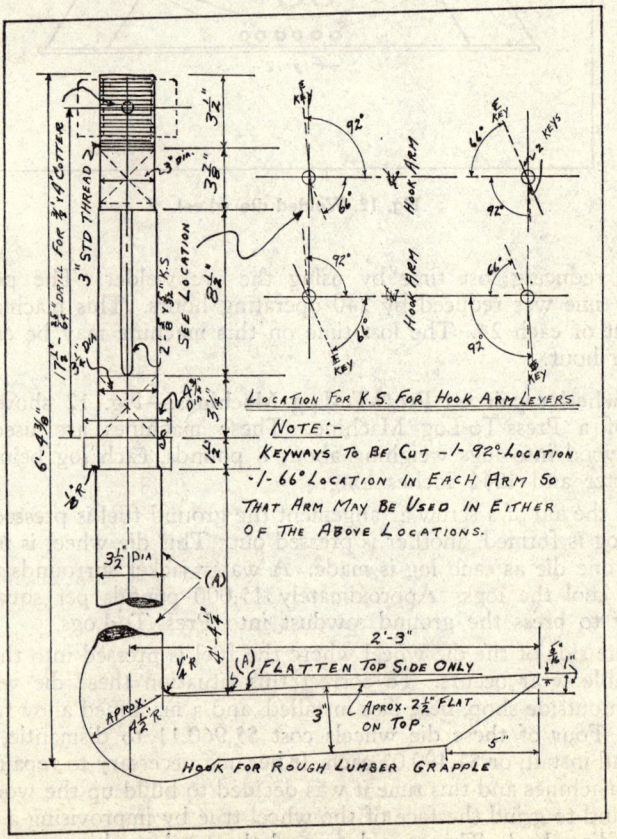

Fig. 13. Design of grapple.

ARC WELDING

There are about 12 of these electric welded arms now in service, some being in use as much as eight months.

A new grapple arm costs about $50.00.

Summary

I have endeavored to give an idea of how arc welding is playing a part in sawmill maintenance by explaining in more or less detail the problems involved in the seventeen examples that I have given. I believe these examples not only show the importance of arc welding in maintenance work but also the importance of arc welding in national defense. Saving and salvaging material for the defense effort is of prime importance.

It is practically impossible to give accurately the actual savings arc welding has made in the items I have listed, but I am going to make a conservative estimate of the approximate saving, on a twelve-months' basis as follows: (Refer to pages 183 and 184 for titles of items.)

Item 1. Saving in material—None
Saving in mill lost time—
Estimated 16 hrs. or 960 min. @ $5.00 per M..........................$4,800.00

Item 2. Saving in material on 50 log chairs @ $11.10 or $555.00............... 555.00

Item 3. Saving on 998 sprockets per year—Assume 5 replacements out of 48 675.00
Saving on 8000 lineal feet of 998 chain per year—
Assume 15% per year, $2,976.00... 2,976.00

Item 5. Considering the number of conveyors in this plant, a conservative twelve-months' savings estimate would be $3,000.00.......................... 3,000.00

Item 6. A conservative estimated savings on eight hogs per year would be $4,000.00 .... 4,000.00

Item 7. Saving on labor in installing sprockets by this method per year= $150.00—Saving in mill lost time at $3.00 per min.=$500.00...... 650.00

Item 8. Due to the large amount of round link chain in this plant, a conservative estimated savings would be $3,000.00............................ 3,000.00

Item 9. Saving on fan per twelve months is about.................................... 100.00

Item 10. Welding saves approximately two sheaves per twelve-month period 178.00

Item 11. Approximately 500 flights per year are salvaged @ $3.75 per flight 1,875.00

Item 12. I believe $100.00 would be a very conservative figure in raising the gang 100.00

Item 13. I believe $175.00 would be a conservative figure in melting cast iron with an arc 175.00

Item 14. No saving occurred on this item during the past year.

Item 15. Saving on this item approximates 250 hours at $3.00 per hour...... 720.00

Item 16. Savings of Press-to-log machines per year approximate $1,000.00.... 1,000.00

Item 17. There are two savings to be accounted for in repairing these lumber grapple arms; namely, the regular savings in repair and that of arc welding over oxy-acetylene welding. A conservative figure for this item is 15 grapples per year at $46.00 each... 690.00

Total of the above figures is $24,494.00.

Chapter XXI—Steel Mill

By J. B. WHITLOCK,

General Maintenance Engineer, The American Rolling Mill Co., Middletown, Ohio.

Subject Matter: A net saving in direct costs of $13,780 is claimed through the use of welding in reclaiming runway rails whose ends had become worn. Guides for cold mill were also welded with a saving of $1,760 per month over new guides. The larger portion of the paper is devoted to a description of the repairing of a large slab mill housing. Welding procedure is given and comparative costs of welding and of new housing are given. A direct saving of $12,850 is claimed with an indirect saving of approximately half a million dollars as a result of welding this housing.

J. B. Whitlock

I. Introduction

Welding in a steel mill has fast become one of the major functions of the maintenance department, and has now reached the important plane occupied by such service departments as the machine shop, pipe shop, and the electric repair shop. In fact, the modern steel mill can no longer be maintained without the use of this valuable tool. The reasons for the gain in importance of welding to a maintenance department are many, and can best be shown by examples which portray the value of this remarkable and valuable tool. From these examples, conclusions can be drawn which will measure this value.

II. Typical Examples of Application of the Arc Welding Process

Repairs Effected to Open Hearth Crane Runway Rails—During the month of February, 1941, the maintenance crews in the open hearth department in one of our plants were having difficulty in maintaining their 125 ton hot metal crane. Crane wheels were breaking, end truck bearings were failing rapidly, and axles were breaking while the crane was carrying its load of hot metal. The cause of all of these crane failures was clearly the fault of the crane runway. Constant pounding, together with high crane speed, coupled with heavy loading, had caused a failure of the rail joints. Some repair had to be made at once in order to keep this unit in operation. Upon inspection, it was found that the main body of the 20 ft. sections of rails was in very good condition, but every joint on this 900 ft. runway was either broken or pounded into a deep recess. Some engineers were of the opinion that new rails should be installed, but others felt that welding could solve the problem.

The welding method was chosen; first, because it could be done at once, while the best possible delivery of rails was ten weeks; second, because the rails erected on the runway would cost $15,070.00, while it was estimated that the welding cost would not be over $1,200.00; and third, because since

Fig. 1. The fractured housing.

the main body of the rail was in excellent condition, many more years of serviceable life could be obtained from the original runway rail investment. Accordingly, the work was scheduled so that it would not interfere with operations, and at the end of fifteen days the work was completed.

The procedure followed in making this repair was:

1. The bad end of each section of rail was carefully scarfed out so that a "V" was formed between the ends of the two adjoining rails. This "V" started at the ball face of the rail and extended into the body of the rail through the web, and stopped at an upper point in the bottom flange. This scarfed face was then ground smooth with a portable grinder in order to remove all voids and pockets and to provide a smooth surface upon which to build the weld metal.

2. The next step consisted of laying a thin layer of 25/20 stainless steel over the entire surface of the "V". This deposit was specified at $5/16$ inch, and was carefully followed by the welders.

3. Over the stainless steel base, horizontal beads of E6010 rod were laid in thin layers, and great care was taken to thoroughly clean each bead before the adjoining beads were laid. This steel electrode was laid in this manner to a point approximately $1/2$ inch from the surface of the ball of the rail.

4. Over the steel weld that had been deposited, hard facing, pressure and abrasion resisting electrode was deposited in single beads and laid in a horizontal position. This weld metal was deposited up to the surface of the ball face.

5. After the weld had cooled sufficiently, the excess weld metal was ground off with a position grinder, and great care was taken in this operation in order to have the welded area ground to the true plane of the virgin rail surface.

This repair has been completed for fourteen months, and no failures of the welded sections have developed. The runway will now serve its purpose for many years to come. Thus, a repair by welding was accomplished which extended the capital life of the original investment many years for an expenditure of $1,200 as against a possible replacement cost of $15,070.00. The repair was completed in a total of fifteen days, while a replacement would have required ten weeks, due to delivery of materials, which was not permissible due to the damage that was being done to the crane by operating over the bad runway.

Most important of all, the repair was made without a shutdown by careful scheduling of each weld, while replacing the bad rails with new sections would have required at least a sixty-hour shutdown in the department.

Development of a Process for Maintaining Cold Mill Guides—A second example of the use of electric welding which has been of great value to our company is the program for salvaging the guides used in the various cold mills. These guides are cast from an alloy of copper, and are purposely made of a soft material so that the strip will not have the edges damaged or marred as it contacts these guides during the rolling process. As a result, small grooves are cut into the guides, which in time become of sufficient depth to prohibit the guide from serving its function in the mill, and the cut guide has to be replaced with a new one. These guides vary in design and weight, and their value covers a range from $30.00 to $65.00 each. An average life of an average guide can safely be given as forty-eight hours, and by using both faces of the guide an average life is found to be ninety-six hours. After the two faces have been used, the guide is scrapped and a new one is put in its place.

This expense, while small per ton of strip rolled, amounted to an average of $2,200 per month on one of our three-stand mills, a sum of money worth saving.

Many tests and experiments were made in an attempt to find a material and a method to make such a repair. No commercial material could be discovered which would deposit a weld of the same physical characteristics as the base metal. And so it was necessary to develop a rod which would meet all of our requirements. Such a rod was finally developed in our foundry after many trials, and after the rod was developed, a welding procedure had to be perfected which would result in good, solid welds.

In June of 1941, all of the difficulties were overcome, and today the welding of cold mill guides is a routine function which requires little or no supervision.

Before the welding procedure was perfected it cost $2,200 each month for new guides.

Today our reclamation cost is $190.00 per month, guide replacement $250.00 per month, which represents a saving of $1,760 each month the mill is in full operation.

Repairs Effected To A Slab Mill Housing—On January 22, 1942, a misunderstanding of signals resulted in two heavy slabs being fed into one of the slab mills. Their total thicknesses was $3\frac{1}{4}$ inches and the horizontal mill rolls were set at 1½ inches. The result was a broken mill housing which put the mill out of service until a repair could be made or a replacement obtained.

Mill manufacturers were contacted, and the best possible promise that could be given for a new mill housing was four months. Such a delay in a time of war was impossible, as this mill produced all of the slabs for the subsequent rolling operations, and its failure meant that the entire plant would have to stop production until the mill was again in operation. Besides the loss of product and the resulting profit, two thousand men would be idle with their resulting loss of wages. Welding was called upon to minimize this delay and to prevent this large economic loss.

The failure of the housing started on the inside or window face of each housing leg and passed through a 2¼ inch hole drilled in the heavy section, then proceeded to the bottom of an 11 inch cored hole in the web of the section. The fracture then advanced approximately 45 degrees upward and followed a horizontal path to the outside face of the leg. This made the fracture complete, and caused a complete separation between the top and the bottom of the housing. The housing in this particular section where the fracture occurred is 28½ inches x 17¾ inches, with a cored area where the section is reduced to 6¼ inches in thickness. Therefore, we had an "H" section where the legs of the "H" are 17¾ inches, the distance between the two faces of the "H" is 28½ inches, and the web of the "H" is 16½ inches, 6¼ inches thick, a difficult section to weld.

Besides the difficult section design, care had to be exercised in the control of overall temperature so that the housing would not be distorted or pulled out of position during the weld period.

Fig. 2. Scarfed areas with the heals in place.

It was decided to weld the housing in place on its own mill shoes and to do all necessary bracing to the second housing by means of existing tie bars and vertical shafts.

After the fractured housing had been placed in its true position and thoroughly braced, tram marks were placed in strategic places on the housing and pin gauges made so that constant checks could be made of the housing position throughout the welding process. Next, the application of secondary heat was carefully studied so that the heavy sections with large areas could be heated to the same temperature as the area surrounding the fractured area.

The method employed in welding the housing consisted of first scarfing out the damaged area in the web section of each leg. This first scarfing started from the 11 inch cored hole and worked towards each face of each leg to a point approximately 2 inches within the $17\frac{3}{4}$ inch section. Care was taken during the scarfing process to remove all dirt and foreign matter from the section in order to provide a clean surface for welding. This scarfed surface was also made as smooth as possible after scarfing by grinding the entire surface. After this first area was completely prepared, the welding was started, using E6010 rod, $\frac{5}{32}$ inch diameter, and having each welding machine set for 150 amperes at 23 volts. Four welders were employed, two on each leg, so that no uneven temperatures would be built up in one localized area. The welding technique employed consisted of laying a horizontal bead or "string" bead continuously from one face of the section to the other. Great care was taken to return each bead so that no crater or depression was left at the end of each pass. As soon as each bead was completed, the slag was thoroughly removed and the single bead peaned with an air operated round nosed peaning tool. Great care was taken not to over pean the weld, and the speed of the peaning was controlled.

With the completion of the peaning, the weld was again cleaned and the process repeated.

After 2 inches of welding was completed in each of the four sections and a "heal" was formed (see Fig. 2), the welding was stopped and preparations were made to scarf the remaining fractured areas of the housing. The remaining area, being in the heavy section, required careful control, and extreme precaution was taken to prevent any great temperature build-up in the section. Care was exercised by alternating the scarfing between the four sections and thus controlling the temperature rise in each section. Also during this period, constant check was made on the housing position, and by the use of the auxiliary heat, the entire casting was kept near a uniform temperature.

After this second step of scarfing was completed and the areas cleaned and ground to a smooth surface, welding was again resumed by the four welders, and continued until the entire area was finished. The same procedure employed in the first or "heal" step, using E6010, $\frac{5}{32}$ inch rod, and cleaning and peaning each bead, was followed in this second step of the process. After all of the area had been welded, finish beads were placed over the face of the welded sections and tie beads were run on the end sections, thereby tying the entire welded area together.

The machining of the housing had to be carried on in the machine shop, and since this shop was some distance away from the mill, and the outside temperature was 10 degrees above zero, it was decided to protect the welded area from any sudden change of temperature by means of rock wool insulation. This was done by building sheet metal boxes around each leg and packing the boxes with the rock wool. With the completion of the machine work, the housing was returned to the mill, the mill was reassembled, and on February 4 at 8:00 A. M., the mill was again rolling steel, thirteen days after the break occurred!

It is interesting to note that 2437 cubic inches had to be filled with weld metal and 896 lbs. of weld rod was used. This metal was deposited in 121 hours with 484 machine hours and 600 man hours, the excess man hours over machine hours being accounted for by "spell" welders.

Figs. 1, 2, and 3 show the fractured housing, the scarfed areas with the heals in place, and one view of the finished weld. A schedule of the process, prepared before the work was started, is also a part of this paper, as it illustrates the estimated time allowed for each step of the work as compared with the actual time used.

The entire cost of this repair, including all welding and machine shop hours, but excluding the dismantling and reassembling of the mill, was $1,658.50. This work, as stated before, was completed in thirteen days. A new mill housing would have cost $12,850, and would have required four months to deliver. When we consider that in four months this mill can produce 240,000 tons of steel and that the loss of production actually amounted to only 26,000 tons, we can readily see the economic value that welding played in making this repair.

III. Recapitulation of the Savings Accrued in the Three Projects Described

Open Hearth Crane Runway Rails—The savings made by effecting a repair to the existing open hearth runway rails can best be shown by balancing the cost of replacing the rails with new rails as against the cost of repairing the existing rails by means of electric welding.

Estimated Cost of Replacing Rails With New Rails

Rails and Clips	$ 2,560.00
Bolts	360.00
Clip Angles and Fillers	432.00
Castings	1,080.00
Misc. Material	200.00
Layout, Drill and Assemble	2,400.00
Field Drilling	1,100.00
Welding Labor	1,830.00
Rigger Labor	3,450.00
Steam Crane	288.00
	$13,700.00
10% Engineering and Contingencies	1,370.00
Cost of Replacement	$15,070.00

Actual Cost of Repairing Runway Rails

Welding Labor	$ 810.00
Supervision and Overhead	81.00
Material and Electric Power	80.60
Grinding Labor	228.40
Cost of Repair	$ 1,200.00
Actual Savings	$13,870.00

Indirect Savings—As has been stated, the electric welding process used in making this crane runway rail repair was carried on without any loss of production in the open hearth department, while to replace the runway rails with new ones would have required a six-hour departmental shut-

Fig. 3. View of finished weld.

down. Since this department produces 100 gross tons of steel per hour, a loss of production equaling 6,000 gross tons of steel would have been suffered if new rails had been installed. The potential profit of the steel at this point, plus the overhead and stand-by charges of the department, equal approximately $6.50 per ton. Therefore, with a loss of 6,000 tons, a direct dollar loss of $39,000 would have been suffered if the rails had not been repaired by electric welding.

The saving, then, that can be attributed to this one repair equals in direct savings $13,870.00, indirect savings $39,000, or a total savings of $52,870.00.

Development of a Process for Maintaining Cold Mill Guides—The replacement cost of the guides on the two cold mills had averaged $2,200 per month for the six months previous to the perfection of a method for salvaging these guides, and during this six months period, an average rolling rate was maintained on these two mills. Since June, 1941, this guide replacement cost has been reduced to an average cost of $250 per month, which with a labor and material cost for salvage work of $190 per month, equals $440 per month. Therefore, a savings of $1,760 per month, or $21,120 per year has been effected.

Since completing the process for salvaging these cold mill guides, the process has been introduced into another plant, where savings of $920 per month, or $11,040 are being made.

We can, therefore, attribute an annual savings of $32,160 to this development besides the material savings of a casting whose basic material is extremely hard to obtain during these war times.

REPAIR SCHEDULE — SLAB MILL HOUSING

[Gantt chart showing repair tasks from Thursday Jan 22 through Thursday Feb 5, 1942, with rows: Dismantle, Clean, Platform, Brace, Scarf "A", Weld "A", Scarf "B", Weld "B", Dismantle, Machine, Reassemble]

Repairs Effected to a Slab Mill Housing—The cost of making the repair to this slab mill housing, exclusive of any dismantling or re-erection cost, was $1,658.50. The dismantling and erection cost, for purpose of comparison, is assumed to be the same whether a new housing was to be installed or a housing repair made. The actual cost of making this repair was as follows:

Preparation Labor	$ 102.60
Welding Labor	647.00
Peaning Labor	184.00
Machine Shop Labor	80.20
Supervision	312.00
Welding Rod	48.37
Power	28.40
Oxygen and Acetylene	54.20
Enclosure	68.40
Service Items—Air, Gas, Lighting	29.75
Bracing Material and Labor	34.60
Misc. Material	68.25
	$1,657.77

Contacts were made with housing manufacturers at the time of the accident, and a firm bid was received from one concern for a housing, to be delivered in four months, for $12,850. Therefore, this repair saved our company $11,192.50. This savings is small in comparison to the loss of production that would have been suffered if the repair had not been made by welding. The time required to make the repair caused a loss of production of 26,000 tons—yet, if we had been forced to wait for the delivery of a new housing, this loss would have been 240,000 tons of material valued at an average selling price of $50 a ton. The making of this repair represents a savings of $546,192.50 to our company, and it is a savings that could not have been made without the use of electric welding.

The most important factor, however, is the savings that was made to the men employed in the division. If this plant had been shut down for four months, 2,000 men whose earnings average $40.00 per week, would have been out of employment for at least sixteen weeks. They would have suffered a loss of income equaling $1,280,000. Such a loss to the community would have been felt by every merchant and landlord in the city, and it would have resulted in untold suffering among the members of the employees' families.

Recapitulation of Savings Accrued in These Welding Projects—

Project	Direct	Indirect
A. Open Hearth Runway Rails	$13,870.00	$39,000.00
B. Cold Mill Guides—Rate per year	32,160.00	
C. Slab Mill Housings	11,192.50	
	$57,222.50	$39,000.00

IV. Conclusion

The experience that has been gained over the past year by members of our organization, together with the application of data determined by research work done by others, has made the application of welding in our maintenance departments successful. The successful application of this process has resulted in making it the most valuable tool we have at our disposal for plant maintenance. Maintenance in a steel plant could not be carried on without the use of electric welding.

These few examples of the application of the process that we have successfully completed during the past year have further proved the economic value of electric welding to the management of our company although they have long been advocates of the use of electrical welding in maintenance work, they are now enthusiastic about its time and money saving advantages.

Each day adds to the value of this process, as each day we find new and important opportunities to use it. Its rapid development and its extended use prove there is a bright future in store for the process of electric welding and for the men engaged in its development and application.

Chapter XXII—Stud Bolts Removed Quickly When Broken

By Alex F. Morton and Wm. F. Kramer,

Welders, Dept. of Sanitation, Central Motor Repair Shops, New York, N. Y.

Subject Matter: Ordinarily when machinists are required to remove broken stud bolts in cylinder heads, motor blocks, wheel carriers, etc., they are drilled out and then shell remaining is taken out by hand tools. Because of these heat treated studs they are relatively hard and average time consumed is about one hour. With electric welding, nuts are welded on studs and they are screwed out. About 20 studs can be removed per 1½ hours of either hardened or unhardened bolts. Authors also claim that cost is about 20 percent less if welder removes the bolts than if machinist does it. Saving of drills, time and getting parts back into service quicker are important considerations.

Alex F. Morton

Wm. F. Kramer

Stud bolts broken off even with, or below the surface of such parts of automotive equipment as wheel carriers, brackets, cylinder heads and motor blocks, etc., are usually a headache to the man assigned to the job of removing them; especially so when the stud bolts are of the hardened type.

Where these bolts break off at an angle, below the surface as shown on the wheel carrier in Fig. 2, drills are dulled with many broken, and an uncertain amount of time lost.

The eight stud bolts in Fig. 2, are broken off at various depths and angles. When removed by the machinist or mechanic, the new stud bolt is sent home with only .003 clearance, and many times the new stud breaks and the operation repeated.

The procedure usually followed by machinists is as follows:—
1. To have the wheel removed and the tire, or tires, dismounted.
2. To drill a pilot hole through the center of the broken stud bolt.
3. To follow this with a larger size drill, large enough to remove all of the bolt possible, without touching the threads, leaving only a thin-walled shell.
4. To remove what is left of this thin shell with a hand tool.
5. To run a tap through the threads to clear them for the new stud post.

Easy out tools do not work on this job, nor Stillson wrenches; other wheel carriers, shown later in this paper, show the results of wrench efforts.

The last four operations listed above take the machinist about one hour. When the broken stud is of the hardened type, no average time is obtainable, a man just does the best he can until it is removed.

Against this average time of one hour per bolt, the electric welder, without trying to establish a record, has on more than one occasion removed as many as 20 stud bolts, broken off above and below the surface, hardened or unhardened, in one hour and a half.

The photo on the next page shows a heap more than 200 stud bolts, removed and accumulated during a period of 20 8-hour working days, 160 hours of welders' time.

During these 160 hours the welder did not work exclusively on stud bolt removal, some days he worked the full 8 hours on this job, other days not at all. But the heap is an accumulation during the period stated. Had the machinist done this work, the very least amount of time that he would have required would have been an average of 1 hour per bolt, on those bolts that could be drilled. This would require 40 hours more time, or about 20 percent more time, than required by the welder. 20 percent is a grossly under-estimated figure, but the 20 percent saving in time is important.

The wheel carrier, Fig. 3, left, plainly shows the bite of the Stillson wrench, and not a bolt removed. Fig. 3, right, shows the start of the electric welders' method of removing broken stud bolts with the electric arc, and is as follows:—

1. Build up the broken off stud bolt until it is level with the wheel carrier surface. Then place over the built up broken off stud either a nut of a size smaller in its inner circumference than the outside circumference of the built up stud bolt, or a blank made of Hex stock, especially for this job. Then weld the blank or nut to the built up stud bolt.

2. Use either a socket, monkey or Stillson wrench and back the bolt out. Fig. 4 shows the nuts welded to the wheel carrier.

When all eight bolts are broken off in this way, there is enough heat transferred to the stud bolt area below the nut from the red hot nuts, which the welder immediately takes advantage of, with the result that he usually gets them all out on the first try.

The time period for removing these bolts between the machinist's method and the electric welder's method is significant.

Estimated gross savings depends on the volume of this particular work, and varies from day to day throughout the year.

The increased service life, is in proportion to the time saved by the fast return of the parts to normal service.

The elimination of broken drills, the saving of time spent on sharpening drills, the use of the drill press, and power used on some other job, as well as the machinist's time on another job, since his release from this stud removal job is also, we believe, an important factor for judgement.

Cost data can only be guessed at. The job is not one of continuous production where a time and cost study could be made. The removal of the studs takes time and varies with each job; some are easily and quickly extracted, while others are very difficult. But the electric welders' method has proven to be so much speedier that the welders now have a monopoly on this work in our shop at least.

Fig. 6 shows tractor drawbar rest bracket with studs removed after nuts had been welded to each broken stud. The one on the left of the picture had to be heated to a bright red around the entire area surrounding it, after which it was backed out with a 36-inch Stillson wrench.

The one on the right was removed first without any heat. The bright threads show an oily appearance while the dull threads on the stud on the left show that the oil was burned out during the heating process.

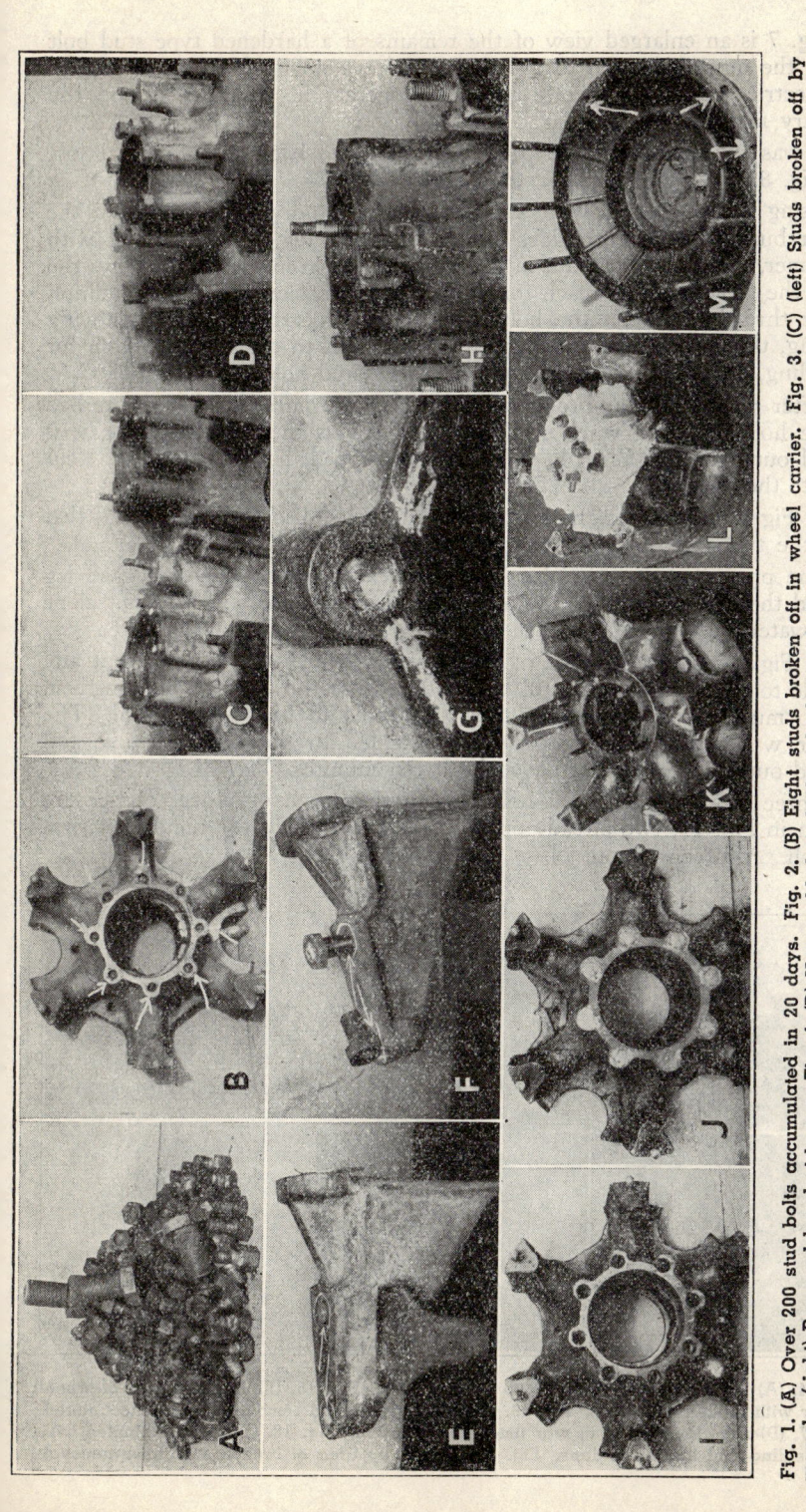

ARC WELDING

Fig. 1. (A) Over 200 stud bolts accumulated in 20 days. Fig. 2. (B) Eight studs broken off in wheel carrier. Fig. 3. (C) (left) Studs broken off by wrench. (right) Removed by electric arc. Fig. 4. (D) Nuts welded on built-up broken stud. Fig. 5. (E) Studs broken off in tractor draw bar rest bracket. Fig. 6. (F) Tractor draw bar rest bracket and arc weld stud removal. Fig. 7. (G) Hardened type stud bolt after attempted drilling out. Fig. 8. (H) With arc welding a tough situation is overcome. Fig. 9. (I) Uneven, distorted threads are often encountered. Fig. 10 (J) Arc welding fills stud holes solid for drilling. Fig. 11. (K) Wheel carrier legs with broken studs. Fig. 12. (L) Wheel carrier in Fig. 11 with leg studs removed, ready for new bolts. Fig. 13. (M) An easy removal job for arc welding.

Fig. 7 is an enlarged view of the remains of a hardened type stud bolt which the machinist tried to drill out, but gave up in disgust and sent to the electric welder to operate on. And operate he did, but not in the ordinary manner.

It was successful and the patient lived, to go back to its normal job. See Fig. 8.

Using a E6010 rod with straight polarity and plenty of amps, the welder burned down both sides of the stud bolt lug, knocked it off with a hammer, then tack welded it in the position shown in Fig. 8. It shows the depth the welder had to reach for the top of the broken stud, the condition of the threads, both on the bolt and the wheel carrier. After removing the slag, this entire section was built up and sent to the machine shop for re-drilling, tapping and the insertion of a new stud bolt.

After removal of the broken stud bolts, many times the threads are bad or the hole has been worn egg shaped. Then as the picture shows, it is drilled out over size filled up solid, drilled, tapped, bolts inserted and sent back to the job.

In Fig. 11 the wheel carrier had the stud bolts all broken in the legs that held the tire and rim in place.

The procedure on this job is the same except that we heated each leg around the broken stud bolts to a bright red, chilled the stud and nut alone with water and backed out with a wrench.

In Fig. 13 is another type of wheel carrier which does not present any trouble to the machinist to drill out, but, because the welder can take them out so much faster and easier, they also come to him for removal. The carrier was turned upside down, nuts welded to the broken studs, and backed out. Three were removed in fifteen minutes. Fig. 14.

Three more broken stud bolts on another type of wheel carrier are shown in Fig. 15; two already out and the third ready for removal with a wrench. A fifteen minute job.

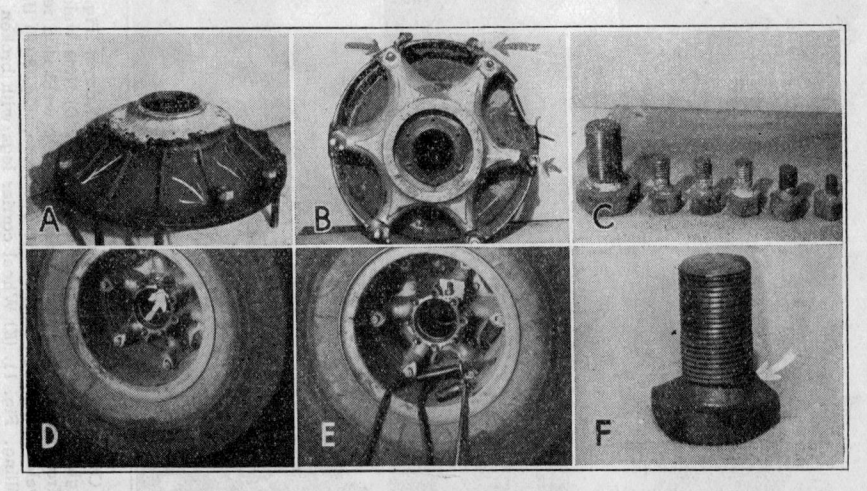

Fig. 14. (A) Method of welding nuts to broken studs. Fig. 15. (B) Another type of wheel carrier with broken stud bolts. Fig. 16. (C) A variety of stud removal jobs is encountered. Fig. 17. (D) A serious delay to war time transportation. Fig. 18. (E) Fifteen minutes with arc welding and the job is done. Fig. 19. (F) Built-up area of broken stud after removal.

Fig. 16 will give a good idea of the various sizes of broken stud bolts that we have removed, the depth that it was necessary to go in order to reach some of them, as well as the angle at which some of them were broken off.

Fig. 17 shows a wheel carrier with a pair of heavy shoes on it. If the machinist would have drilled this bolt, he would have had the tires removed for ease in handling and setting up. The welder merely pushed the entire assembly over on its side walls, welded a nut to the broken stud and backed it out. Another fifteen minutes operation, Fig. 18.

Fig. 19 is a slight enlargement of the tractor bolt shown in Fig. 6. We wish to call attention to the area sandwiched between the lower ends of the threads and the upper part of the nut to which it is welded. The undercut appearance shows the effects of the use of welders moulding compound around the wall of a threaded area, which we use to protect the wall threads from arc splatter, which sometimes interferes with the easy removal of a broken stud. Welder's moulding compound is now in regular use when the bolt is broken off below the surface and there is a chance of tieing into the threads instead of the top of the bolt.

In closing we wish to say that we have had our best results with a heavy flux-coated manganese type rod. This does not mean of course, that some other type rod, with a high tensile strength, would not do the job as well or better. We use what we have on hand and make the best of it. The heavy flux-coating aids in keeping the rod from welding itself to the sides of the stud bolt hole. It helps the welder put the building up material where he wants it, and not where the rod wants to go at times.

We have also had to weld more than one nut to the same broken stud, but we stick to them until it appears hopeless, then we resort to the major operation as shown in Fig. 8.

Our employer operates one of the largest automotive fleets in the U. S., at least, we did up to the time we motorized our Army.

Since the date of our first experiment with this idea in August 1940, we have continuously used this method at least once a day, and many times eight hours per day, on nothing else but wheel carriers and other parts of auto equipment. We are conservative when we state that we have saved the department many hundreds of hours, many unbroken drills, much power, a considerable amount of machinists' time, and a drill press for other purposes.

We have used this method to remove broken off studs with the tire rim and wheel carrier in place on the truck, but not with the same speedy or satisfactory results that we obtained when the job was in position for a down hand weld.

Chapter XXIII—Trestle for Stocking Iron Ore

By EARL M. VER BUNKER,

Mining Engineer, The Montreal Mining Co., Montreal, Wisconsin.

Earl M. Ver Bunker

Subject Matter: In order to increase the stock pile of iron ore at shaft it was necessary to reinforce the stock pile trestle which had six branches or "bays". A mining engineer discusses fully and illustrates clearly how arc welding was used to: 1, reinforce the bottom chords of trestle girders; and 2, reinforce the top chords. Cost of arc welded fabrication was $374.60 per bay while riveted construction was $684.60 per bay. A total saving for the six bays was $1,860.

INTRODUCTION

When additional ore hoisting capacity was required, new aluminum skips (11.2 ton capacity) were placed in service at the central hoisting shaft of a large iron ore mining company located on the Gogebic range in the Lake Superior district. The amount of ore handled per hour was thereby increased and to stock this ore, the load in the larry cars, operating on the stocking trestles, was also increased to a maximum of 22.4 tons. This load was more than the trestles were originally designed to carry, and the resulting safety factor was too low to be considered good practice. It was recommended that a member of sufficient cross-section area be added to the top chord of each girder comprising the trestle. Fig. 1 shows a plan of the present ore stocking trestles.

Another recommendation was the placing of additional bracing in the bottom chord, including diaphragm bracing about the middle of the span, designed to resist the horizontal thrust of the iron ore caused by stocking the ore to the top of the trestle girder. When stocking ore to the top of the girder or track elevation, a considerable increase in the capacity of the trestle is attained over filling the trestle only to the bottom of the girder. This increased capacity is essential especially during a lean shipping season when the capacity of all ore stocking facilities is taxed to the maximum. Figs. 2 and 3 indicate the end view and side elevation, respectively, of the steel stocking trestle.

The discussion of the above trestle reinforcing by electric arc welding is divided in two parts: (1) Reinforcing the bottom chords of the trestle girders. (2) Reinforcing the top chords of the trestle girders.

The mining company maintains an engineering department in which the author is employed as a mining engineer. All new work is planned and estimated by this department. When the trestle repair request came up, the engineering and planning work was assigned to the writer.

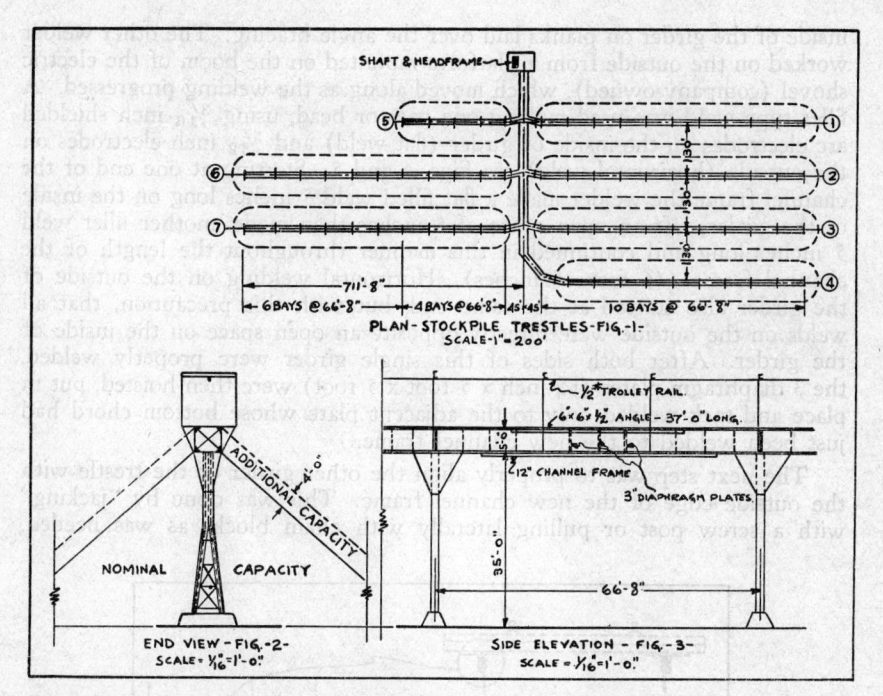

Fig. 1. Stock pile trestle plan. Fig. 2. End view steel stocking trestle. Fig. 3. Side elevation stocking trestle.

The company's mechanical and welding crews did the actual erection under the supervision of the master mechanic. All the steel for this reinforcing work was fabricated by an outside contracting firm.

Period Covered by the Work—The work described in this paper was planned during the early part of 1940. Actual welding work began in June 1940 and continued intermittently until fall. Work was again resumed in the summer of 1941 and carried on to the fall as the stockpiles became available.

Bottom Chord Reinforcing of the Trestle Girders—The steel for this reinforcing consisted of two 12 inch #25 channels 46 feet—6 inches long per bay connected as a unit by angle bracing. (See Fig. 5) Each complete section weighed approximately 2,675 lbs. and was lifted to within one foot of the bottom of the girder by means of two long ½ inch cables, 2 snatch blocks and a larry car moving on top of the trestle furnished the lifting power. The channel reinforcing unit was then raised the remaining distance, and held snugly in place by two ½ ton chain blocks. This unit was then clamped to the girders using heavy "C" clamps after properly aligning the bottom chord of one girder only. The bottom of this girder was then tacked by electric arc welds to the channel unit. Care was exercised in aligning the channel unit to the bottom of the trestle girder.

Welding to the girder then proceeded. Two welders and four assistants were used on all this work. A 200 ampere and a 150 ampere machine were used. One machine was connected to the trolley rail, (see photograph Fig. 8), and the other machine was connected to a power supply line nearby. Due to the height of these girders, (see Figs. 2 and 3), one welder worked on the inside of the girder on planks laid over the angle bracing. The other welder worked on the outside from a platform mounted on the boom of the electric shovel (company owned), which moved along as the welding progressed. A fillet type weld was used making one pass or bead, using $3/16$ inch shielded arc electrodes on the inside of girder (flat weld) and $5/32$ inch electrodes on the outside (horizontal weld) see Figs. 4 and 5. Starting at one end of the channel frame the welder made a flat filled weld 5 inches long on the inside of the girder, left an open space of 5 inches then made another fillet weld 5 inches long and continued in this manner throughout the length of the channel frame (46 feet—6 inches). Horizontal welding on the outside of the girder also started at the same end, but with this precaution, that all welds on the outside were directly opposite an open space on the inside of the girder. After both sides of this single girder were properly welded, the 3 diaphragm plates ($1/4$ inch x 5 foot x 5 foot) were then hoisted, put in place and tack welded only to the adjacent plate whose bottom chord had just been welded to the new channel frame.

The next step was to properly align the other girder of the trestle with the outside edge of the new channel frame. This was done by "jacking" with a screw post or pulling laterally with chain blocks as was needed.

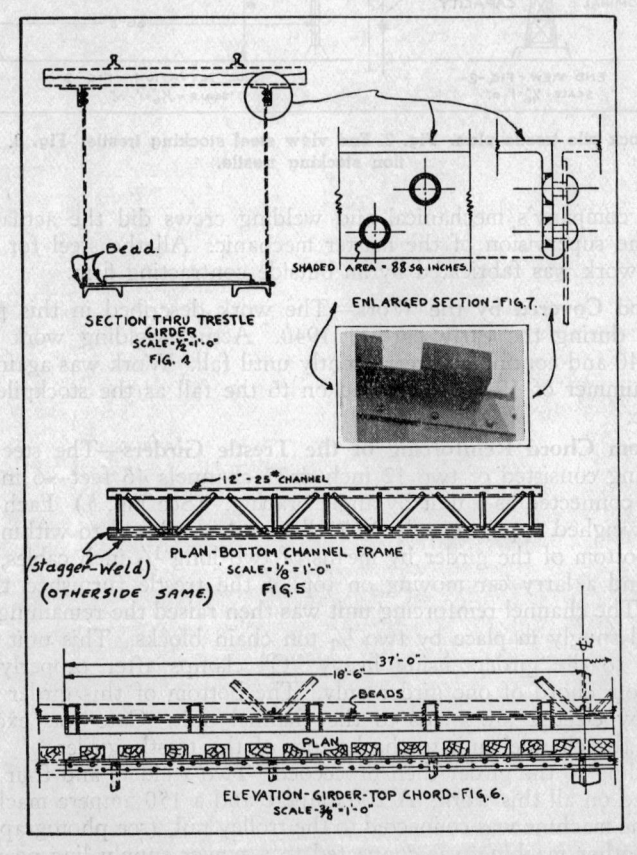

Fig. 4. Section through trestle girders. Fig. 5. Bottom channel frame plan. Fig. 6. Elevation of girder-top chord. Fig. 7. Enlarged section trestle girder.

Having accomplished this alignment, the three diaphragm plates were then welded, two vertical sides only, using $3/16$ inch and $5/32$ inch electrodes.

The purpose of the three diaphragm plates ($1/4$ inch x 5 foot x 5 foot) placed about the center of the girder span was to aid in maintaining a true parallelogram form, as the maximum stress occurs in this portion. $5/32$ inch electrodes were used making a one pass weld 3 inch followed by a 4 inch space on the two vertical sides and along the angle cross-bracing on the sides of the diaphragm plates. (See Fig. 2)

Cross-bearing was also welded to the diaphragm plates at this time. Welding the second girder to the new channel frame was then started, following the same procedure as with the first girder: 1 pass weld 5 inch long followed by a 5 inch space—weld staggered on opposite side.

While the work was being planned a contract bid for the fabricating and erecting of the steel for the bottom channel frame including the diaphragm plate angle cross-bracing was requested of a jobber.

The proposal for the contract was exorbitantly high over our own estimate, therefore, we decided to do the work ourselves.

The cost per bay was as follows:

Method by Welding
Fabricated steel channel frame..$178.60
Erection—Labor (mechanical and welders), welding material
 and electricity 196.00
                                                                                    ————
                                                                                    $374.60

Contracts Bid Using Rivets
Fabricated steel channel frame..$178.60
Erection—(Labor and freight on tools, etc.)................................ 506.00
                                                                                    ————
                                                                                    $684.60

This shows a considerable saving, namely $310 per bay. There is no doubt that welding had a major share in this saving using the welding method over riveting. Some saving was also made in using our own equipment.

Top Chord Reinforcing of the Trestle Girders—The steel for this reinforcing consisted of one (6 inch x 6 inch x $1/2$ inch) angle (37 foot-0 inch) and ten tie plates—size (6 inch x $1/2$ inch x 1 foot-0 inch) per bay welded to the outside and top of each girder. (See Fig. 4) One hundred thirty pieces of angles were required for the sixty-five bays. (See Fig. 1) The proposition of welding the angles to the present riveted structure entailed much discussion before a final decision was reached. It was first suggested to burn out every other rivet and then re-rivet the new member to the present girder. There were two lines of $3/4$ inch rivets in the riveted structure over which the new (6 inch x 6 inch x $1/2$ inch) reinforcing angles had to be fitted and made snug against the old member itself before welding could be started. It was finally decided to have the holes in the new angles drilled $1 \, 9/16$ inch diameter. The nominal size of a $3/4$ inch rivet is $1 \, 5/16$ inch, giving the drill holes in the angle $1/4$ inch clearance. It was also recommended to temporarily support the present girder at the mid-point with timber posts and jack-screws to relieve the dead load stresses in the present structure. By doing this, the new reinforcing members would receive the same stress as the present structure, thus avoiding an overload in the old members.

The (6 inch x 6 inch x $1/2$ inch) angles were next placed in the mid-section of the girder bay, and clamped by means of "C" type clamps. These clamps were sufficiently large to pass over the two (6 inch x 6 inch x $1/2$

Fig. 8. Arc welding machine with swinging platform attached to truck. Fig. 9. Reinforcing completed by arc weld.

inch) angles, binding the two angles tightly. The tie plates (6 inch x $\frac{1}{2}$ inch x 1 foot-0 inch) across the top of the angles and the space between the wood ties were spot welded. The spot welding was then followed by flat and vertical welding. Three-sixteenth inch shielded-arc electrodes were used in making a fillet type weld (one pass or bead) at the edges of the tie plates and the open space between the 6 inch x 12 inch ties, throughout the entire length of the angle. (See Fig. 6) One welder performed the top welding (flat) operation, starting at one end of the angle reinforcing while the second welder started at the opposite end to weld around the rivet heads on the vertical (outside) leg of the angle. A special platform connected to the arc welding machine truck was used for welding the vertical leg. (See Fig. 7)

Three sixteenths inch shielded-arc electrodes were used in welding the holes around the lower part of the $\frac{3}{4}$ inch rivet heads. Five thirty-seconds inch electrodes were used around the upper part of the holes. (Overhead welding) Special care was taken in welding these side holes, to obtain a good penetration and at least a $\frac{3}{16}$ inch circular weld adjacent to the walls of the hole. The area of this circular weld is .88 square inches, which is equal to the area of two $\frac{3}{4}$ inch rivets. (See Fig. 7) There were 86 side holes to weld in each (6 inch x 6 inch x $\frac{1}{2}$ inch) reinforcing angle.

The reinforcing project has proven very satisfactory to the management, both in workmanship and cost. Arc welding was the direct contributing factor in the efficient manner in which the work was performed, and the substantial saving in the cost.

The cost per bay was as follows:—

Method by Welding

Steel—Furnished and drilled by jobber..$ 64.67
Erection—Labor (mechanics and welders), welding material and electricity 48.78

Total cost per bay..$113.45

Comparing this with a riveted job it would have required burning and punching out one half of the old rivets in the top chord and replacing them with longer rivets through both members. This would have required more field labor and material, thereby increasing the cost. The completed work is stronger with the extra top cross-plates and additional welding at the top of the chord between the wood ties. The completed reinforcing assembly is shown in Fig. 9.

Chapter XXIV—Truck Wheel Carrier

By Clinton Stutter,

Foreman of Mechanics, City of New York, Dept. of Sanitation, New York, N. Y.

Subject Matter: Cast steel wheel carriers were salvaged by first making a jig so that thick spokes of wheels could be torch cut. Wheel carriers to be salvaged are put into another special jig for tacking so that the spokes will be lined up properly. These large cast steel wheel carriers cost $53.50 when new and it is estimated that a saving of 94 per cent can be made by welding them. Formerly broken carriers were scrapped. Any large fleet owner can cut costs at least 50 percent and salvaging is especially economical at this time because of difficulty in obtaining new steel wheels.

Clinton Stutter

In September of 1941, a salesman employed by "Wheels Inc." of New York City, visited our shop on a routine business call. While walking through our machine shop, he noticed a pile of cast steel rear wheel carriers which were awaiting repairs. Some of these seemed beyond repair. He told me to hold onto them as it would be practically impossible to obtain replacements, due to defense programs. He then explained that his company was salvaging a great many carriers which were worn on the felloe parts, by cutting them down and welding a complete new felloe ring to the old hub and spokes. It so happened that in the pile of carriers in our shop, each had one or two broken, missing, cracked or twisted spokes and after looking them over, he said, "well we can't do anything with those". That started a train of thought in my mind—(Why can't we save some of these? If a carrier has only one or two broken spokes, why can't we cut those spokes out and replace them with good spokes cut from other carriers which have three broken ones. In that way we may be able to save at least 50 percent of these carriers which, heretofore, had been junked.)

I knew this would require a jig or fixture to cut the spokes accurately enough to be interchangeable. The jig was designed and built in our machine shop shortly after. There were no elaborate drawings or blue prints. I laid the basic setup out on a piece of black cardboard, marking the various dimensions full scale with chalk. This permitted easy erasure and changes which were numerous.

The accompanying photographs and following description will, I trust, convey the idea comprehensively.

The bed in Fig. 1 is a piece of $\frac{1}{2}$ inch boiler plate 22 inches square. This sets in an angle iron tray 1 inch x $\frac{5}{8}$ inch x $\frac{1}{8}$ inch iron. The legs are $1\frac{3}{4}$ inch x $\frac{1}{8}$ inch angle iron 30 inches high, braced about half way down with the same size angle iron used for the tray. The frame is arc welded into one unit but the bed plate is removable. Four old steering arm balls are welded to the legs to facilitate moving the unit. The center shaft

Fig. 1. Cutting set-up.

is a piece of cold rolled steel 1½ inches x 6 inches, this is centrally located in an old 5¾ inch O. D. thrust bearing, which is protected from flying oxide by a steel ring ¼ inch thick by 1 inch high. A guide plate to fit the hub bore of wheel carrier and center stud is placed over the thrust bearing. A stop to locate the wheel carrier through any of the brake drum bolt holes is provided with a removable pin.

The outside cutting torch carrier guides are 1¼ inch round stock 14 inches high above the plate. The center guide is $1^{5}/_{16}$ inch round.

The torch carrier presented the greatest problem. Motion in all directions was necessary and has been provided, vertical, horizontal and lateral. The torch can be swung in a 360° circle in the vertical or horizontal plane, but is prevented once set from changing its lateral or center distance from the hub, by two binder screws which clamp the tubes of the torch tightly in a two piece revolvable and removable flanged block. Block is placed in a ring on the carrier which must be large enough to permit the head of the torch to pass through.

The counterweights are just heavy enough to allow the torch carrier assembly to move down slowly by its own weight. The cables were taken from a discarded speedometer drive and are run over small grooved sheaves.

The carriers to be salvaged are set properly on the center guide, the stop pin is inserted, the cutting torch is set laterally in the most advantageous position regarding the cracked or broken part, and the cut is made on one side. The carrier is then transferred to the other guide post and the cut is made on the opposite side. We now have the damaged spoke removed

Fig. 2. Set-up for arc "tacking". Fig. 3. Completed weld-carrier ready for use.

and the cut is clean, straight and true. This carrier is then removed and the hopeless carrier with several remaining good spokes is handled the same way with the same lateral setting of the cutting torch. This, of course, leaves a gap when set in the fixture for arc welding, but this gap is readily filled and provides for 100 percent bond by the filler rod.

The set up for arc welding is simple, the proper size spacer rim is shipped over the wheel carrier and clamped tightly to two good spokes, evenly spaced. An extra deep "C" clamp is used so as to clamp the rim in the center of the length of the spoke. A $\frac{1}{2}$ inch thick flat steel ring $18\frac{1}{4}$ inch O. D. and $14\frac{1}{8}$ inch I. D.; notched out to clear the rim lug studs in the spokes, is clamped on the end faces of the fixed spokes; the replacement spoke is then set in place and clamped to the steel ring by means of a hand wheel, screwed onto the rim lug stud. The beveled felloe end of the spoke is brought snugly up against the spacer rim and clamped with another "C" clamp. The welder then proceeds to "tack" the spoke securely. After this is done the plate and rim is removed and the regular weld is completed in the usual way.

The jig heretofore described, cost approximately $227 to build. Material, $8 for steel and angle iron, plus labor, $219 for machinists and welder. (Salvaged auto parts used not evaluated).

Assembly weighs..................................205 pounds.
Construction took place..................Sept.—Oct. 1941.
First wheel carrier finished..............Oct. 6th 1941.

The jig and process is not patented.

The basic design was devised by the author with some modifications suggested by the two machinists who built it.

Savings effected—A new wheel carrier costs $53.50. The average salvage time is two hours labor at $1.40 per hour and two pounds of mild steel arc rod at six cents per pound.

Oxygen and acetylene for the cutting operation was eighteen cents.
Proportionate cost saving compared to price of new carrier 94 percent.
Estimated annual gross cost saving $3,210.

To explain: Should the number of wheel carriers salvaged thus far (twenty in four months) continue at the same rate, it would mean that we would have had to purchase sixty wheels at the aforementioned gross cost.

Any large fleet owner faced with the same condition, could cut carrier costs at least 50 percent, bearing in mind that all carriers cannot be salvaged and some must be destroyed to obtain replacement spokes.

Note: Overhead has not been figured as it varies greatly as to locality and circumstances.

In these times when replacement parts are difficult or impossible to obtain quickly, salvaging processes must be employed as extensively as possible. It means a saving to the department or fleet owner, a saving in raw materials and productive man hours that are so vital to our war effort. The useful life and service of parts formerly junked is now greatly extended.

Chapter XXV—Hydraulic Turbine Maintenance on Municipal Power System

By ERIC F. BLADHOLM,

Mechanical Engineering Associate, General Plant Division, Department of Water and Power, Los Angeles, California

Subject Matter: Paper deals exclusively with the maintenance of hydraulic turbines for Los Angeles and covers 4 years' work. The pitted surfaces of turbines were welded with mild steel, stainless steel and 4–6% chromium steel electrodes. The relative merits of these electrodes are pointed out including the techniques used in their application. Details of preparation and finishing of the turbines are given. Carefully prepared tables show the areas repaired, rod consumption, man hour per square inch of repaired surface and the total man hours. 9 units were repaired in the period covered.

E. F. Bladholm

Maintenance problems on the power system of the Department of Water and Power, City of Los Angeles, are probably the largest of their kind. The total connected generating capacity is approximately 800,000 kilowatts, of which 495,000 kilowatts are represented by six 82,500 kilovolt amperes hydro-electric generators at Boulder Power Plant. The first of these units was placed in operation October, 1936.

Maintenance of the hydraulic turbine runners on these units was started in 1938. The work was progressed by the general plant division shops, and to date a total of 31,566 square inches of pitted surface, due to cavitation, has been repaired. During this time approximately 3,460-pounds of welding rod have been used, of which 2,735-pounds was mild steel, 650-pounds was 18-8 stainless, and 75-pounds was 4-6 chromium. A total of 12,577 man hours was required for completion of repairs. A high standard of continuity service has been maintained with a minimum of outage in line with the policy of the operating division.

The hydraulic turbine runners described in this paper are of the Francis type, developing 115,000 brake horsepower at approximately 2,500-cubic feet per second at 500-foot head. The runners are of immense proportions, being approximately 15½-feet in diameter and weighing approximately 75,000-pounds.

They are of cast steel construction, having approximately the following analysis: carbon .32, silica .35, manganese .70, sulphur .025, and phosphor .025.

The inside diameter of the runners at the top of the draft tube is 11-feet, allowing ample space for working. There are 19 vanes, which from the draft-tube side are approximately 39 inches high and 1 inch thickness at the trailing edge. Fig. 1 shows a view of the under side of the runner from the draft-tube side.

Cavitation, which has caused pitting and loss of metal on the runners at Boulder Power Plant, has been described by many authorities. Many

Fig. 1. View beneath runner from draft-tube side.

theories have been advanced and they will not be discussed here. However, it is generally conceded that the discontinuity or roughness of surface increases the intensity or activity of cavitation. This point is important when considering welded and cast runner surfaces, as will be discussed later in this report.

During the operation of the units at the Boulder Power Plant, which started when unit N-2 was placed in service in October, 1936, periodic turbine inspections disclosed cavitation damage. After 4- to 6-months of operation, pitting had progressed only to minor extent, and was found in the low-pressure areas of the vanes near the trailing edge. The areas were small, and the maximum depth only a little over $\frac{1}{16}$-inch, and during this time, the head on the turbines had increased from approximately 378-feet to 450-feet.

At the low heads, considerable noise was experienced in turbine operation, and as a result vane struts, as shown in Fig. 1, were installed by the manufacturer. Some varied successes were experienced, but a few months later the struts were removed.

In February, 1938 approximately 16-months after unit N-2 was placed in service, inspection showed that the pitting had advanced seriously. In fact, cavitation was propagating so fast, it was necessary to plan an extensive repair program for the low peak season which was only a short time away. The extent of cavitation on the other units N-1, N-3, and N-4 was similar to that found in unit N-2, but varied in degree of intensity. The general picture of the deteriorating effect is shown on Figs. 2 and 3. In some places the vanes which were approximately 1-inch in thickness at the trailing edge were cavitated clear through the metal. It was felt that, at the increased rate of cavitation shown by inspection, the units would not operate through the next winter peak season without serious damage.

With only a short time available for preparation, the general plant division's engineering and shop sections cooperated in laying out equipment, materials, and methods for handling the job. Available information of the methods used on similar jobs was studied and some good suggestions were obtained, but the program was much larger and differed in many respects. Time did not allow much experimentation or testing.

Qualification of welders was not a problem, as welders were qualified periodically and many good welders were available for carrying on the welding phase of the work. Test plates were made so that the best repair methods could be developed. Plates were set up in vertical positions to simulate actual field conditions. The plates were chipped in steps of approximately one welding bead. Chipping methods and tools were tried out and found to be satisfactory. Various types of rods were used in order to determine bonding and depositing characteristics. Current and potential settings were also noted for the different rods. The deposited weld metal was peened and then ground to determine the grinding characteristics of the metal and the best types of grinding wheels and tools for resurfacing.

Test plates served to determine the ability of the shop men to chip, weld, peen, and grind, and in addition were used for demonstration and for training new men. A full size floor plan of the runner area was laid out in the shops to determine the number of men that could efficiently work on a runner.

A wood staging, Fig. 4, was so constructed that it could be readily installed through the draft tube inspection doors and yet not sacrifice any strength. The platform was set at an elevation so that the men could conveniently work on the vanes and still have complete access to the inspection doors in case of an emergency. Foot benches in varying heights were used

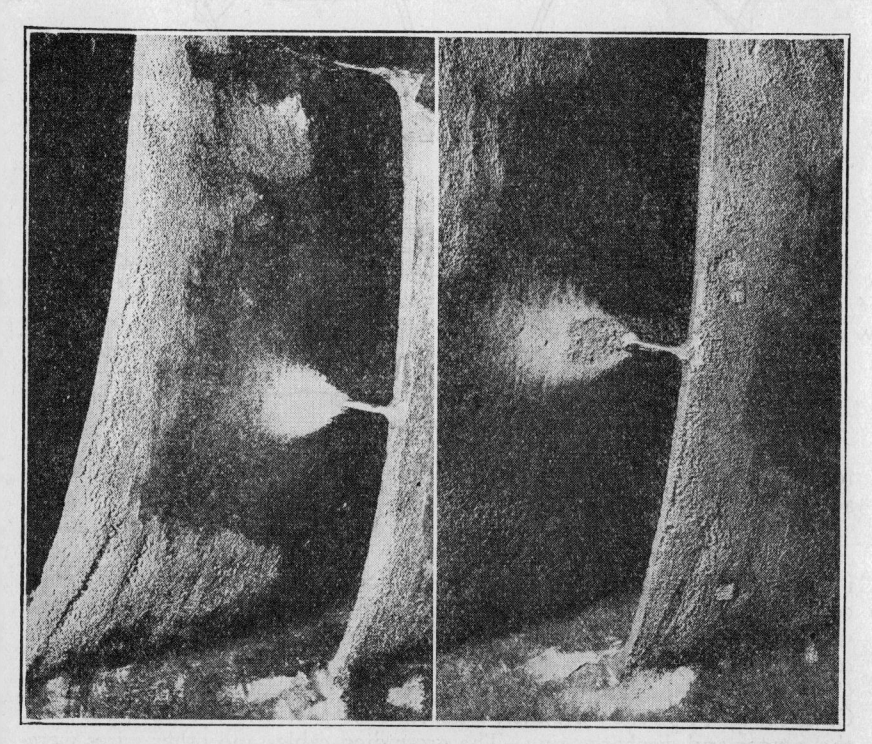

Figs. 2 and 3. Deteriorating effect of cavitation.

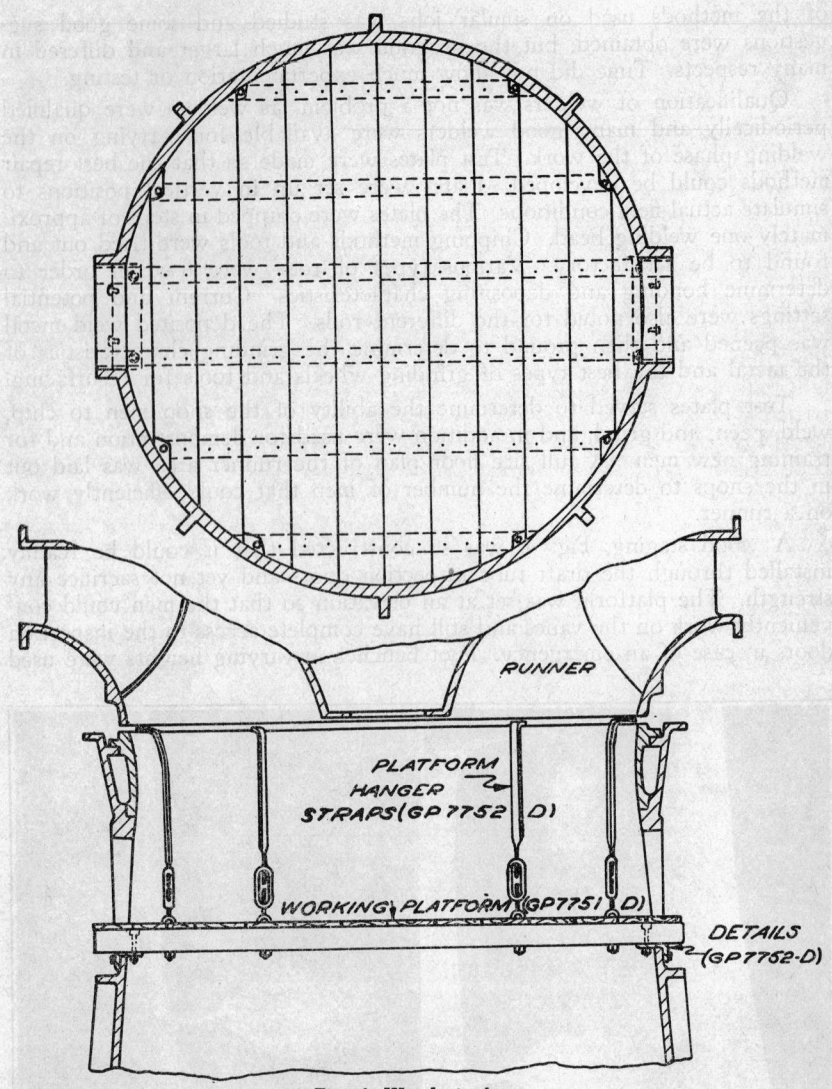

Fig. 4. Wood staging.

for the convenience of both tall and short men. Drawing, Fig. 5, shows additional details of the platform.

Portable power switchboards, drop cords, welding leads, grounding cables and other miscellaneous wiring were installed. A master switch was installed in the draft tube, Fig. 5, so that ventilation and welding machines could be shut down in case of fire or other emergency. Considerable thought was given to making the ground connections for welding operations. In order to prevent a heavy flow of current from the turbine shaft to the guide bearings, the runner and draft tube were both grounded with 500,000 C.M. cable. A 1/4-inch x 2-inch mild steel strap was also welded between the runner and discharge ring. The grounding cables and other wires were passed in under the platform and up through holes in the center of the platform, under the runner cone. The master switch was attached to the runner cone where it could be conveniently reached.

Ventilation was maintained by two blowers, which forced air into the draft tube through the inspection doors, and a fan which exhausted through a manhole in the top of the scroll case. There was always plenty of fresh air and the draft was strong enough to pull the grinding wheel dust out of the working area. Space heaters were placed in the manways leading to draft tube inspection doors to heat the ventilating air as needed.

Two one-inch air hoses were passed into the draft tube under the platform and were brought out into manifolds having five ½-inch air hose connections. These were used for chipping, peening, and grinding operations. Gloves and special helmets were furnished for the grinding operations. The helmets were constructed with safety glass windows. They were light, but were designed to protect the operator's face and neck from grinding particles. Chrome leather aprons, gloves and shoulder protectors were furnished for the welders. Conventional type helmets and extra light electrode holders were used. Stools with adjustable legs, arm rests, and everything of a practical nature were used for the comfort and safety of the men. Grinder pedestals were made with telescopic legs so the height could be readily adjusted.

One of the bays in the eductor gallery was closed off to form a room where the men could change clothes and eat their meals. The room was large enough so that tools, supplies and equipment could also be stored and was conveniently located to all units which were repaired. Minor repairs and adjustments to equipment were made in this room, although chisel tempering

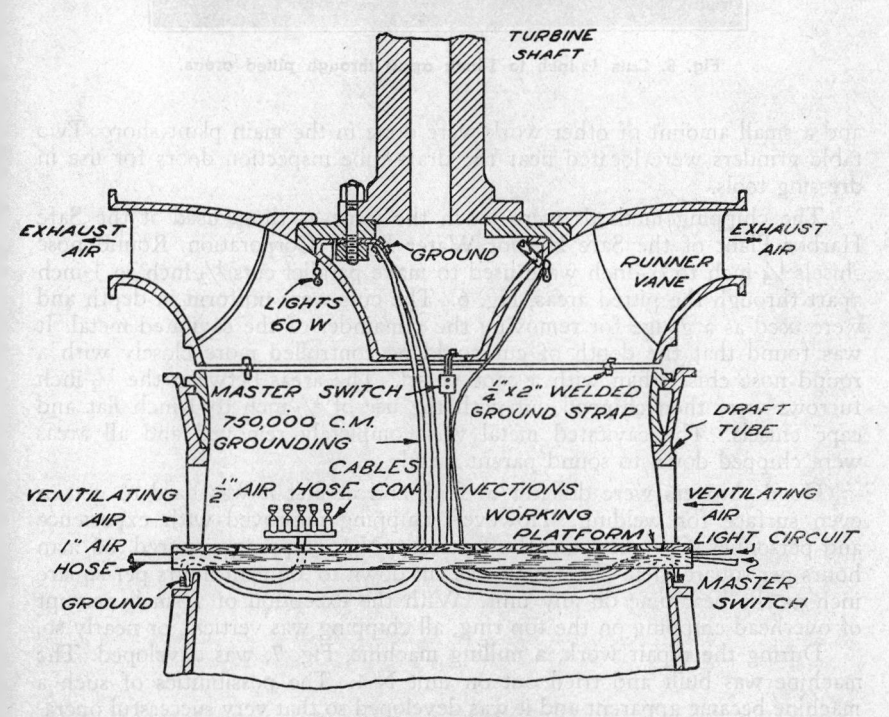

Fig. 5. Details of platform.

Fig. 6. Cuts ½-inch to 1-inch apart through pitted areas.

and a small amount of other work were done in the main plant shop. Two table grinders were located near the draft tube inspection doors for use in dressing tools.

The chipping methods were much the same as those used at the Safe Harbor Plant of the Safe Harbor Water Power Corporation. Round nose chisels ¼-inch to ½-inch were used to make parallel cuts ½-inch to 1-inch apart through the pitted areas, Fig. 6. The cuts were uniform in depth and were used as a gauge for removing the remainder of the cavitated metal. It was found that the depth of cut could be controlled more closely with a round nose chisel than with a cape chisel. The areas between the ½-inch furrows were then chipped out with the use of ½-inch to 1-inch flat and cape chisels. The cavitated metal was completely removed and all areas were chipped down to sound parent metal.

Good chippers were difficult to find, and at first it was hard to get an even surface for welding. However, chipping improved with experience and personnel selections. On the first unit, N-1, chipping required .08 man hours per square inch. This time was cut down to .06 man hours per square inch as the best time on any unit. With the exception of a small amount of overhead chipping on the top ring, all chipping was vertical, or nearly so.

During the repair work, a milling machine, Fig. 7, was developed. The machine was built and tried out on unit N-4. The possibilities of such a machine became apparent and it was developed so that very successful operation was obtained. The milling head was driven by an air motor and was constructed with an adjustable feed for accurate and rapid adjustment to depth of cuts and to release the milling cutter in an emergency. Cuts were made, Fig. 8, in even steps, approximately 1/8-inch deep, so that successive welding layers could be laid on uniformly. Small sections of cavitated metal, which still existed after the milling operation, were chipped out to sound parent metal.

The primary object of the milling machine was to get an even surface, Fig. 9, on which to build up successive layers of welding. This objective was attained, and, in addition, it was found that the metal could be removed in .04 man hours per square inch as compared with .06 to .08 man hours per square inch by chipping.

In addition to the above saving, the smooth surface was conducive to better welding and subsequently faster grinding.

In welding, due consideration was given to established practice of the

Fig. 7. Special milling machine developed.

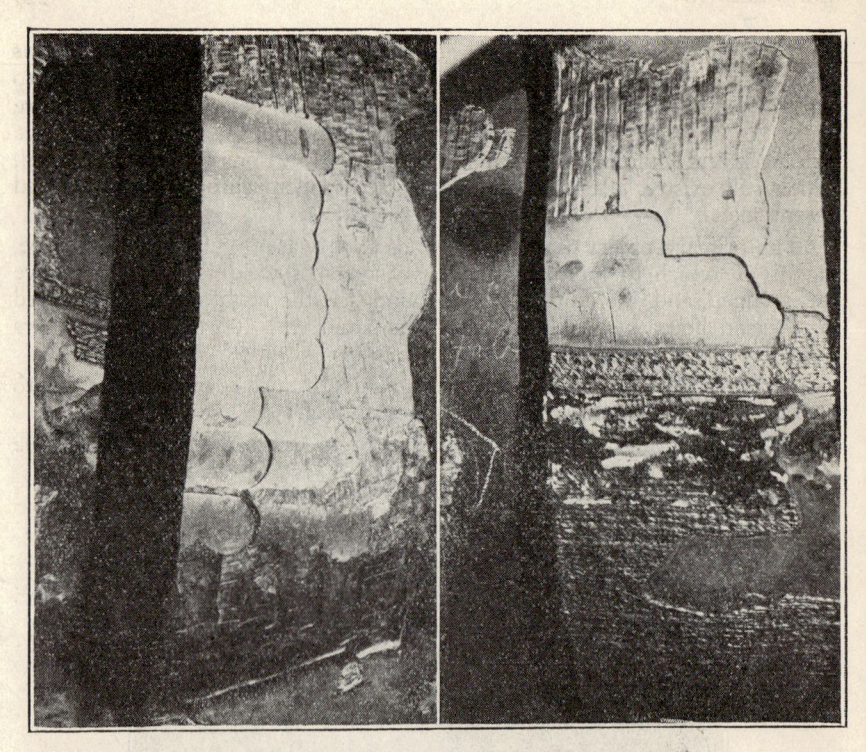

Fig. 8, (left). Cuts made in even steps approximately ⅛-inch deep. Fig. 9, (right). Use of milling machine provided even surface on which to build weld metal.

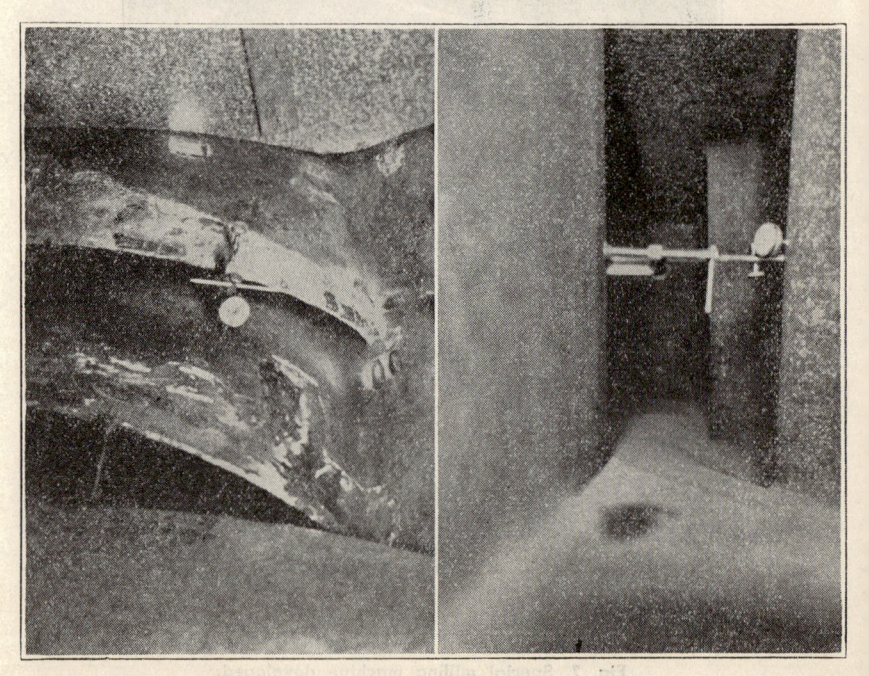

Fig. 10, (left). Metal partitions used to separate the welders. Fig. 11, (right). Dial indicators used to obtain clearance between stationary and runner wearing rings.

department, and of the industry. The turbine manufacturer was freely consulted and a method of repairs was developed which was satisfactory to all interested. Shop tests were also closely studied. As a result, a close overlapping bead was laid on, so that a minimum of patch welding would be necessary to fill valleys, between beads, left after grinding. Studding was not used, as it was not practical. Good fusion was obtained with the cast steel runners.

Crews of five men each were used on each welding shift. The welding was well coordinated with the chipping and grinding. Each repair job was started with chipping, and, as the work advanced, welding and then peening and grinding were progressed. The crews were rotated so that no phase of the work had to wait.

The runner was divided into four parts and only four welders worked at one time. The fifth welder was a relief man. Metal partitions, shown in Fig. 10, which were painted black, were used to separate the welders working on the runner. Four 200-amp. D.C. welding machines were used. Extreme care was taken to avoid warping, distortion, or overheating of runner sections. Before welding was attempted on a production basis, a dial indicator and thermometer, Fig. 10, were mounted on one of the vanes and distortion was noted as welding progressed. It was found that warping could be neglected if section welding was progressed from vane to vane to allow dissipation of the heat.

Two dial indicators were also placed, 90-degrees apart, on the runner

Fig. 12, (left). Smooth bright surface after grinding. Fig. 13, (right). Mild steel bead along edge of chipped area.

Fig. 14, (left). Cup wheels used for finishing. Fig. 15, (right). Two finished mild steel vanes.

vane tips, Fig. 11, and feeler gauge readings were taken at four points, 90 degrees apart, to obtain the clearance between stationary and runner wearing rings. At first, these readings were taken every half hour, but as it became apparent that there would be no distortion, readings were recorded once every hour. The dial indicators showed .001-inch to .002-inch variation. However, this was not considered the result of welding because the change coincided with a change in scroll case temperature as the penstock was being filled. Feeler gauge measurements were averaged by adding diametrically opposite readings. Then, if the runner became distorted, the change in reading along one axis would show a corresponding change along the other axis. Measurements varied somewhat with the different men taking readings; however, careful scrutiny of the figures disclosed a maximum probable movement of not more than .002-inch.

Tram marks were made on the lower flange face of the runner cone and on the center trailing edge of each vane. The marks were made the length of a tram, about three feet long, which was used to check the distance between the vanes and runner cone so that warping, if any, could be detected. Later, the long tram was discarded and a shorter tram, about five inches long, was used to check the distance from one vane edge to the adjacent vane in about the same place that the struts were previously located. The measurements at this point, using the short tram, showed an average maximum deflection of .025 inch.

Unit N-1 was repaired with an austenitic 18-8 (18 percent chromium, 8 percent nickel) stainless steel coated rod, having .07 maximum carbon and a columbium to carbon ratio of not less than 10. No test samples were made and the tensile strength and ductility are not known. The stainless steel rod was laid on with a close overlapping bead and the metal gave a smooth, bright polish, Fig. 12, after grinding operations.

Before applying the stainless steel rod, all low spots and deeply chipped areas were built up with a mild steel rod. The welding beads were laid on horizontally, and all succeeding layers were applied parallel to the underlayers. After each layer of welding beads was laid on, the beads were carefully wire-brushed and peened. The low areas were built up to within not more than .1-inch of the final contour as determined by the templates. A minimum thickness of .1 inch was maintained for the stainless steel layer which was applied last.

There was a slight tendency for undercutting at the edge of the chipped areas when using 18-8 rod. This was due to porosity and sand holes in the parent metal. The condition was corrected early by running a mild steel bead along the edge of the chipped area before the stainless steel rod was applied. This can be seen by the narrow band around the edge of the round area in the center of Fig. 12 and also in Fig. 13.

A small amount of work hardening of the stainless 18-8 is shown by the fact that the Brinell hardness was approximately 200 to 210. The hardness was obtained with a portable Brinell set using a 5 millimeter ball and 750 kilogram pressure. The 18-8 rod was applied with reverse polarity, 90-95 amperes and 27-30 volts. Three sizes of 18-8 stainless steel rod were used: $5/32$-inch,

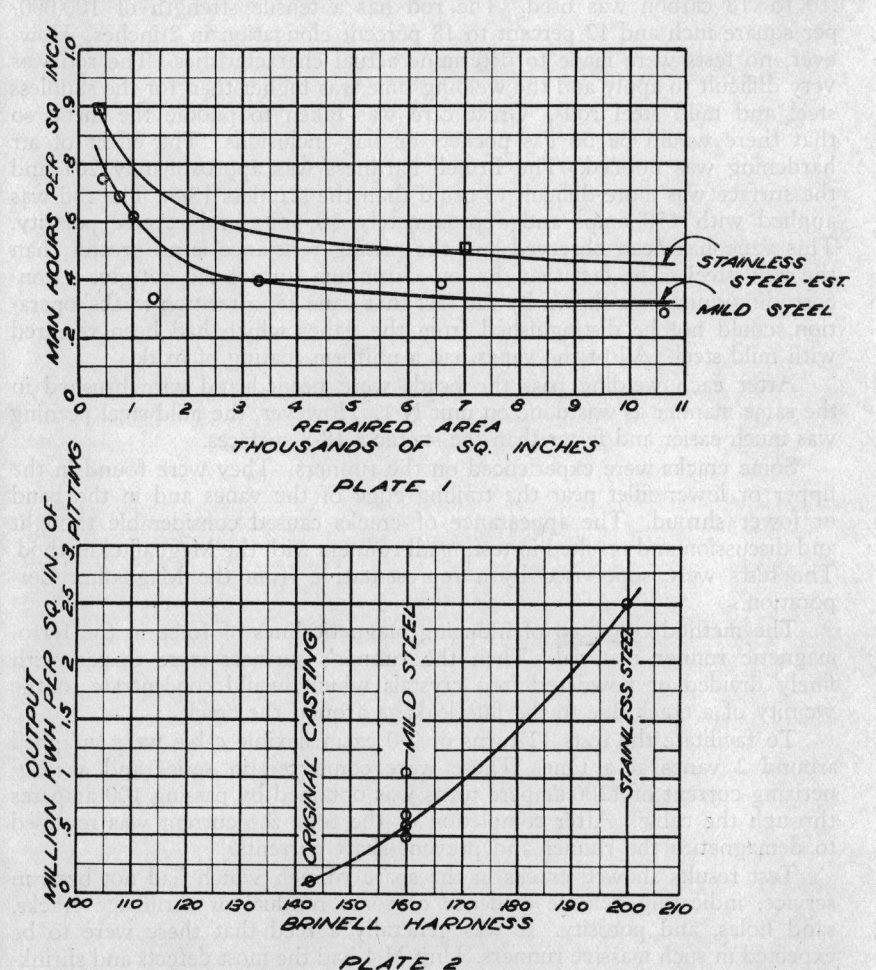

Fig. 16. Comparative costs and wearing qualities of mild and stainless steel.

1/8-inch and 3/32-inch. The 3/32-inch rod was used mainly for patching low areas during grinding operations. The amount of rod used is shown in Table I.

Units N-4, N-2 and N-3 were repaired with a mild steel rod, having approximately .14 carbon content, 70,000-80,000 per square inch tensile strength, and 20 percent elongation in 2 inches.

The mild steel rod was applied with straight polarity, 150 amperes and 25-30 volts. The method used was the same as that used on unit N-1. In some areas where pitting was deep, as many as 7 welding beads were necessary to build up some of the vanes to the original contour. The size of mild steel welding rod used was 5/32-inch, 1/8-inch, and a small amount of 3/16-inch. The Brinell hardness was approximately 145-160, using a 5 millimeter ball and 750 kilogram pressure. This was approximately the same hardness as the parent metal.

On vane 15, unit N-4, a special low chromium rod having 4 percent to 6 percent chromium, a small amount of vanadium and molybdenum, and .10 to .18 carbon was used. The rod has a tensile strength of 100,000 per square inch and 12 percent to 18 percent elongation in 2-inches. However, no tests were made to determine actual characteristics. The rod was very difficult to apply and the welding time was higher than for the stainless steel and mild steel rods. Great care was taken to puddle the metal so that there would be no gas pockets or slag inclusions. The effect of air hardening was noticed. The Brinell hardness was approximately 205 and the surface was more difficult to grind than the stainless 18-8. The rod was applied with 150 amps and approximately 30 volts and reverse polarity. This vane has been observed and the pitting resistance is no greater than the mild steel. The fact that the low chromium surface did not give a non-corroding finish was shown by the fact that vane 15, after two weeks' operation, could not be distinguished from the vanes which had been repaired with mild steel. All of the vanes had a uniform coating of oxide.

After each welding pass the beads were peened and wire brushed in the same manner as was done on unit N-1. However, the mild steel peening was much easier and faster than the stainless 18-8 surfaces.

Some cracks were experienced on the runners. They were found in the upper or lower fillet near the trailing edge of the vanes and in the band or lower shroud. The appearance of cracks caused considerable thought and discussion and resulted in testing all runners with the Magnaflux method. The tests were supervised by a representative from the Magnaflux Corporation.

The method consisted of inducing magnetic lines of force in the ferromagnetic runner material. Then the runner's surfaces were dusted with finely divided or powdered iron crystals which would concentrate in the vicinity of a crack due to the flux leakage around the crack.

To facilitate the tests 12 turns of 2-0 extra flexible cable were wrapped around 2 vanes at a time. These were connected in series and a magnetizing current of 1200-ampere turns was obtained by passing 100 amperes through the cable. After completion of the tests the current was reversed to demagnetize the runner and prevent shaft currents.

Test results showed cracks in the spare runner, which had not been in service, indicating definite evidence of some residual or shrinkage cracks, sand holes, and porosity. It was generally agreed that these were to be expected in such massive runners. Unit N-4 had the most defects and shrinkage cracks, but this runner was also cavitated over a larger area than units

N-1, N-2, and N-3. Subsequent welding repairs from 1938 to February 1942 have not disclosed any cracks.

As a result of the tests and experience gained, Magnaflux tests have been included in the specifications for new runners.

After building up the vanes with welded metal, 5-man crews were used in grinding the welded areas to conform to the original contour. Horizontal templates were made to insure close accurate control of the work. The templates were constructed from the manufacturer's detail drawings and were then checked on the spare runner. Considerable variation in vane contour was found when checking from vane to vane on the spare runner. As a result, it was necessary to alter the templates to get an average vane contour. The templates were constructed to maintain one-inch thickness of the trailing edge.

Multivane and piston type grinders were used with flat and recessed wheels. A medium soft bakelite wheel with size 14 aluminum oxide grit proved to be the most successful wheel for grinding the stainless weld metal. The wheel wore faster, but clogged less than any of the others which were tried. The vitrified wheels clogged considerably. The best results were obtained at a speed of about 6,000 revolutions per minute with a 6-inch wheel. Radial wheels cut faster than the recessed type, but they frequently gouged the metal and were harder to control. As a result, they were used for rough grinding only and the cup wheels, Fig. 14, were used for finishing.

A 24-grit aluminum oxide hard grade bakelite bonded wheel was used on the mild steel welded surfaces. Grinding was much faster but the surfaces showed marks of the grinding wheels. The surfaces were then finished with aluminum oxide paper discs which gave a smooth mirror finish. Fig. 15 shows 2 finished mild steel vanes on unit N-4. There was a tendency for the operators to overgrind the trailing edge of the vane. This was checked closely with the templates during repairs.

In studying the cost analysis, Table 1, Table 2, Plate 1 and Plate 2, Fig. 16, should be observed closely. Unit N-1 is high in man hours per square inch of repaired area. This is due to the harder surface and the greater difficulties in grinding the stainless steel. It will also be noticed that there is some variation in man hour requirements, depending on the size of the area

Table I—Boulder Power Plant Labor Distribution on Cavitation Repairs

Unit	Date	Area Repaired Sq. In.	Man Hours	Man Hours per Sq. In.	Million K.W.H. per Man Hr.	Welding Rod, Lbs.	Lbs. Rd. per Sq. In.
N-1	4- 7-38	7,000	3,570	.51	.12	596	.085
N-4	5-15-38	10,600	2,930	.28	.15	1,175	.111
N-2	6-27-38	6,670	2,502	.38	.20	1,000	.150
N-3	8-14-38	3,300	1,266	.39	.35	350	.106
N-4	3-23-39	460	346	.75	.83	40	.087
N-4	7-29-40	1,000	612	.61	.81		
N-2	8-19-40	1,400	465	.33	1.74	250	.071
N-3	9-12-40	768	521	.68	1.53		
N-1	10- 9-40	368	365	.99	2.52		
Total		31,566	12,577	.398		34,11	

Table II—Boulder Power Plant Labor Distribution of Cavitation Repairs

Operation	Unit N-1 Man Hours	Unit N-1 Man Hours per Sq. In.	Unit N-4 Man Hours	Unit N-4 Man Hours per Sq. In.	Unit N-2 Man Hours	Unit N-2 Man Hours per Sq. In.	Unit N-3 Man Hours	Unit N-3 Man Hours per Sq. In.	All Units Man Hours	All Units Man Hours per Sq. In.
Chipping	586	.08	644	.06	240	.08	120	.06	1,590	.07
Machining					160	.04	96	.07	256	.05
Welding	794	.11	784	.07	678	.10	306	.09	2,562	.09
Peening and Grinding	773	.11	448	.04	468	.07	232	.07	1,921	.07
Electrical	394	.06	176	.02	168	.03	224	.07	962	.04
Misc.	1,023	.15	880	.08	788	.12	288	.09	2,979	.11
Total	3,570	.51	2,932	.28	2,502	.38	1,266	.39	10,270	.37
Area Sq. In.	7,000		10,600		6,670		3,300		27,570	
Weight Welding Rod	596*		1,175†		1,000		350		3,121	
Man Hrs. Welding per lbs.	1.3		.67		.68		.87		.80	

*—546 lbs. 18-8 stainless steel rod, 50-lbs. mild steel rod.
†—70 lbs. 18-8 stainless steel rod, 1030-lbs. mild steel rod, 75-lbs. 4-6 chromium rod.

Fig. 17. The original runner surface.

to be repaired. The reason for this is obvious. Costs of installing the platform and other equipment necessary for repairs, remain constant regardless of the size of area. Table 2 shows how the detail studies were made.

Plates 1 and 2, Fig. 16, show the comparative costs and wearing qualities of mild steel and stainless steel. The low chromium surface showed no advantages and was difficult to apply and grind.

The advantages of welding resulted in finished vanes which conformed more accurately to correct contour than the original castings. The surface was smoother and more dense and was free from sand holes and porosity, as compared to the original runner surface, shown in Fig. 17. The result was an increase in output of approximately 4 percent more horsepower than was obtained prior to welding repairs. It is obvious also that the cost of a runner replacement is saved and the useful life prolonged where otherwise it would have been necessary to remove the runners after approximately three years' operation.

As a result of the experience obtained during this maintenance program, the specifications for a new unit at Boulder Power Plant included a definite advancement. The new runner is required to have a stainless steel welded surface at the entrance and discharge edges of the vanes, crown, and band. Approximately 321.5 square feet of welded surface was required. The runner patterns could allow for 1/8-inch stainless steel build-up in the heavier sections of the castings, but not on the vanes where the sections were thinner.

This unit will be placed in operation in a few months and the operation over the next few years will give added information as to the advantages obtained by welding.

Index

	Page		Page
Bakery, Modern	1	Ore, Iron, Trestle for Stocking	210
Blast Furnace Shell, Welded	7	Oven Doors, Coke	60
Bolts, Studs, Removed Quickly When Broken	205	Pipe, Drill, of Integral-Joint Construction	85
Bridge, Railway	157	Plant, Cement	26
Broken, Stud Bolts Removed Quickly When	205	Ceramic	47
Carrier, Truck Wheel	215	Chemical	55
Cement Plant	26	Copper	67
Ceramic Plant	47	Fibre and Plastics	96
Charging Pump, Cracking Still	82	Furniture Manufacturing	114
Chemical Plant	55	Gravel	124
Coke Oven Doors	60	Plastics and Fibre Plant	96
Construction, Drill Pipe of Integral-Joint	85	Power Generating Station	149
Contents, Table of	vi	Power System, Municipal, Hydraulic Turbine Maintenance on	219
Control, Corrosion, in Refinery Pressure Vessels	165	Preface	v
Copper Plant	67	Pressure Vessels, Corrosion Control in	165
Corrosion Control in Refinery Pressure Vessels	165	Pump, Cracking Still Charging	82
Cracking Still Charging Pump	82	Railway Bridge	157
Doors, Coke Oven	60	Rammers, Foundry Sand	110
Drill Pipe of Integral-Joint Construction	85	Refinery Pressure Vessels, Corrosion Control in	165
Farm Machinery	91	Sand Rammers, Foundry	110
Fibre and Plastics Plant	96	Saw Mill	183
Foundry Sand Rammers	110	Shell, Welded Blast Furnace	7
Furnace, Blast, Shell, Welded	7	Station, Power Generating	149
Furniture Manufacturing Plant	114	Steel Mill	196
Generating Station, Power	149	Still Charging Pump, Cracking	82
Gravel Plant	124	Still, Oil, Tubes	143
Hydraulic Turbine Maintenance on Municipal Power System	219	Stocking Iron Ore, Trestle for	210
Integral-Joint Construction, Drill Pipe of	85	Stud Bolts Removed Quickly When Broken	205
Iron Ore, Trestle for Stocking	210	System, Municipal Power, Hydraulic Turbine Maintenance on	219
Machine Tools	134	Table of Contents	vi
Machinery, Farm	91	Tools, Machine	134
Maintenance, Hydraulic Turbine, on Municipal Power System	219	Trestle for Stocking Iron Ore	210
Manufacturing Plant, Furniture	114	Truck Wheel Carrier	215
Mill, Saw	183	Tubes, Oil Still	143
Mill, Steel	196	Turbine, Hydraulic, Maintenance on Municipal Power System	219
Modern Bakery	1	Vessels, Refinery Pressure, Corrosion Control in	165
Municipal Power System, Hydraulic Maintenance on	219	Welded Blast Furnace Shell	7
Oil Still Tubes	143	Wheel Carrier, Truck	215